THE THEORY OF THE SCATTERING MATRIX

For the Interactions
of Fundamental Particles

THE THEORY OF THE SCATTERING MATRIX

For the Interactions
of Fundamental Particles

A. O. BARUT
University of Colorado

THE MACMILLAN COMPANY, NEW YORK
COLLIER-MACMILLAN LIMITED, LONDON

Library of Congress catalog card number: 67–15547

THE MACMILLAN COMPANY, NEW YORK
COLLIER-MACMILLAN CANADA, LTD., TORONTO, ONTARIO

Printed in the United States of America

PREFACE

Investigations published during the last ten years have greatly increased our knowledge of the properties of the scattering matrix (S-matrix) of the reactions of fundamental particles. We have in mind here the S-matrix introduced directly between the asymptotic states of particles, as was originally done by Heisenberg in 1942. Let us emphasize that the mathematical concept of the S-matrix, defined as the unitary matrix connecting the states in the Hilbert space of (irreducible) unitary representations of the inhomogeneous Lorentz group, is rigorous and comes, with some modifications in certain cases, reasonably close to the observed transition probability amplitudes. (And the motivation behind the original idea of introducing the S-matrix was indeed to have a quantum theory in terms of directly observable quantities.) We say "reasonably close" because continuous quantum numbers, like energy and momenta, are never measured with absolute accuracy. Furthermore, the modifications referred to above arise in the case of electromagnetic interactions where charged particles experimentally are never produced alone, but are always accompanied by their electromagnetic fields or photons. The scope of the S-matrix can be extended to overcome these two limitations of an empirical nature—namely the nonexact measurement of continuous quantum numbers, and the long-range electromagnetic or gravitational fields accompanying the particles—by defining the S-matrix between the states of special types of reducible representations of the inhomogeneous Lorentz group.

Thus we can ask about the properties of the S-matrix so defined, and about the additional physical requirements or postulates which would allow us to determine the elements of the S-matrix completely. Once the S-matrix of a reaction is known, all observable quantities, like cross sections, lifetimes, bound states, can be derived from it. As a result, a new branch of theoretical physics has gained some momentum which formulates the relativistic quantum theory in terms of the S-matrix. This development has been largely guided by what is known and by what can be derived in relativistic quantum field theory. In fact, the Hilbert space of states of the unitary representations of the inhomogeneous Lorentz group is the basic framework of the quantum field theory as well. However, the formulation of the laws of physics in terms of the S-matrix is much more close to the experimental situation than the formulation in terms of the unobservable fields; it is at least quite a bit more economical. On the other hand, the actual determination of the S-matrix depends largely on the assumed analytic properties of its elements as a function of the momenta. These properties are derived in field theory and, in the case of two-body interactions, in nonrelativistic potential scattering. In fact a great deal of insight into the physical meaning of the analyticity properties has been developed from a study of the analyticity properties in potential scattering, such as the discovery of the bound states and resonance poles of the scattering amplitudes in the unphysical regions of the momenta.[1] That the values of the scattering amplitude outside the physical range of the momentum variables for one process contain information about the bound states and resonances, and, more generally, about the amplitudes of related antiparticle processes, is really the basic physical content of analyticity. Because analytic functions are determined by their singularities, and because of the physical interpretation of these singularities (poles = bound states or resonances, branch point = threshold of a new channel, etc.), the mathematics here is inseparably related to physics, in much the same manner as the hermitian operators and their eigenvalues are related to physical observables in quantum theory. We expect, therefore, that every singularity of the amplitude in all its Riemann sheets has a physical significance and that analyticity is the way to show the mutual relationships of these physical inputs. From the S-matrix point of view the analyticity properties can be made, by virtue of TCP theorem and crossing relations, extremely plausible, but in the end they must be postulated as additional requirements. Postulates of the type of analyticity are essentially mathematical in nature and the implied dynamical principles are not clearly spelled out, with the exception of the connection of the singularities with the physics discussed above. It is largely for this reason that some people are very reluctant to make the S-matrix the starting point of a physical theory. We recall, however, that the derivation of most of the properties of atomic spectra by the use of group theory in the early thirties—without the use of Lagrangians or Hamiltonians—has also been accepted with great reluctance.[2]

At any rate, the elegance, the economy and simplicity of the formulation (absence of renormalization and second quantization techniques), use of directly observable quantities, and, above all, the successes of the theory compel us to see how the laws of physics can be formulated and how the calculations can be performed starting from the S-matrix. The purpose of this book is just this. We also believe that the theory has reached a sufficient stage of elegance and maturity to warrant such a book.[3]

---

[1] Potential scattering as such is not considered in this book except to show how it arises as a limiting case from the relativistic two-body scattering. A very detailed treatment of it and a general theory of scattering processes can be found in M. L. Goldberger and K. M. Watson, *Collision Theory* (New York: Wiley, 1964). See also A. Martin in *Progress in Cosmic Rays and Elementary Particle Physics*, Vol. VIII (Amsterdam: North Holland Publ. Co., 1965), for rigorous results in potential scattering theory; and V. de Alfaro and T. Regge, *Potential Scattering* (New York: Interscience Publishers, 1965).

[2] See preface to E. P. Wigner, *Group Theory* (New York: Academic, 1959).

[3] *Remark on References.* References in this very rapidly developing field are quite extensive. We have tried to give the original references as often as possible, especially in Chapter 10, in the case of experimental results. A bibliography of monographs and review articles on S-matrix theory can be found at the end of the book.

The first part of the book (Chapters 1 to 9) deals with the general principles of the theory. We introduce in some detail the group theoretical specification of the S-matrix with emphasis on the theory of the unitary representations of the inhomogeneous Lorentz group, and develop related machinery in Chapter 2 and in the Appendixes. The statements and the results of the theory of group representations belong to the more permanent part of relativistic quantum theories and are independent of the underlying "field" concept for the particles. The connection of the group theoretical results with the form of the amplitudes and with the observable quantities is discussed in Chapters 3 and 4.

Discrete symmetry transformations are treated in Chapter 5 as extra restrictions on the results of Chapter 4. In particular, it is shown how the effort to give a physical meaning to the discrete operations T, or PT, leads to the postulate of crossing, analytic continuation, CPT theorem, and analyticity itself.

In Chapter 7 we discuss the process of analytic continuation explicitly, with emphasis on some of the important singularities and the corresponding Cauchy relations. The singularity structure of many particle amplitudes is much more complicated and lengthy, and we have not attempted to include in such a textbook these topics which are still in the development stage.[4] It will be a sign of vitality of the S-matrix theory if its center of interest shifts in the future toward the study of multiparticle amplitudes.

In Chapter 8, we indicate how the practical calculations are made; these are treated on the basis of specific examples in the second part of the book. Finally, we discuss the asymptotic properties of the scattering amplitudes, which also belongs within the scope of general principles. The point at infinity in the complex plane and the behavior of the amplitudes there must also reflect some physics; some existing ideas in this respect, together with what can be proved rigorously from some very general principles, are discussed in Chapter 9.

The second part of the book is devoted to an explicit discussion of fundamental particle processes, in agreement with the desirable notion that writings in theoretical physics should not only contain mathematical formalisms but also their application to nature. We begin with the identification of particles observed—i.e., their quantum numbers and the recognition of conservation laws. In Chapter 11, we discuss pion-pion scattering, and in Chapter 12 the pion-nucleon scattering. These prototypes of scattering processes show how the dispersion relations techniques are actually carried out in detail. In Chapter 13 electromagnetic processes are discussed. It is shown how simply one can obtain the results of already renormalized perturbation series of quantum electrodynamics.

---

[4] For this particular topic see, for instance, R. Eden, V. Landshof, D. I. Olive, and J. Pollinghorne, *Analytic S-Matrix Theory* (Cambridge: Cambridge University Press, 1966).

This book is intended to serve students, and others who may want to study the field from the beginning. A knowledge of quantum field theory is not required. It can also be used as a textbook for beginning graduate students if a rapid entry into the field of fundamental particles is desired. The material has been used by the author in the past years for just this purpose at several places.

I express my gratitude to the multitude of collaborators, colleagues, and students who over the years consciously or unconsciously have helped the formation of this book. I should like to name specifically W. Au, R. Blade, E. Branscomb, W. E. Brittin, A. Bussian, F. Calogero, G. F. Chew, J. Dilley, C. Fronsdal, C. Lee, G. Leung, I. Muzinich, K. H. Ruei, M. Samiullah, E. J. Squires, H. P. Stapp, B. Unal, D. Williams, F. Zachariasen, C. Zemach, and D. Zwanziger. My thanks are due to The Macmillan Company for its co-operation and for the excellent work achieved in the production of my books.

Boulder, Colorado A. O. B.

CONTENTS

PART ONE

General Principles

CHAPTER 1

Kinematical Principles of Quantum Theory in Terms of the S-Matrix

> It does not seem likely that the first principles
> of things will ever be adequately known . . .
>
> *Voltaire*

1.1 S-Matrix

The S-matrix was introduced by Heisenberg[1] in 1942 for the purpose of having a theory of elementary particles in terms of the "observable quantities" only. Heisenberg took as observable quantities the energies of the stationary states of the systems and the asymptotic parameters in scattering experiments. These two types of quantities, though seemingly different, need not be introduced separately as is the case in ordinary quantum mechanics. If we enclose a scattering system in a large box, the discrete energies of the system are determined by the phase shifts only, and vice versa. This shows that discrete stationary energies and energies and momenta of the outcoming particles in a scattering experiment are basically quantities of the same type. It will turn out that the S-matrix describes both stationary states and the scattering states, although the name "scattering matrix" points only to the latter situations.

We take as the so-called *primary observable quantities* energies, momenta, and other internal variables (such as rest mass, spin and charge degrees of freedom) of the free physical particles. These quantities arise, as we shall see in Chapter 2, from the invariance or symmetry conditions imposed on the physical processes. We do not make any distinction at this point between elementary particles or composite systems. The special theory of relativity

---

[1] W. Heisenberg, *Z. Physik*, **120**, 513, 678 (1942–43). For early developments of the S-matrix theory, see also C. Møller, Kgl. Dansk Videnskab, *Selskab. Math.-phys.*, **23**, nos. 1, 19 (1945); *Nature*, **158**, 143 (1946); W. Heisenberg, *S. Naturforschung*, **1**, 608 (1946). The S-matrix had been introduced earlier in nuclear reactions by J. Wheeler, *Phys. Rev.*, **52**, 1107 (1937).

can be formulated in terms of energies and momenta—i.e., we do not need to introduce position coordinates or localization of the particles at this stage. We assume that the four moments $k = (k_0, \mathbf{k})$ of the asymptotic incoming and outgoing free physical particles obey the special relativistic relation

$$k_0^2 - \mathbf{k}^2 = m^2. \tag{1.1}$$

Here we have taken $c = 1$; then k_0, the energy, k, the momentum, and m, the rest mass of the particle or the system all have the same dimension.[2] The sign of the physical energy is positive

$$k_0 \equiv E = +\sqrt{\mathbf{k}^2 + m^2}. \tag{1.2}$$

The fourvector k is a timelike ($m^2 > 0$) or a lightlike ($m = 0$) vector in the forward cone. For fixed m^2, k lies on a hyperboloid, which is called the *mass shell*. For $m = 0$ the mass shell coincides with the forward light cone itself. Unlike in field theory, we consider the mass always to be the physical mass and energy momentum fourvector always on the mass shell, except for some mathematical manipulations.

The other variables will be discussed as we go along. We assume the rest masses m of the particles to be given; they may be determined in some cases theoretically from the self-consistency of the theory (Sec. 11.4 for an example). If a particle is known to be a composite particle (by explaining its properties in terms of its constituents), then its mass must be calculated dynamically. The masses are certainly measurable. The spin degree of freedom is a consequence of relativistic invariance (Chap. 2) and is measured by various polarization experiments. Other properties (charge, strangeness) are consequences of the additional symmetry or invariance properties of the world of particles.

The actual measurements of the interactions of the particles are expressed in terms of *derived quantities* which include:

   (i) *Cross sections* for elastic, inelastic, and production processes in various energy-momentum spin, and charge states.

  (ii) The *energy values of stationary (or excited) states* of the systems, again measured on the basis of emitted or absorbed particles; all spectroscopic measurements belong to this group.

 (iii) *Lifetimes* of resonant states or unstable particles.

In fact, all measurements in physics can be reduced to these three types. The derived quantities must be expressed as functions of the observable properties of particles. The object of the theory of "elementary" particles is

---

[2] The nature of c is outside the scope of special theory of relativity. Planck's constant $\hbar$ will enter through the measurement (see Chap. 3). If we take $c = \hbar = 1$ all physical quantities will have the dimension of a power of length. In particular, m, k_0, and $\mathbf{k}$ will have the dimension of inverse length. If there would be a universal length ℓ_0 and we set $c = \hbar = \ell_0 = 1$, all physical quantities would be dimensionless. There is, at present, no accepted theory incorporating an elementary length.

then to correlate and explain the experimental results and obtain from here the nature, properties, and unity of the particles.

In Table 1–1 we list the parameters and quantum numbers that enter into the theory and the quantities to be calculated.

Table 1–1

Parameters, Quantum Numbers and Observables

PROPER LORENTZ GROUP	FULL LORENTZ GROUP	SUPERSELECTION RULES	
Mass	P	Q	Charge
Spin	T, CP	N	Baryonic charge
$k = (E,\mathbf{k})$	Antiparticles	L_t	Leptonic charges

STRONG INTERACTIONS QUANTUM NUMBERS	INTERNAL SYMMETRIES	
Y	Hypercharge	(a) Isospin
I	Isospin	(b) Approximate higher symmetries
C	Charge conjugation	Kinematical branching ratios under
P	Parity	the above symmetries

PARAMETERS	DYNAMICAL CALCULATIONS
Coupling constants	Cross sections
Normal magnetic moments	Lifetimes
	Masses and coupling constants of composite particles
	Anomalous magnetic moments

We remark that in ordinary quantum mechanics quantities referring to the positions of the particles, such as the probability distribution of the electron within the hydrogen atom, are considered in principle as observable. Such quantities will be discarded here as unobservable. They can be indirectly inferred, if need be, from the scattering experiments of, for example, electrons from the hydrogen atom in various states.

In Appendix 1 we list the empirical properties of the known "particles," stable or unstable, to which we shall frequently refer. These are the primary observable quantities that we want to interpret and understand.

We shall now define a function of the initial and final primary quantities of the particles, the so-called *S-matrix element*, in terms of which all derived quantities will be expressed.

There is one *S*-matrix for the whole universe; we shall look at individual elements and submatrices of this one continuously infinite matrix.

With the choice of variables discussed above we write an *S*-matrix element in the form

$$S([k_i,s_i,t_i]_{\text{initial}};\ [k_j,s_j,t_j]_{\text{final}}) \equiv S(\alpha_i,\alpha_f),$$

where "initial" and "final" indicate the set of parameters belonging to the initial and final particles—e.g., the four momenta spins, and types or other "quantum numbers" collectively. When the spin and types indices are discrete we shall write simply $S(K_i; K_f)$, suppressing all the discrete matrix indices and denoting by K the set of four momenta. It should be remarked that energy and momenta are never measured with absolute accuracy by the uncertainty principle. This fact has to be taken into account eventually. Nevertheless we now make the idealization that they are the measurable quantities.

What is the physical meaning of the S-matrix elements? It is the *transition probability amplitude* from the initial state i to the final state f. It is in the use of probability amplitudes rather than probabilities that the quantum principle enters into the theory. Our first task is then to formulate the *kinematical postulates* of quantum theory in terms of transition probability amplitudes between states, rather than in terms of state vectors and linear operators.

1.2   The Quantum Principle

Having introduced the transition probability amplitudes S_{if} between initial and final states, the *probability of* transition (or *conditional probability*) is given by

$$w_{if} = |S_{if}|^2 = S_{if}^* S_{if}. \tag{1.3}$$

The initial and final states are specified by a number of measurements, to be precise, by a *complete set of measurements*. They consist in finding the relative frequencies or probabilities of occurrence of certain values of the parameters. If we write these probabilities w_i and w_f in the form

$$w_i = |a_i|^2, \quad w_f = |a_f|^2, \tag{1.4}$$

then the *quantum transition process* is described by[3]

$$a_f = \sum_i S_{if} a_i \tag{1.5}$$

where S depends on the states only but not on the values of a_i and a_f or on the magnitude of probabilities. It is valid for *all* a_f and all a_i. The postulate (1.5) is of course tested experimentally in ordinary quantum mechanics for electromagnetic interactions.[4]

---

[3] We assume the physical meaning of the quantum principle and the related superposition principle to be well known to the reader. See, for example, P. A. M. Dirac, *Quantum Mechanics* (Oxford U. P., 1958), chap. I; W. Pauli, *Handbook of Physics*, vol. 1 (Berlin: Springer, 1958).

[4] More general nonlinear relations replacing Eq. (1.5) are conceivable; for a non-relativistic nonlinear model, see E. A. Power and I. Saaverda, *Proc. Cambridge Phil. Soc.*, **57**, 121 (1961). The quantum principle, Eq. (1.5), should perhaps be tested directly in strong interactions.

In contrast to Eq. (1.5) a classical transition process, such as a Markov chain or a Chapman-Kolmogroff process, is described by a linear equation among probabilities:

$$w_f = \sum_i w_{if} w_i.$$

In Eq. (1.5) we sum over all possible initial states, as the system may have started from any of the possible initial states to arrive at the particular final state considered. If the initial state is "prepared" to be in a definite state with probability one, then Eqs. (1.4) and (1.5) reduce to Eq. (1.3).

1.3   The Unitarity Condition

In any probabilistic theory we have the condition that the sum of probabilities must equal unity:

$$\sum_f |a_f|^2 = \sum_i |a_i|^2 = 1, \tag{1.6}$$

or, from Eq. (1.5),

$$\sum_{ijf} S_{if} S_{jf}^* a_i a_j^* = 1. \tag{1.6'}$$

This equation must hold for *all* possible choices of a_i, a_j, and is, therefore, satisfied if and only if

$$\sum_f S_{if} S_{jf}^* = \delta_{ij}, \tag{1.7}$$

or, in matrix notation,[5]

$$SS^\dagger = 1. \tag{1.7'}$$

For we can choose, e.g., $a_i = \delta_{ik}$ and find, from (1.6'),

$$\sum_f S_{kf} S_{kf}^* = 1, \tag{1.8}$$

which expresses the normalization of conditional probabilities, $\sum_f w_{kf} = 1$ for all k. We can also choose, e.g.,

$$a_i = \frac{1}{\sqrt{2}} (\delta_{ik} + \delta_{im} e^{i\phi})$$

and obtain

$$\tfrac{1}{2} \sum_f S_{if} S_{if}^* (\delta_{ik} + e^{i\phi}\delta_{im})(\delta_{jk} + e^{-i\phi}\delta_{jm}) = 1;$$

[5] In the case of classical Markov processes the corresponding equation is

$$\sum_f w_{if} w_{jf} = \delta_{ij}.$$

Here the matrix $\|w_{if}\|$ is the so called stochastic matrix and is the basis of the algebraic theory of Markov chains.

or with Eq. (1.8),

$$\sum_f (S_{mf}S_{kf}^* e^{i\phi} + S_{kf}S_{mf}^* e^{-i\phi}) = 0.$$

We then get for $\phi = 0$:

$$\sum_f S_{mf}S_{kf}^* + \text{c.c.} = 0,$$

and for $\phi = \pi/2$:

$$\sum_f S_{mf}S_{kf}^* - \text{c.c.} = 0.$$

Hence

$$\sum_f S_{mf}S_{kf}^* = 0, \quad m \neq k,$$

and one gets Eq. (1.7).   Q.E.D.

Similarly, using Eq. (1.7) and the fact that Eqs. (1.5) and (1.6) are also valid for all a_f, we shall prove the relation

$$\sum_f S_{fi}^* S_{fj} = \delta_{ij}, \quad \text{or} \quad S^\dagger S = 1. \tag{1.9}$$

To see this, we multiply both sides of Eq. (1.7) with a_i and sum over i,

$$\sum_{fi} S_{if}S_{jf}^* a_i = a_j,$$

or, by Eq. (1.5),

$$\sum_f S_{jf}^* a_f = a_j.$$

Now we insert this into the relation $\sum_j a_j a_j^* = 1$ and obtain

$$\sum_{jff'} S_{jf}^* a_f S_{jf'} a_f^* = 1, \quad \text{for all} \quad a_f.$$

Again choosing once $a_f = \delta_{fk}$ and once $a_f = (1/\sqrt{2})(\delta_{fk} + \delta_{fm}e^{i\phi})$, as before, we get Eq. (1.9).

Equations (1.7) and (1.9) together show that S considered as a matrix is a unitary matrix. We shall, however, use always the matrix elements as the S-"functions" and in this sense the relations (1.7) and (1.9) are more like a completeness or normalization relation.

If $S = I$, there is no scattering; initial and final states are the same. The actual scattering is given by the difference

$$R_{ij} = S_{ij} - \delta_{ij}, \tag{1.9'}$$

which we shall call the scattering amplitude and which satisfies from Eq. (1.7) the equations $RR^\dagger = -(R + R^\dagger)$, and $R^\dagger R = -(R + R^\dagger)$, or

$$R_{ij} + R_{ij}^* = -\sum_k R_{ik}R_{jk}^*,$$

$$R_{ij} + R_{ji}^* = -\sum_k R_{ki}^* R_{kj}. \tag{1.10}$$

These equations clearly show the nonlinear character of the unitarity equation. As a consequence there are relations between the first-order and second-
order scattering parameters. In particular, the units and dimensions are
determined; we *cannot* multiply R by an arbitrary constant. Furthermore,
the phase of the amplitude R_{ij} is determined by Eq. (1.9′) by taking the phase
of the δ_{ij}-term ("no-scattering" term) to be zero.

So far we have used discrete indices for simplicity. We must actually
operate with continuous-energy-momentum indices as well as discrete
indices. Equations (1.7) and (1.10) become in this case

$$\sum_k \int S(\alpha_i ; \alpha_k) S^*(\alpha_f ; \alpha_k) = \delta(\alpha_i ; \alpha_f)$$

$$\sum_k \int S^*(\alpha_k ; \alpha_f) S(\alpha_k ; \alpha_i) = \delta(\alpha_i ; \alpha_f), \tag{1.11}$$

and

$$R(\alpha_i ; \alpha_f) + R(\alpha_f ; \alpha_i)^* = -\sum_k \int R(\alpha_i ; \alpha_k) R(\alpha_f ; \alpha_k)^*$$

$$= -\sum_k \int R(\alpha_k ; \alpha_f)^* R(\alpha_k ; \alpha_i), \tag{1.12}$$

where we integrate over the momenta and sum over the discrete indices of
the set α_k; $\delta(\alpha_i ; \alpha_f)$ means Kroenecker deltas for the discrete indices and
δ-functions for momenta.

We have still to specify precisely the integrals in Eqs. (1.11) and (1.12).
We do this in a relativistically invariant manner in the next section after the
discussion of the invariance properties of the S-matrix elements. The
appearance of δ-functions in Eq. (1.11) indicates the singular character of the
S-matrix, and care must be taken to interpret the integrals correctly.

The unitarity condition is perhaps the most fundamental relation of
S-matrix theory. It alone does not determine the S-matrix, but coupled with
invariance and analyticity principles it will, in principle, determine the
S-matrix.

As was already noted by Heisenberg, the S-matrix treats the elementary
and composite particles on the same footing. For, in the course of the
scattering process, particles may form other composite systems that would
leave the scattering center with definite energy, spin, mass, etc., so that in the
final situation we have states with the quantum numbers of composite
particles.

1.4 The "Diagonalization" of the S-Matrix

The S-matrix connects any state into every other state in nature. There is,
fortunately, some order in nature; not all transitions are possible—either
strictly or approximately. Many of the S-matrix elements will thus be zero.

We can, then, reorder the matrix elements in such a way that the S-matrix is "diagonalized" in block form, which shows that there are only transitions within each block. Clearly it is then sufficient to consider these submatrices separately. Each such block is itself unitary and we can characterize each block by certain properties, or *quantum numbers*, which remain unchanged under transitions. These properties indicate the underlying *symmetry or invariance principles* of transitions. A large part of the elementary-particle physics consists in uncovering these symmetry and invariance principles, as will be discussed in later chapters. The diagonalization of the S-matrix involves a choice of observables or, mathematically, a choice of the basis in which the representations of the symmetry groups are expressed.

It should be remarked that the quantities invariant under transitions are not necessarily the same as the so-called constants of the motion[6] although the converse is always true. We shall talk about only what might be called "constants of collisions."

Heisenberg's idea of formulating the theory of elementary particles in terms of the S-matrix is another step towards a fundamental theory in terms of directly observable quantities. It is worth recalling here the situation at the beginning of quantum theory. In order to explain the discrete spectral lines of atoms it was again Heisenberg who put the idea forward that the theory should be formulated in terms of the observed frequencies of the spectral lines. These frequencies satisfied the Rydberg-Ritz combination principle and therefore were represented by a set of two integers, or as the difference of two terms (term structure):

$$\nu(n,m) = T_n - T_m.$$

Hence the combination principle

$$\nu(n,m) + \nu(m,k) = \nu(n,k).$$

Heisenberg's method was then to assume that in the Fourier decomposition of the coordinates and momenta of a multiple periodic motion, only certain terms should occur; further, that the coordinates and momenta are also given as a function of a set of two integers—an array of terms $q_{nm} \exp(2\pi i t \nu(nm))$, i.e., as matrices. The Hamiltonian, being a function of these quantities, becomes also a matrix, and consequently the Poisson bracket equation of classical mechanics goes over to the matrix equation of motion

$$\dot{q} = i[H,q], \quad \dot{p} = i[H,p].$$

Of course, we know now that q_{nm} is the matrix element of the operator q between the stationary states n and m of the system.

The S-matrix approach remained, without the powerful implications of analyticity, insufficient and incomplete. It took more than fifteen years before it was seriously reconsidered, although the concept of S-matrix came into fundamental usage even in quantum field theory.

---

[6] Example: kinetic energy in elastic collisions.

1.5   Definition of Space-Time and Passage to a Space-Time Description

We started our discussion with the observable properties of particles and considered observable scattering events only. The S-matrix is a function of "intrinsic" properties of the particles. The space-time coordinates need not be introduced in the formulation of the laws of physics, nor in the course of dynamical calculation. The only place in S-matrix theory where space-time enters is after an S-matrix has been evaluated, in comparison of the theory with the experimental setup, i.e., in calculating the cross sections and lifetimes (see Chapter 3).

It is intuitively clear, however, that if the various scattering events occur separately from each other in a sufficiently localized manner, it is meaningful to assign space and time coordinates to them. In this way the events themselves make their space-time. This is clearly an operational definition: the succession of localized events themselves generate space-time. But what one obtains is a sort of coarse-grained (macroscopic) space-time. The space-time continuum to which we are accustomed may be considered as an abstraction from here. This microscopic space-time is usually introduced by the so-called "interpolating fields" to the free fields describing the initial and final states of a scattering process. Certainly a deep fundamental question arises whether a microscopic space-time continuum is meaningful independent of the physical events.

In order to introduce a time and a space interval between two scattering events we must discuss the composition of the two scattering events. Clearly if two events occur very close to each other the S-matrix does not satisfy a simple composition law. That is, we cannot calculate from the knowledge of the two S-matrices the S-matrix for the total process. Some of these questions and the problem of causality have been recently discussed in the literature[7] but the answers are by no means complete. We shall have occasions to refer to the problem of the composition of successive S-matrices in a later chapter; here we only indicate how a microscopic time coordinate may be introduced.

The time coordinate may be formally introduced by the Fourier transform of the amplitude in the energy variable. Let us exhibit the dependence of the S-matrix on the total energy alone, $R(E)$, and write

$$\tilde{R}_{fi}(t) = \frac{1}{2\pi} \int_{-\infty}^{\infty} dE\, e^{-iEt} R_{fi}(E),$$

then $|\tilde{R}_{fi}(t)|^2\, dt$ may be very roughly interpreted as the probability that the states (fi) are interacting for a time between t and $t + dt$. If $R(E)$ is peaked

---

[7] M. L. Goldberger and K. M. Watson, *Phys. Rev.*, **127**, 2284 (1962); M. Froissart, M. L. Goldberger, and K. M. Watson, *Phys. Rev.*, **131**, 2820 (1963); D. Branson, *Phys. Rev.*, **135**, B1255 (1964); D. Iagolnitzer, *J. Math. Phys.*, **6**, 1576 (1965).

around some resonance value, the Fourier transform is quite broad in the corresponding region in agreement with the intuitive idea that during a resonance (or the formation of a compound state) the interaction takes a long time.

CHAPTER 2

Invariance Principles

> Whenever groups disclosed themselves or
> could be introduced, simplicity crystallized
> out of comparative chaos. . . .
>
> *E. T. Bell*

2.1 Formulation of the Invariance Condition

Because of the use of probability amplitudes, all laws in quantum theory have a strong and a weak form, depending whether they are formulated in terms of amplitudes or in terms of probabilities. Consider the transition probability W_{if} for a process. The process viewed in a different frame of reference has the transition probability W'_{if}. The *weak* (or macroscopic) *relativistic invariance* says that

$$W'_{if} = W_{if}. \tag{2.1}$$

The *strong* (or microscopic) *relativistic invariance* equates, after a suitable choice of the phases, the probability amplitudes:

$$S'(\alpha_i; \alpha_f) = S(\alpha_i; \alpha_f). \tag{2.2}$$

In other words, two different observers operating with the same values of the initial and final variables measure the same transition amplitudes. We now assume that the S-matrix elements have some definite transformation property, symbolically [1]

$$S'(\alpha'_i, \alpha'_f) = U S(\alpha_i, \alpha_f) \tag{2.3}$$

under the inhomogeneous Lorentz transformations, then Eq. (2.2) says that S is invariant under these transformations and satisfies the equation

$$S(\alpha'_i; \alpha'_f) = U S(\alpha_i; \alpha_f). \tag{2.4}$$

---

[1] Note that we are considering directly the transformation property of the individual matrix elements considered as functions. In field theory the invariance principles are formulated in terms of the transformation of the whole S-matrix in the form $S = USU^{-1}$. See, e.g., J. M. Jauch and F. Rohrlich, *Theory of Photons and Electrons* (Reading, Mass.: Addison-Wesley, 1955), p. 117.

Thus, the principle of relativistic invariance restricts the form of the scattering-matrix elements; only those functions satisfying Eq. (2.4) are candidates for scattering-matrix elements.

Equation (2.4) is valid for all other invariant transformations, including improper Lorentz transformations, isospin, and other internal symmetry transformations, etc. In all these cases we determine the transformation property of S and then equate the transformed S into the original one at the same values of the arguments. These further invariance principles will be discussed in Chapters 5 and 10.

We now show quite generally that U in Eq. (2.4) must be a unitary or antiunitary operator; both constructed out of products of unitary representations, in other words, the S-functions essentially transform according to unitary representations of the underlying symmetry or invariance group. This theorem is a simple consequence of the unitarity relation, which must be valid in every frame.

Symbolically the idea of the proof is as follows. Let S' be the S-matrix in the transformed frame with

$$S'S'^\dagger = S'^\dagger S' = I.$$

If we insert Eq. (2.3), we get

$$USS^\dagger U^\dagger = U^\dagger S^\dagger SU = I,$$

hence

$$UU^\dagger = U^\dagger U = I.$$

The unitarity condition has also played here the role of an invariant scalar product.

More precisely, if we separate the transformations acting on the first and second indices of S in the form

$$S'_{fi} = V_{fm} W^*_{in} S_{mn} \quad \text{or} \quad S' = VSW^\dagger, \tag{2.5}$$

we get

$$VSW^\dagger WS^\dagger V^\dagger = WS^\dagger V^\dagger VSV^\dagger = I,$$

which is consistent with both V and W being unitary; hence $U = VW$ is also unitary. On the other hand, we notice that the unitary condition

$$\sum_j S_{fj} S^*_{ij} = \sum_j S^*_{jf} S_{ji} = \delta_{fi}$$

is invariant under V and W alone: one because $\sum_j S_{ij} S^*_{ij}$ is an invariant scalar product, the other because δ_{if} is itself invariant:

(1)

$$\sum_{jmn} V_{fm} S_{mj} V^*_{in} S^*_{nj} = \sum_j S_{jn} W_{ni} S^*_{jm} W^*_{mf}$$

$$= \delta_{fi} = \sum_{nm} V_{fm} V^*_{in} \delta_{mn}$$

$$= \sum_{nn} W^*_{mf} W_{ni} \delta_{mn}$$

(2)

$$\sum_{jmn} S_{fm}W_{mj}S_{in}^*W_{nj}^* = \sum_{jmn} V_{jm}^*S_{mf}^*V_{jn}S_{ni} = \delta_{fi},$$

for all S.

From (1) and (2) we get the result that

$$VV^\dagger = V^\dagger W = W^\dagger W = WW^\dagger = I.$$

Consequently V and W are unitary.[2] In the case of continuous variables, the integrations are over an invariant volume element.

The second possibility is the so-called *antiunitary* operators in which case the transformation law is

$$S' = VS^TW^\dagger \qquad (2.5')$$

and it can be shown in a similar way that again V and W are unitary representations. The discrete transformations of time reversal, for example, is of this type and we shall see how we are led to such a transformation (Chap. 5). Proper inhomogeneous Lorentz transformations as well as parity are all of the type (2.5)—i.e., unitary.

To summarize, the formulation of the invariance principles quite generally is given by the following table:

	CONTINUOUS INDEX	DISCRETE INDEX
Invariance	$S'(\alpha) = S(\alpha)$	$S'_\alpha = S_\alpha$
Transformation Property	$S'(\alpha') = US(\alpha)$	$S'_{\alpha'} = U_{\alpha'\alpha}S_{\alpha'}$
Equation for S	$S(\alpha') = US(\alpha)$	$S_{\alpha'} = U_{\alpha'\alpha}S_\alpha$
		$UU^\dagger = U^\dagger U = I$

In particular, we see from the case of the discrete index that S must be an invariant or *isotropic geometric object* (e.g., isotropic tensor or spinor); α stands for the collection of all indices.

The internal degrees of freedom of the particles such as charge, strangeness, etc., are independent of the four momenta of the particles. We, therefore, shall omit the indices on the S-matrix corresponding to these properties in the discussion of relativistic invariance.

We consider now the S-matrix element as a function of the four momenta of both the incoming and the outgoing particles, $S(K_i,K_f)$. We assume that $S(K_i,K_f)$ has some well-defined transformation property, not necessarily a (covariant) tensor or spinor function; it may even be more complicated. To illustrate Eq. (2.4) we see that if S is a scalar function under Lorentz transformations Λ, it must satisfy:

$$S(K_i;K_f) = S(\Lambda^{-1}K_i;\Lambda^{-1}K_f). \qquad (2.6)$$

This equation is satisfied if S depends only on the invariant scalar products $(k_i \cdot k_j)$; we shall later see that this is also necessary under the assumption of analyticity (Chap. 6).

[2] A. O. Barut, *Phys. Rev.*, **127**, 321 (1962).

But more general transformation properties than Eq. (2.6) must also be allowed. For example, we can have,

$$S(K_i; K_f) = QS(\Lambda^{-1}K_i; \Lambda^{-1}K_f) \tag{2.7}$$

where the operator Q is such that first transforming the arguments of S alone, then applying Q, we must get back to the original S-function. Our objective in the following sections is to determine these more general forms of the S-matrix.

2.2   Unitary Representations of the Symmetry Groups

Properly speaking, this and the following sections of the present chapter, which are purely of mathematical character, should belong in an appendix. However, the form of the unitary representations of the inhomogeneous Lorentz group will play such a fundamental role in this book that we have preferred to treat this subject as part of the text.

Consider a group of transformation of elements $L_1, L_2, \ldots$. Let there correspond to every element L_1 another transformation or operator $D(L_1)$ in such a way that $D(L_1)D(L_2) = D(L_1 L_2)$. [In quantum mechanics the right-hand side is multiplied with a "phase" factor $\omega(L_1 L_2)$.] Then $D(L)$ is a *representation* of L, the dimension of D is the dimension of the representation. The "vectors" (or functions) in the representation space transform under L according to the law

$$S'(\alpha') = D(L)S(\alpha), \quad \alpha' = L\alpha. \tag{2.8}$$

In particular, L itself is its own representation. The representation is *faithful* if $L_1 \neq L_2$ implies $D(L_1) \neq D(L_2)$. We shall also require $D(I) = I$ so that $D(L^{-1}) = D(L)^{-1}$.

If a representation is unitary,

$$D^\dagger(L) = D^{-1}(L), \tag{2.9}$$

then a quadratic form (S,S) in the representation space is invariant. Two representations D_1 and D_2 are (unitarily) *equivalent* if there exists an arbitrary fixed (unitary) matrix B such that

$$D_2 = BD_1 B^{-1}.$$

For a finite group, more generally a *compact group* (a group in which the accumulation point of every sequence belongs to the group such as the rotation group), any representation by matrices with nonvanishing determinants is equivalent to a unitary representation[3] (Schur-Auerbach theorem). The unitary representation $U(L)$, corresponding to a given representation $D(L)$, is explicitly given by

$$U(L) = d^{-\frac{1}{2}}V^{-1}D(L)Vd^{\frac{1}{2}} = d^{-\frac{1}{2}}Dd^{\frac{1}{2}}$$

---

[3] See, for example, E. P. Wigner, *Group Theory* (New York: Academic, 1959), pp. 74, 101; L. Pontryagin, *Topological Groups* (Princeton U. P., 1939).

where V is the unitary matrix, which diagonalizes the hermitian expression $Z = \sum_L D(L)D^\dagger(L)$, where the summation (or the so-called Hurwitz integral in the case of continuous groups) is over all group elements, and d the positive definite diagonal form of Z and $d^{1/2}$ is the positive square root of d.

[*Proof*: Because

$$d = V^{-1}ZV = \sum_L \bar{D}(L)\bar{D}^\dagger(L), \quad V^{-1}DV = \bar{D}$$

or

$$I = d^{-1/2} \sum \bar{D}\bar{D}^\dagger d^{-1/2}$$

we have

$$\begin{aligned}
U(L)U^\dagger(L) &= d^{-1/2}\bar{D}d^{1/2}\big(d^{-1/2} \sum \bar{D}\bar{D}^\dagger d^{-1/2}\big)d^{1/2}\bar{D}^\dagger d^{-1/2} \\
&= d^{-1/2}\bar{D}(L) \sum_{L'} \bar{D}(L')\bar{D}^\dagger(L')\bar{D}^\dagger(L)d^{-1/2} \\
&= I].
\end{aligned}$$

Given a representation D, then D^*, D^{T-1} and $D^{\dagger-1}$ are also representations as can be seen from $D(L_1)D(L_2) = D(L_1L_2)$. Here $*$, T, and $\dagger$ stand for complex conjugate, transpose, and the hermitian conjugate, respectively.

The formulation of the invariance condition is essentially complete with Eq. (2.4), where U is a unitary representation of the symmetry group. The remaining problem is now partly of physical nature, namely to recognize or discover what are the symmetry groups; and partly mathematical, to find explicitly the unitary representations of these groups. The following groups are of importance:

(i) the three-dimensional rotation group for isospin—more precisely, its quantum mechanical counterpart, the 2×2-unitary group SU_2;
(ii) other unitary groups for possible *higher symmetries* (SU_3, SU_6, ...);
(iii) the Poincaré group for *momenta and spin*;
(iv) the full inhomogeneous Lorentz group, including reflections.

The first two groups are compact, hence all representations, finite or infinite, are equivalent to unitary representations, therefore of physical interest. On the other hand, the Lorentz group is *not compact* and it turns out that all finite dimensional representations of it are nonunitary. These are the representations used in wave equation, such as the Dirac equation, and will not interest us here. We need the unitary representations of the Poincaré group, which are all infinite-dimensional and have been first determined by Wigner.[4]

---

[4] E. P. Wigner, *Ann. Math.*, **40**, 149 (1939); see also A. S. Wightman in C. deWitt and R. Omnès (eds.), *Dispersion Relations and Elementary Particles* (New York: Wiley, 1960); E. P. Wigner in *Theoretical Physics*, International Atomic Energy Commission, Vienna (1963). E. P. Wigner in F. Gürsey (ed.), *Group Theoretical Methods in Elementary Particle Physics* (New York: Gordon and Breach, 1964).

This is discussed in the next section. The discussion of the other groups is postponed to later chapters.

2.3 Determination of the Unitary Representations of the Poincaré Group

Let us turn back to the Poincaré group (a,A) (see first Appendices 2 and 3), and denote its unitary representations by $U(a,A)$, which we want to determine. From the group property we have

$$U(a_2 A_2)U(a_1 A_1) = U(a_2 + \Lambda(A_2)a_1, A_2 A_1). \tag{2.10}$$

Instead of Λ we use the 2×2 unitary-unimodular matrices A (see Appendix 3). Actually, in quantum mechanics one must consider representations up to a phase factor $\omega(1,2)$ on the right-hand side of Eq. (2.10), but this factor can be chosen to be $+1$ when A is used.[5]

The translations T which we diagonalize form a commutative subgroup with

$$U(a_2,1)U(a_1,1) = U(a_2 + a_1, 1). \tag{2.11}$$

Their representations are all direct products of one-dimensional representations. For the functions $X(K_i; K_f)$ transforming under the representations of translations, we can then write, up to a unitary equivalence,

$$X'(K_i; K_f) = \exp\left(i \sum_j k_j a\right) X(K_i; K_f), \tag{2.12}$$

where the sum $\sum_j k_j a$ includes all the particles incoming and outgoing, if we draw in the S-matrix, for convenience, all particles as outgoing, for example.

Next we consider the representations $U(0,A)$ which we split into two parts

$$U(0,A) = Q(A)T(A), \tag{2.13}$$

where $T(A)$ is defined to act on the arguments K only:

$$[T(A)X](K) = X[\Lambda(A^{-1})K]. \tag{2.14}$$

Under $T(A)$, X transforms like a scalar. Because the unitarity condition involves an invariant integration, $T(A)$ is unitary. Hence $Q(A)$ in Eq. (2.14) must also be unitary if $U(0,A)$ is unitary. The definition (2.14) fixes the transformation property of $Q(A)$ which is supposed to affect X itself, not the arguments.

---

[5] V. Bargmann, *Ann. Math.*, **59**, 1 (1954). The phase ω can first be reduced to ± 1 using the continuity and associativity properties of the group. Then because the correspondence between A and Λ is 2-to-1; i.e., $\pm A \leftrightarrow \Lambda(A)$, the remaining phase can be taken to be $+1$. The groups with the phase factors properly taken care of, are called the *quantum mechanical groups*. Thus the quantum mechanical group of relativistic invariance is the group $SL(2,c)$, the 2×2 unimodular group which is the covering group of Λ.

The translations $U(a,1)$ do not commute with $U(0,A)$. However, we show now that the $Q(A)$ part of $U(0,A)$ commutes with the translations: Indeed, from the group property

$$U(0,A)U(a,1) = U(\Lambda(A)a,1)U(0,A)$$

we have

$$Q(A)T(A)U(a,1)T^{-1}(A)Q^{-1}(A) = U[\Lambda(A)a,1]. \qquad (2.15)$$

By direct computation from its definition,

$$[T(A)U(a,1)X](K) = T(A)e^{i\sum_j k_j a}X(K)$$
$$= \exp\left(i\sum_j k_j a\right)X[\Lambda(A^{-1})K] = [U(\Lambda(A)a,1)T(A)X](K)$$

for all X; hence

$$T(A)U(a,1) = U(\Lambda(A)a,1)T(A) \qquad (2.16)$$

so that T and $U(a,1)$ do not commute, but from Eq. (2.15) we now get

$$Q(A)U(\Lambda(A)a,1) = U(\Lambda(A)a,1)Q(A), \qquad (2.17)$$

which is the desired result.

Any operator F which commutes with the translations cannot affect the momentum arguments of the function X, for if $[F,U(a,1)] = 0$ we get $\exp\left(i\sum_j k_j a\right)FX = U(a,1)FX$. Hence $Q(a)$ must act as follows[6]

$$[Q(A)X](K) = \left[\prod_i Q_i(k_i,A)\right]X(K), \qquad (2.18)$$

where $Q_i(k_i,A)$ are operators acting on the additional indices of X, one for each k_i. These additional degrees of freedom on X will be interpreted as the "spin" indices. In this sense the separation given in Eq. (2.13) is one which separates spin and orbital angular momenta.

To determine $Q(A)$ or $Q(k,A)$ we use the group property

$$U(0,A_1)U(0,A_2) = U(0,A_1A_2)$$

or

$$Q(A_1)T(A_1)Q(A_2)T(A_2) = Q(A_1A_2)T(A_1A_2). \qquad (2.19)$$

Let us operate both sides of Eq. (2.19) on X and use Eq. (2.18). We have in

---

[6] "Every bounded operator commuting with translations has the spectral representation $(FX)(k) = F(k)X(k)$, where $F(k)$ is a bounded operator." See SNAG (Stone-Neumark-Ambrose-Godement) theorem, in M. M. Stone, *Ann. Math.*, **33**, 643 (1932), M. Neumark, *Iz. Akad. Nauk USSR*, **7**, 237 (1943), W. Ambrose, *Duke Math. J.*, **11**, 589 (1944), R. Godement, *C. R. Acad. Sci.*, **218**, 901 (1944).

successive steps (note that the transformations act on the variables not the argument as a whole)

$$T(A_2)X(K) = X[\Lambda(A_2^{-1})K)] \equiv Y(K).$$

$$Q(A_2)T(A_2)X(K) = Q(A_2)Y(K) = \left[\prod Q_i(k_i, A_2)\right]X[\Lambda(A_2^{-1})K]$$

$$T(A_1)Q(A_2)T(A_2)X(K) = \left[\prod_i Q_i(\Lambda(A_1^{-1})k_i, A_2)\right]X[\Lambda(A_1 A_2)^{-1}K]$$

$$Q(A_1)T(A_1)Q(A_2)T(A_2)X(K)$$
$$= \left[\prod_i Q_i(k_i, A_1)\right]\left[\prod_i Q_i(\Lambda(A_1^{-1})k_i, A_2)\right]X[\Lambda(A_1 A_2)^{-1}K]$$

The left-hand side of Eq. (2.19), on the other hand, gives

$$Q(A_1 A_2)T(A_1 A_2)X(K) = \left[\prod_i Q_i(k_i, A_1 A_2)\right]X[\Lambda(A_1 A_2)^{-1}K]$$

for all X. Therefore we obtain for each Q_i the following equation

$$Q_i(k_i, A_1)Q_i(\Lambda(A_1^{-1})k_i, A_2) = Q_i(k_i, A_1 A_2). \tag{2.20}$$

This equation is almost a group property, but not quite. It is a group property for the subgroup g of Lorentz transformations which leave a given fourvector k_i invariant:

$$g : \Lambda(A^{-1})k_i = k_i \quad \text{or} \quad \Lambda(A)k_i = k_i. \tag{2.21}$$

Clearly all Lorentz transformations satisfying Eq. (2.21) form a group, *the little group* of the vector k_i. Thus, $Q_i(k_i, A)$ are unitary representations of the little groups. These representations can be finite dimensional, because the little groups can be, as we shall see, compact subgroups of the Lorentz group. It remains to determine the little groups and their representations.

First we express $Q(k, A)$ for arbitrary k in terms of a fixed momentum p. Let p be a fixed fourvector and let

$$\Lambda(B_{k \leftarrow p})p = k. \tag{2.22}$$

We have

$$\Lambda(B_{k \leftarrow p}^{-1}) = \Lambda(B_{k \leftarrow p})^{-1} = \Lambda(B_{p \leftarrow k})$$

and hence

$$\Lambda(B_{k \leftarrow p}^{-1})k = p. \tag{2.23}$$

From Eq. (2.20) we obtain the following relation:

$$Q(k, A) = Q(k, B_{k \leftarrow p})Q(p, B_{k \leftarrow p}^{-1}AB_{q \leftarrow p})Q(p, B_{q \leftarrow p}^{-1});$$

in fact the first two terms on the right-hand side are equal to $Q(k, AB_{q \leftarrow p})$, and the product of this matrix with the last term gives the left-hand side by another application of Eq. (2.20). Because $Q(k,B_{k\leftarrow p}) = Q(p,B_{k\leftarrow p}^{-1})^{-1}$, by Eq. (2.20), again we rewrite the last equation in the form

$$Q(k,A) = Q(p,B_{k\leftarrow p}^{-1})^{-1}Q(p,B_{k\leftarrow p}^{-1}AB_{q\leftarrow p})Q(p,B_{q\leftarrow p}^{-1}), \tag{2.24}$$

which expresses $Q(k,A)$ in terms of factors of the form $Q(p,A)$.

In Eq. (2.24) the transformation $B_{k\leftarrow p}^{-1}AB_{q\leftarrow p}$ belongs to the little group of p. We choose p to be the rest frame of the particle in the case of nonzero mass. (For the case $m = 0$ see below.) Therefore $Q(k,A)$ is given essentially by the representations of the little group of the momentum in the rest frame. The first and the third factors on the right-hand side of Eq. (2.24) are arbitrary; they correspond to the choice of spin bases. If we choose the spin indices to have the same meaning as in the rest frame we can choose these factors equal to unity. Up to a unitary equivalence we can therefore write

$$Q(k,A) = Q(p,B_{k\leftarrow p}^{-1}AB_{q\leftarrow p}). \tag{2.25}$$

In terms of the representations of the little groups in the rest frame the final form of the unitary representation is

$$[U(a,A)X](K) = [U(a,1)U(0,A)X](K)$$

$$= \exp\left[i\sum_j k_j a\right] \prod_i Q_i(p_i,B_{k_i\leftarrow p_i}^{-1}AB_{q_i\leftarrow p_i})X[\Lambda(A^{-1})K]. \tag{2.26}$$

2.4   Representations of the Little Groups

We shall consider two cases, p timelike or lightlike. There are two other cases: p spacelike and $p = 0$. Their relevance will be indicated later (Chap. 10, Exercise 14).

Case (a): $\qquad\qquad\qquad p = (m,0,0,0).$

The matrices A, which take p into itself, satisfy $Ap^\mu\sigma_\mu A^\dagger = p^\mu\sigma_\mu$, which in this case reduces to

$$AA^\dagger = I. \tag{2.27}$$

That is, the little group is just the 2×2 unimodular unitary group u. The corresponding Lorentz transformations have the form

$$\Lambda = \begin{pmatrix} 1 & 0 \\ 0 & \mathbf{R} \end{pmatrix}, \quad \text{where } \mathbf{R} \text{ is a } 3 \times 3 \text{ rotation.}$$

The unitary irreducible representations of u are the $(2j + 1)$-dimensional matrices $D^j(u)$ (see App. 3). Therefore the spin matrices $Q_i(k_i,A)$ are given by

$$Q_i(k_i,A) = D^j(B_{k_i\leftarrow p}^{-1}AB_{q_i\leftarrow p_i}). \tag{2.28}$$

Here the matrices B satisfy

$$B_{k \leftarrow p} p^\mu \sigma_\mu B^\dagger_{k \leftarrow p} = k^\mu \sigma_\mu,$$

or

$$B_{k \leftarrow p} B^\dagger_{k \leftarrow p} = k^\mu \sigma_\mu / m. \tag{2.29}$$

Similarly,

$$B_{q \leftarrow p} B^\dagger_{q \leftarrow p} = q^\mu \sigma_\mu / m. \tag{2.29'}$$

The matrices B are not uniquely determined by Eqs. (2.29). Because every nonsingular matrix B can be decomposed uniquely into a product of a unitary matrix U and a positive definite hermitian matrix H: $B = HU$ (see Exercise 6), where $BB^\dagger = H^2$. Consequently if B is a solution of Eq. (2.29) then BU is also one, where U is an element of the little group.

In the next section we shall define two amplitudes depending on the choice of U. If we choose $U = I$, $BB^\dagger$ has a unique square root and we denote the corresponding matrices by $A_{k \leftarrow p}$:

$$A_{k \leftarrow p} = (k^\mu \sigma_\mu / m)^{1/2} \quad \text{and} \quad A_{q \leftarrow p} = (q^\mu \sigma_\mu / m)^{1/2}. \tag{2.30}$$

In another case we shall choose U different from I to define the helicity amplitudes. The matrix $(k^\mu \sigma_\mu / m)^{1/2}$ can also be written as

$$(k^\mu \sigma_\mu / m)^{1/2} = \cosh \frac{\chi}{2} + \hat{\mathbf{k}} \cdot \boldsymbol{\sigma} \sinh \frac{\chi}{2},$$

$$(k^\mu \tilde{\sigma}_\mu / m)^{1/2} = \cosh \frac{\chi}{2} - \hat{\mathbf{k}} \cdot \boldsymbol{\sigma} \sinh \frac{\chi}{2},$$

where

$$\cosh \chi = k^0 / m, \quad \sinh \chi = k/m, \quad \mathbf{k} = k\hat{\mathbf{k}},$$

or,

$$\cosh \frac{\chi}{2} = \frac{1}{\sqrt{2}} \left(\frac{k^0}{m} + 1 \right)^{1/2}, \quad \sinh \frac{\chi}{2} = \frac{1}{\sqrt{2}} \left(\frac{k^0}{m} - 1 \right)^{1/2}.$$

We have the useful relation

$$(k^\mu \tilde{\sigma}_\mu / m)^{1/2} (k^\nu \sigma_\nu / m)^{1/2} = 1$$

because $k \cdot \tilde{\sigma} k \cdot \sigma = k^2 = m^2$. Equation (2.26) now takes the form

$$[U(a,\Lambda)X](K) = \exp \left(i \sum_j k_j a \right) \prod_i D^{j_i}(B^{-1}_{k_i \leftarrow p_i} A B_{q_i \leftarrow p_i}) X(\Lambda(A^{-1})K). \tag{2.31}$$

These representations are determined by two sets of parameters, m_i and the spins j_i, and will be denoted by $[m,j]$.

Case (*b*): $p = (1,0,0,1)$. Any lightlike vector can be brought to this form. We find

$$p^\mu \sigma_\mu = \begin{pmatrix} 2 & 0 \\ 0 & 0 \end{pmatrix}.$$

The elements A_0 of the little group must satisfy

$$A_0 \begin{pmatrix} 1 & 0 \\ 0 & 0 \end{pmatrix} A_0^+ = \begin{pmatrix} 1 & 0 \\ 0 & 0 \end{pmatrix}.$$

The solutions of Eq. (2.31) can be written as follows

$$A_0 = \begin{pmatrix} e^{i\varphi/2} & a_{12} \\ 0 & a_{12} \end{pmatrix}.$$

The condition det $A_0 = +1$ implies

$$A_0 = \begin{pmatrix} e^{i\varphi/2} & a_{12} \\ 0 & e^{-i\varphi/2} \end{pmatrix}.$$

The coefficient a_{12} is arbitrary and we write it in the form

$$a_{12} = e^{-i\varphi/2}(x + iy).$$

Hence

$$A_0 = \begin{pmatrix} R & R^{-1}z \\ 0 & R^{-1} \end{pmatrix}, \; R = e^{i\varphi/2} \tag{2.32}$$

or

$$A_0 = \cos\frac{\varphi}{2}\sigma_0 + i\sin\frac{\varphi}{2}\sigma_3 + \frac{z}{2}R^{-1}(\sigma_1 + \sigma_2).$$

Let us look at the group property of the matrices (2.32). If we denote the elements of the little group by (z,R) or (z,φ), we see from the multiplication of two matrices of the form (2.32) that

$$(z_2,R_2)(z_1,R_1) = (z_2 + R^2z_1,R_2R_1). \tag{2.33}$$

This is exactly the group property of inhomogeneous transformations in the plane (Euclidian group E_2): $R = e^{i\varphi/2}$ is a rotation around the third axis and z a translation: $r' = Rr + z$, where r is a complex number. Note the exact analogy of Eq. (2.33) with that of inhomogeneous Lorentz transformations, Eq. (2.10). There is, however, one difference with the Euclidian group, namely $(z,-I) = (z, \varphi = 2\pi) \neq (z, \varphi = 0)$. But this is due to the choice of the parameter φ and, as we did in the Poincaré group, the representations up to a factor can be reduced to those without such a factor. Thus we can restrict the range of φ between 0 and 2π.

The group element (z,R) can be factorized as follows

$$(z,R) = (z,I)(0,R)$$

where both (z,I) and $(0,R)$ are commutative subgroups of (z,R) but

$$(0,R)(z,I) = (Rz,I)(0,R)$$

which is the counterpart of Eq. (2.15). Or, in terms of unitary representations,

$$U(0,R)U(z,I) = U(Rz,I)U(0,R).$$

The representations of the translations are given by

$$[U(z,I)X](t) = e^{iz \cdot t} X(t).$$

We know the representations of $(0,R)$, but it is instructive anyway to apply the same approach of the so-called induced representations that we used in the Poincaré group. Let us put $U(0,R) = Q(R)T(R)$ such that

$$T(R)X(t) = X(R^{-1}t)$$

where $t = (t_1,t_2)$ are the variables corresponding to k's in Poincaré group. Then $T(R)U(z,I) = U(Rz,I)T(R)$ and we obtain

$$Q(R),U(z,I) = 0.$$

Consequently, we can put

$$U(0,R)X(t) = Q(tR)X(R^{-1}t)$$

and obtain as before

$$Q(t,R_1)Q(R^{-1}t,R_2) = Q(t,R_1R_2).$$

Thus $Q(t,R)$ is a representation of the "little group" of this little group: Transformations such that $R^{-1}t = t$. There are two essentially different cases:

(a) $$t_1^2 + t_2^2 = 0, \quad \text{i.e., } t_1 = t_2 = 0.$$

It follows from Eq. (2.34) that the irreducible representations are all one dimensional and of the form

$$Q(0,R) \equiv Q(R) = e^{ij\varphi}, \tag{2.34}$$

where, if we take one- and two-valued representations, j is integer or half-integer.

(b) $$t_1^2 + t_2^2 = \Xi \neq 0.$$

In this case "the little group" of the little group consists of matrices I and $-I$. The corresponding unitary representations are infinite dimensional, as it is seen from Eq. (2.34), and are characterized by a number Ξ.

Note that the 2×2 representation $(0,z) = \begin{pmatrix} 1 & z \\ 0 & 1 \end{pmatrix}$ is reducible, but not fully reducible. The Euclidian plane is not compact.

By direct calculation we find the Lorentz transformation corresponding to Eq. (2.32) to be

$$\Lambda_\nu^\mu = \begin{bmatrix} 1 + |z|^2/2 & x\cos\varphi + y\sin\varphi & x\sin\varphi - y\cos\varphi & -|z|^2/2 \\ x & \cos\varphi & \sin\varphi & -x \\ -y & -\sin\varphi & \cos\varphi & y \\ |z|^2/2 & -x\cos\varphi - y\sin\varphi & -x\sin\varphi + y\sin\varphi & 1 - |z|^2/2 \end{bmatrix}.$$

$$\tag{2.35}$$

We recognize the one-parameter subgroup of rotations by angle φ in the k^1k^2-plane.

Next we calculate the matrices $B_{k \leftarrow p}$ which now satisfy the equation

$$B_{k \leftarrow p}\tfrac{1}{2}(1 + \sigma_3)B^{\dagger}_{k \leftarrow p} = \tfrac{1}{2}k^{\mu}\sigma_{\mu} = \frac{k^0 + \boldsymbol{\sigma}\cdot\mathbf{k}}{2\omega}. \tag{2.36}$$

Again if B is a solution, BA_0 is also one, where A_0 is an element of the little group. From Eq. (2.36) and $\det B = +1$ we obtain the general solution

$$B_{k \leftarrow p} = \begin{bmatrix} \sqrt{\dfrac{k^0 + k^3}{2\omega}}\, e^{i\theta/2} & ze^{-i\theta/2}\sqrt{\dfrac{k^0 + k^3}{2\omega}} \\[3mm] \dfrac{(k^1 + ik^2)e^{i\theta/2}}{\sqrt{2(k^0 + k^3)\omega}} & \sqrt{\dfrac{2\omega}{k^0 + k^3}}\, e^{-i\theta/2}(1 + b_{12}\cdot b_{21}) \end{bmatrix}$$

$$= \begin{bmatrix} \sqrt{\dfrac{k^0 + k^3}{2\omega}} & 0 \\[3mm] \dfrac{k^1 + ik^2}{\sqrt{2(k^0 + k^3)\omega}} & \sqrt{\dfrac{2\omega}{k^0 + k^3}} \end{bmatrix} \begin{bmatrix} e^{i\theta/2} & e^{-i\theta/2}z \\[3mm] 0 & e^{-i\theta/2} \end{bmatrix} \tag{2.37}$$

We take the first term as the standard solution $B^0_{k \leftarrow p}$; the second term is an element of the little group. The Lorentz transformation corresponding to the standard $B^0_{k \leftarrow p}$ is

$$\Lambda^0_{k \leftarrow p} = \frac{1}{\omega}\begin{bmatrix} \dfrac{a^2 + b + 4\omega^2}{4a} & a^{-1}k^1_{\omega} & a^{-1}k^2_{\omega} & \dfrac{a^2 + b - 4\omega^2}{4a} \\[3mm] \dfrac{k^1}{2} & \omega & 0 & \dfrac{k^1}{2} \\[3mm] \dfrac{k^2}{2} & 0 & 1 & \dfrac{k^2}{2} \\[3mm] \dfrac{a^2 - b - 4\omega^2}{4a} & -a^{-1}k^1_{\omega} & -a^{-1}k^2_{\omega} & \dfrac{a^2 - b + 4\omega^2}{4a} \end{bmatrix}$$

where $a = (k^0 + k^3)$, $b = k^{1^2} + k^{2^2}$. For lightlike vectors $k^{1^2} + k^{2^1} = k^{0^2} - k^{3^2}$, and it is easily verified that $\Lambda_{k \leftarrow p}$ takes the vector $(1,0,0,+1)$ into k. The most general form of $\Lambda_{k \leftarrow p}$ is the product of this matrix with the matrix (2.35).

We shall give now the solution of Eq. (2.36) in a different, more convenient form. Let us take the standard form of the momentum of the massless particle as

$$p = \lambda(1001), \quad \lambda = \text{arbitrary.}$$

Then

$$B_{k \leftarrow p}\frac{1 + \sigma_3}{2}B^{+}_{k \leftarrow p} = \frac{\mathbf{k}\cdot\boldsymbol{\sigma}}{2\lambda}, \tag{2.36'}$$

and the most general solution of this equation is of the form

$$B_{k \leftarrow p} = F(k)U(k)A_0, \tag{2.37'}$$

where A_0 is an element of the little group of the form (2.32) and $U(k)$ is a rotation taking the z-axis into the direction $\hat{\mathbf{k}}$:

$$U(k) \frac{1 + \sigma_3}{2} U(k)^\dagger = \frac{1 + \boldsymbol{\sigma} \cdot \hat{\mathbf{k}}}{2},$$

and $F(k)$ is a dilatation, i.e.,

$$F(k) \frac{1 + \boldsymbol{\sigma} \cdot \mathbf{k}}{2} F^\dagger = \frac{k \cdot \sigma}{2\lambda} = \frac{k^0}{\lambda} \frac{1 + \boldsymbol{\sigma} \cdot \hat{\mathbf{k}}}{2}.$$

This is given explicitly by

$$F(k) = \frac{1}{2\sqrt{k^0/\lambda}} \left[\frac{k^0}{\lambda} + 1 + \left(\frac{k^0}{\lambda} - 1 \right) \boldsymbol{\sigma} \cdot \hat{\mathbf{k}} \right].$$

Clearly for the special choice $\lambda = k^0$ we have $F(k) = I$, and the form of $B_{k \leftarrow p}$ simplifies to a rotation (up to an element of the little group).

We can now write the one-dimensional unitary representations of the Poincaré group in the mass zero case as follows:

$$[U(a,\Lambda)X](K) = e^{i \sum_\alpha k_\alpha a} e^{i \sum_\alpha j_\alpha \varphi(A,k)} X(\Lambda^{-1}K). \tag{2.26'}$$

This is the equation which takes the place of Eq. (2.26) in the massless case. The j_α is the spin of the αth particle and $\varphi(A,k)$ is the parameter appearing in the following element of the little group

$$A_0(\varphi) = B_{k \leftarrow p}^{-1}(\varphi)AB_{q \leftarrow p}(\varphi),$$
$$\Lambda(A)q = k, \tag{2.38}$$

with B given by Eq. (2.37) or Eq. (2.37'). We also note for further use that A_0 satisfies the equation

$$A_0 \frac{1 + \sigma_3}{2} = e^{i \varphi(K,A)} \frac{1 + \sigma_3}{2}. \tag{2.39}$$

The connection between φ and A_0 can also be written as

$$\frac{\varphi}{2} = \text{arcos} \left(\tfrac{1}{2} \operatorname{tr} A_0 \right).$$

This completes the discussion of the representations in the zero mass case.

2.5 *S*-Matrix and the Amplitudes

We now apply the unitary irreducible representations of the Poincaré group discussed in the previous section to the S-matrix elements and amplitudes.

The S-matrix elements transform according to Eq. (2.31); they are moreover invariant under these transformations. To formulate the conservation laws in a simple form, we have to distinguish between the incoming and the outgoing particles. If the outgoing particles transform with e^{ika}, $D^j(B_{k \leftarrow p}^{-1} A B_{q \leftarrow p})$, or $e^{is\varphi}$, $D^I(u)$ under translations, Lorentz transformations, and isotopic spin rotations respectively, then we take the incoming particles to transform with e^{-ika}, $D^{j*}(B^{-1}AB)$, or $e^{-is\varphi}$, $D^{I*}(u)$. The opposite choice is also possible, as long as the incoming and outgoing particles are transformed according to conjugate representations.

It would be more convenient to draw all particles as ingoing in which case all particles would transform according to the same representation D^j, if antiparticles are introduced. The antiparticles and the relation of particle processes to antiparticle processes will be introduced in Chap. 5.

With these conventions the S-matrix satisfies the following fundamental equations:

$$S(K_i, K_f) = \exp\left(i \sum_f k_f a\right) \exp\left(-i \sum_i k_i a\right)\left[\prod_f D^{(S_f)}(A'_f)\right]$$
$$\times \left[\prod_i D^{(S_i)*}(A'_i)\right] S(\Lambda^{-1}K_i, \Lambda^{-1}K_f), \quad (2.40)$$

where

$$A' = B_{k \leftarrow p}^{-1} A B_{k \leftarrow q}, \quad B_{k \leftarrow p} = \left(\frac{k^\mu \sigma_\mu}{m}\right)^{1/2} U. \quad (2.41)$$

The new quantum numbers S_i, S_f occurring in this equation are defined to be the *spins* of the particles. Correspondingly the S-matrix will have spin indices, m_i, one for each particle: $-S_i < m_i < +S_i$. When one of the particles has a zero mass the corresponding D-term must be replaced by $\exp(iS\varphi)$; we have always only two inequivalent representations. Mass zero particles of opposite helicities may be counted as different particles.

From the fact that the S-matrix is invariant under translations alone we obtain the conservation of total linear energy momentum:

$$P_f = \sum_f k_f = \sum_i k_i \equiv P_i. \quad (2.42)$$

The same transformation property (2.40) holds for the amplitudes $R = S - I$. Let us write as an example the Eq. (2.40) for the amplitude explicitly with their spin indices for a two-body scattering process, $1 + 2 - 3 + 4$,

$$R^{m_1 m_2}_{m_3 m_4}(k_1 k_2; k_3 k_4) = D^{(S_1)*}{}^{m_1}{}_{n_1}(A') D^{(S_2)*}{}^{m_2}{}_{n_2}(A') D^{(S_3)n_3}_{m_3}(A')$$
$$\times D^{(S_4)n_4}_{m_4}(A') R^{n_1 n_2}_{n_3 n_4}(\Lambda^{-1}k_1, \Lambda^{-1}k_2; \Lambda^{-1}k_3, \Lambda^{-1}k_4). \quad (2.43)$$

We recall that the phase of the amplitudes is so fixed that the "no-scattering" part I of the S-matrix has the phase 1.

Let us introduce at this point the *isotopic spin* of the particles to point out the analogies and differences with the ordinary spin. Empirically, the strongly interacting particles possess an intrinsic quantum number, such that the corresponding indices of the S-matrix transform according to irreducible representation of the group SU_2 (covering group of the rotation group R_3, as in the case of spin). We have

$$R^{\alpha_1\alpha_2}_{\alpha_3\alpha_4}(K) = D^{(I_1)*\alpha_1}{}_{\beta_1}(u)D^{(I_2)*\alpha_2}{}_{\beta_2}(u)D^{(I_3)\beta_3}_{\alpha_3}(u)D^{(I_4)\beta_4}_{\alpha_4}(u)R^{\beta_1\beta_2}_{\beta_3\beta_4}(K), \quad (2.44)$$

where the new quantum numbers I_i are the isospins of the particles. There are two differences between the two equations (2.43) and (2.44): In the spin case we have the argument $\Lambda^{-1}K$ of R in the right-hand side and the k-dependent arguments A' of $D^{(S)}$. Both of these show coupling of the spin to linear momenta, whereas the isospin is a quantum number completely independent of momenta. One consequence of the simpler transformation property of the isospin quantum number is that we can immediately define amplitudes $R^{II'}$ corresponding to *total isotopic spins* I and I' of the incoming and outgoing particles. These amplitudes have the transformation property

$$R^{(II')\alpha}_{\alpha'} = D^{(I)*\alpha}{}_{\beta}(u)D^{(I')\beta'}_{\alpha'}R^{(II')\beta}_{\beta'}, \quad (2.45)$$

or, in matrix rotation

$$R^{(II)} = D^{(I')}RD^{(I)\dagger}. \quad (2.45')$$

But because $D^{(I)}$ is unitary and irreducible, we find by Schur's lemma that

$$R^{(I'I)}_{\alpha'\alpha} = R^I\delta^{I'I}\delta_{\alpha'\alpha}. \quad (2.46)$$

Thus the *total isotopic spin* I is conserved and the amplitudes are independent of the third components α of the total isospin. This result is a special case of the Wigner-Eckhart theorem.[7] Later on we shall express R^I in terms of $R^{(I_1\cdots I_4)}$, and vice versa and prove Eq. (2.45) again indirectly.

We could also define amplitudes corresponding to *total spin* transforming as

$$R^{(SS')m}_{m'}(K) = D^{(S)m}{}_n(A')^*D^{(S')n'}_{m'}(A')R^{(SS')n}_{n'}(\Lambda^{-1}K). \quad (2.47)$$

But the Schur lemma is no longer applicable and the total spin is *not* conserved. Amplitudes corresponding to total angular momentum will be introduced later by the partial wave projection techniques. Angular momentum can also be introduced directly if we represent the Poincaré group in the angular momentum basis (see Exercise 24).

Our problem is now to find the most general solutions of Eqs. (2.40) and (2.44), i.e., to determine the most general form of amplitudes compatible with relativistic invariance. (Reflections not yet included.)

According to the choice of $B_{k\leftarrow p}$ in Eq. (2.40) we shall define two amplitudes:

[7] See, for example, E. P. Wigner, *Group Theory* (New York: Academic, 1959); M. E. Rose, *Elementary Theory of Angular Momentum* (New York: Wiley, 1957).

a. R-amplitudes

$B_{k \leftarrow p} = H = (k^\mu \sigma_\mu / m)^{1/2}$, which means that all spin components are measured with respect to a fixed $z =$ axis.

b. H- or Helicity Amplitudes

The spin component of each particle is measured in the direction of the motion of that particle.[8]

Let the spatial part of the momentum $\mathbf{k}$ be in the direction (φ, θ); we need then a rotation from the z-direction to the direction of (φ, θ). The unitary matrix corresponding to this rotation is now the matrix U, which enters in the expression of $B_{k \leftarrow p}$, Eq. (2.40). Hence

$$B_{k \leftarrow p} = HU = \left(\frac{k^\mu \sigma_\mu}{m}\right)^{1/2} e^{-i\sigma_3 \phi/2} e^{i\sigma_2 \theta/2} e^{i\sigma_3 \phi/2}$$

$$= e^{-i\sigma_3 \phi/2} e^{i\sigma_2 \theta/2} e^{i\sigma_3 \phi/2} (\bar{k}^\mu \sigma_\mu / m)^{1/2} \tag{2.48}$$

where $\bar{k} = (k^0, 0, 0, |\mathbf{k}|)$.

2.6 Spinorial Amplitudes

In order to bring the spin equation (2.40) into a manageable form (because of the appearance of the complicated argument A') and for the purpose of analytic continuation, we shall now define new amplitudes, the *M-amplitudes*, or the "Spinorial amplitudes," or the "analytic amplitudes." These amplitudes arise from a natural decomposition of A'.

Because A' is unitary we have

$$D^{(S)}(A') \equiv D^{(OS)}(A') = D^{(OS)}(B_{k \leftarrow p}^{-1}) D^{(OS)}(A) D^{(OS)}(B_{q \leftarrow p}); \quad (q = \Lambda^{-1} k) \tag{2.49}$$

where in the last step we have used the group property of $D^{(OS)}$, the irreducible representations of the *homogeneous* Lorentz group. If we insert Eq. (2.49) into Eq. (2.40) and define the M-functions in terms of the R-amplitudes by

$$M(K) = \prod_i D^{(OS_i)}(B_{k_i \leftarrow p})^* \prod_f D^{(OS_f)}(B_{k_f \leftarrow p}) R(K) \tag{2.50}$$

then we obtain the following equation for the M-amplitudes[9]:

$$M(K) = \prod_i D^{(OS_i)}(A)^* \prod_f D^{(OS_f)}(A) M(\Lambda^{-1} K). \tag{2.51}$$

Thus the M-amplitudes transform according to the direct product of irreducible $D^{(OS)}$-representations of the *homogeneous Lorentz group*. In other words, they are just the Lorentz covariant spinors. It will be easier to construct

---

[8] For an entirely different derivation of helicity amplitudes, see M. Jacob and G. C. Wick, *Ann. Phys.*, **7**, 403 (1959).

[9] The M-functions for spin $\frac{1}{2}$ case have been discussed by H. P. Stapp, *Phys. Rev.*, **125**, 2139 (1962) by a different method. Our formulae are automatically valid for all spin values and coincides with Stapp's in the case of spin $\frac{1}{2}$-particles. See also A. O. Barut, I. Muzinich, and D. Williams, *Phys. Rev.*, **130**, 442 (1963).

the *M*-functions from Eq. (2.51). Once *M* is known we go back to Eq. (2.50) and calculate *R* and consequently the cross sections and probabilities.

As an example, consider the scattering problem with one spin $\frac{1}{2}$ particle such as π-*N* scattering. Because $D^{(0\,\frac{1}{2})}(A) = A$, the equations (2.51) and (2.50) reduce to

$$M_{\dot{m}m}(k) = A_{\dot{m}}^{*\dot{n}} A_m{}^n M_{\dot{n}n}(\Lambda^{-1}K)$$

and

$$M_{\dot{m}m}(k) = \left(\frac{k_1 \cdot \sigma}{m_1}\right)^{\frac{1}{2}\cdot \dot{n}}_{\dot{m}} \left(\frac{k_3 \cdot \sigma}{m_3}\right)^{\frac{1}{2}n}_{m} R_{\dot{n}n}^{(K)}(K). \tag{2.52}$$

Or, in matrix rotation, and, writing the outgoing indices first,

$$\begin{aligned} M(K) &= AM(\Lambda^{-1}K)A^\dagger \\ &= (k_3 \cdot \sigma/m)^{\frac{1}{2}} R(K)(k_1 \cdot \sigma/m)^{\frac{1}{2}\dagger}, \end{aligned} \tag{2.52'}$$

respectively. Note that in *R* a lower dotted index is equivalent to an upper undotted one, because $D^{(j)T-1} = D^{(j)*}$.

We shall now consider the spinorial amplitudes in the mass zero case. In order to have a formalism similar to the massive case we use an amplitude which is a $(2j + 1)$-spinor with a projection operator in front to pick up just a single polarization state:

$$R_{(m=j)} = D_{mn}^{(j)}\left(\frac{1 + \sigma_3}{2}\right) R_n(K), \tag{2.53}$$

where we considered, for simplicity, a single outgoing massless particle only. We now show that the transformation property (2.38), namely

$$D^j\left(\frac{1 + \sigma_3}{2}\right) R(K) = e^{ij\varphi(A,k)} R(\Lambda^{-1}K), \tag{2.54}$$

is equivalent to

$$D^j\left(\frac{1 + \sigma_3}{2}\right) R(K) = D^j(A_0) D^j\left(\frac{1 + \sigma_3}{2}\right) R(\Lambda^{-1}K) \tag{2.54'}$$

where $A_0 = B_{k \leftarrow p}^{-1}(\varphi) A B_{q \leftarrow p}(\varphi)$ is the element of the little group of the massless particle, as discussed before, Eq. (2.32'). Indeed, because the D^j matrices can also be defined for nonunitary arguments, we can rewrite the last equation as

$$\begin{aligned} D^j\left(\frac{1 + \sigma_3}{2}\right) R(K) &= D^j\left(A_0 \frac{1 + \sigma_3}{2}\right) R(\Lambda^{-1}K) \\ &= D^j\left(e^{i\frac{1}{2}\varphi(k,A)} \frac{1 + \sigma_3}{2}\right) R(\Lambda^{-1}K) \\ &= e^{i\varphi(k,A)} D^j\left(\frac{1 + \sigma_3}{2}\right) R(\Lambda^{-1}K) \end{aligned}$$

where we have used Eq. (2.39) and the fact that $D^j(cA) = c^{2j} D^j(A)$, where *c* is a complex number.

The spinorial amplitudes M can again be defined in the same way as before

$$M(K) = D^{0j}(B_{k \leftarrow p})R(K) \tag{2.55}$$

and have the transformation property

$$M(K) = D^{0j}(A)M(\Lambda^{-1}K). \tag{2.56}$$

Because the actual amplitude is picked up by the projection operator as shown above we get the relation

$$D^{0j}(B^{-1})M(k)|_{m=j} = D^{0j}\left(\frac{1 + \sigma_3}{2}\right)D^{0j}(B^{-1})M(K).$$

Hence

$$M(K) = D^{0j}\left(B\frac{1 + \sigma_3}{2}B^{-1}\right)M(K).$$

Or, using Eq. (2.36), we get

$$M(K) = D^{0j}\left(\frac{k \cdot \sigma}{2k^0}\right)M(K). \tag{2.57}$$

This is the fundamental equation to be satisfied by the spinor index describing a massless particle; it takes care of the fact that such a particle has only one degree of polarization and not $(2j + 1)$. We shall impose this condition in determining the amplitudes. The above condition can be written also in a different form. Because

$$k \cdot \tilde{\sigma} k \cdot \sigma = k^2 = 0$$

for a massless particle, we get

$$D^{0j}\left(\frac{k \cdot \tilde{\sigma}}{2k^0}\right)M(K) = 0, \tag{2.58}$$

which has the form of the neutrino wave equation, but M is the amplitude and not a wave function. Spinors satisfying the above equation may be called "nullspinors"[10] or "polarization spinors."

As an example, consider the case of spin $\frac{1}{2}$ and $k^2 = 0$. The nullspinor $\xi(k)$ in this case can be constructed from the factorization property (see Exercise 16):

$$(k \cdot \sigma)_{\alpha\dot\alpha} = \xi_\alpha(k)\xi_{\dot\alpha}(k) \quad \text{(if } k^2 = 0\text{)}, \ \xi_{\dot\alpha} \equiv \xi_\alpha^*. \tag{2.59}$$

Indeed, $\xi(k)$ has the correct transformation property: from

$$Ak \cdot \sigma A^+ = A\xi(k)\xi^*(k)A^\dagger = (\Lambda k) \cdot \sigma = \xi(\Lambda k)\xi^*(\Lambda k)$$

we have

$$D^{0\frac{1}{2}}(A)\xi(\Lambda^{-1}k) = A\xi(\Lambda^{-1}k) = \xi(k). \tag{2.60}$$

[10] See also D. Zwanziger, *Phys. Rev.*, **133**, B1036 (1964).

In addition, the property of being the nullspinor

$$\left(\frac{k \cdot \sigma}{2k^0}\right)_{\alpha\dot{\alpha}} \xi^{\dot{\alpha}} = \xi_\alpha, \tag{2.61}$$

or

$$(k \cdot \tilde{\sigma})\xi(k) = 0, \tag{2.61'}$$

follows from the explicit form of ξ:

$$\xi_\alpha = \begin{bmatrix} \sqrt{k^0 + k^3} \\ \dfrac{k^0 + ik^2}{\sqrt{k^0 + k^3}} \end{bmatrix}, \quad \xi_{\dot{\alpha}} = \xi_\alpha^*. \tag{2.62}$$

A neutrino therefore must be described by an amplitude of the form ξ_α. There is also a (parity) conjugate nullspinor

$$\eta(k) = \xi(\tilde{k}), \quad \tilde{k} : (k^0, -\mathbf{k})$$

satisfying

$$\left(\frac{k \cdot \tilde{\sigma}}{2k^0}\right)\eta = \eta, \quad \text{or} \quad (k \cdot \sigma)\eta = 0, \tag{2.63}$$

with the factorization

$$k \cdot \tilde{\sigma} = \eta\eta^*, \quad k^2 = 0. \tag{2.64}$$

We now turn to the connection between M and R, Eq. (2.55). We have seen that, in Eq. (2.37'), with the choice $\lambda = k^0$, $B_{k \leftarrow p}$ is a rotation up to an element of the little group. Choosing the arbitrary element of the little group to be unity we are left with a rotation which precisely measures the spin index in the direction of the 3-momentum $\mathbf{k}$. Hence we get automatically the *helicity index* for such particles. And with this choice of the spin measurement there is actually no difference between M- and R-amplitudes for massless particles.

Finally we give a convenient matrix notation of our transformation equations. Let us introduce the short notations

$$D^F \equiv \prod_f D^{(S_f)}(A'), \quad D^S \equiv \prod_i D^{(S_i)}(A'),$$

$$D^{0F} \equiv \prod_f D^{(0S_f)}(B_{k_f \leftarrow p_f}), \quad D^{0S} \equiv \prod_i D^{(0S_i)}(B_{k_i \leftarrow p_i}), \tag{2.65}$$

$$\Delta^{0F} = \prod_f D^{(0S_f)}(A), \quad \Delta^{0S} = \prod_i D^{(0S_i)}(A).$$

We have then the transformation equations in matrix form as far as the spinor indices are concerned

$$R(K) = D^F R(\Lambda^{-1}K)D^{S\dagger}$$
$$M(K) = \Delta^{0F} M(\Lambda^{-1}K)\Delta^{0S\dagger}, \tag{2.65'}$$

and the equation connecting M and R is

$$M(K) = D^{0F} R(K) D^{0S\dagger}. \tag{2.65''}$$

In these equations the matrix indices are the sets of indices for initial and final particles.

In equations of the type (2.64) and (2.65) one should write R with dotted indices, $R_{m\dot{n}}$ instead of R_m^n. Wek now that these are equivalent in R. But in M-functions we have four different types of spinors. Also in R-functions the operation of complex conjugation changes dotted and undotted indices:

$$(R_{m\dot{n}})^* = R_{\dot{m}n}. \tag{2.66}$$

2.7 An Application: Selection Rule on the Number of Fermions

At this point we can prove the theorem that *in any scattering process the sum of incoming and outgoing fermions must be even.*[11]

To see this we use in Eq. (2.43) or (2.51) the transformation $\Lambda(-I)$. Because

$$D^{(S)}(-A) = (-1)^{2S} D^{(S)}(A), \quad D^{(0S)}(-A) = (-1)^{2S} D^{(0S)}(A),$$

and

$$\Lambda(-A) = \Lambda(A)$$

we have

$$R(K) = (-1)^{2 \sum_j S_j} \prod_j D^{(S_j)}(I) R(\Lambda(-I)K) = (-1)^{2 \sum_j S_j} R(K); \tag{2.67}$$

hence $\sum_j S_j$ (sum over both initial and final particles) must be an integer. *The same* result holds also for isospin: *The sum of the initial and final isospins must be an integer.*

Problems and Further Developments

1. Show that the Lorentz transformations $\Lambda_+^\uparrow$ with $\det = +1$ and $\Lambda_0^0 > +1$ form a subgroup.
2. Find the rotation $R(u^*)$ and the Lorentz transformations $\Lambda(A^*)$, $\Lambda(A^{T-1})$, $\Lambda(A^{\dagger-1})$ and compare them with $R(u)$ and $\Lambda(A)$.
3. Show that the representations $D^j(u)$ and $D^{j_1 j_2}(A)$ are irreducible.
4. Introduce angular coordinates in the spinors X_m^j transforming under $D^j(u)$ and show that they are associated Legendre polynomials Y_m^j and transform under $D^j(u)$ for fixed j.
5. Using Schur's lemma show that the only matrices which transform hermitian and traceless matrices into again hermitian and traceless matrices are multiples of unitary transformations.

[11] This rule on the number of fermions is sometimes cited as a superselection rule, but in fact it follows from relativistic invariance.

6. Show that any given nonsingular matrix B can be decomposed in one and only one way into $B = HU$ where H is a positive definite hermitian matrix and U is unitary. (Polar decomposition.) Every real matrix of determinant 1 may be written in the form OH where O is an orthogonal matrix and H a positive definite matrix, both of determinant 1.

7. Extend to compact groups the proof (given in text for finite groups) that any representation by matrices with nonvanishing determinants is equivalent to unitary representations.

8. All unitary representations of compact groups are finite dimensional. [P. Koosis, *Proc. Amer. Math. Soc.*, **8**, 712 (1957); L. Nachbin, *Notas de Fiska*, VI, No. 3 (1960), Brasil.]

9. Every representation of a finite or compact group is *discrete*; i.e., the representation is fully reducible into irreducible representations and nothing else.

10. Show that the spinor indices of σ_μ are $\sigma_{\mu\alpha\dot\alpha}$ and that of $\tilde\sigma_\mu$ are $\tilde\sigma_\mu^{\dot\alpha\alpha}$.

11. Show that a second-rank hermitian spinor $X_{\alpha\dot\alpha}$ represents a fourvector a^μ by the relation $X_{\alpha\dot\alpha} = \sigma_{\mu\alpha\dot\alpha}a^\mu$.

12. Show that the Lorentz transformations corresponding to $A_r = \exp\left(\dfrac{\theta}{2}\,i\mathbf{n}\cdot\boldsymbol\sigma\right)$, n real are pure rotations; those corresponding to $A_w = \exp\left(\dfrac{\theta}{2}\,\mathbf{n}\cdot\boldsymbol\sigma\right)$ are pure timelike. A general homogeneous proper Lorentz transformation can be decomposed into the product of a rotation and a pure timelike Lorentz transformation. Thus a general 2×2 unimodular matrix can be written in the form $A = \exp\left(\dfrac{\theta}{2}\,i\mathbf{n}\cdot\boldsymbol\sigma\right)\exp\left(\dfrac{\theta'}{2}\,\mathbf{n}'\cdot\boldsymbol\sigma\right)$. In particular find the rotation corresponding to

$$e^{-i\frac{\sigma_3}{2}\varphi}e^{i\frac{\sigma_2}{2}\theta}e^{i\frac{\sigma_3}{2}\varphi}.$$

13. Show that $C^{-1}M^TC = M^{-1}\det M$ and $D^{0j}(C)^{-1}D^{0j} \times (M^T)D^{0j}(C) = D(M)^{-1}\det D(M)$; for any 2×2 matrix M.

14. Prove the relations

$$(k^\mu\sigma_\mu/m)^{1/2} = \cosh\frac{\chi}{2} + \hat{\mathbf{k}}\cdot\boldsymbol\sigma\sinh\frac{\chi}{2}$$

$$(k^\mu\tilde\sigma_\mu/m)^{1/2} = \cosh\frac{\chi}{2} - \hat{\mathbf{k}}\cdot\boldsymbol\sigma\sinh\frac{\chi}{2}$$

where $\cosh\chi = k^0/m$ and $\mathbf{k} = k\hat{\mathbf{k}}$, and find the corresponding Lorentz transformations $\Lambda_{k\leftarrow p}$.

15. For $k^2 = 0$ find the Lorentz transformation $\Lambda_{k\leftarrow p}$ where $p = (1001)$. Show that $B_{k\leftarrow p} = \overset{(0)}{B}_{k\leftarrow p}A_0$, where A_0 is an arbitrary element of the little group, and $\overset{(0)}{B}_{k\leftarrow p}$ is given in Eq. (2.37).

16. For $k^2 = 0$ show that $k^\mu \sigma_\mu = \xi_\alpha(k)\xi_{\dot\alpha}^*(k)$ where

$$\xi_\alpha = \begin{bmatrix} \sqrt{k^0 + k^3} \\ \dfrac{k^1 + ik^2}{\sqrt{k^0 + k^3}} e^{i\varphi} \end{bmatrix}$$

and ξ^* is the conjugate complex of ξ. Or, introducing the polar coordinates $k^1 + ik^2 = k^0 \sin\theta e^{i\varphi}$ and $k^3 = k^0 \cos\theta$, we can write

$$\xi = \sqrt{2k^0} \begin{bmatrix} \cos\dfrac{\theta}{2} \\ \sin\dfrac{\theta}{2} e^{i\varphi} \end{bmatrix}.$$

17. Similarly, for $k^2 = m^2$, show that most generally

$$B_{k \leftarrow p} = (k\cdot\sigma/m)^{1/2} U$$

where U is a unitary (i.e., an element of the little group).

18. Show that for $k^2 = m^2$, a spinor decomposition

$$\frac{1}{m} k^\mu \sigma_{\mu\alpha} = \xi_\alpha \eta_{\dot\alpha}$$

is not possible.

19. The 2×2 unimodular matrix $B_{b \leftarrow a}$ corresponding to a Lorentz transformation taking the fourvector a_μ into the fourvector b_μ satisfies

$$B_{b \leftarrow a} a^\mu \sigma_\mu B_{b \leftarrow a}^\dagger = b^\mu \sigma_\mu;$$

show that the most general solution of this equation for $b^2 = a^2 \neq 0$ is given by

$$B_{b \leftarrow a} = \frac{1}{|a|} (\sqrt{b\cdot\sigma}\, U \sqrt{a\cdot\tilde\sigma}).$$

20. Solve the same problem in the case $a^2 = b^2 = 0$.

21. Show that all real 2×2 matrices of determinant one represent (2 to 1) the group of three-dimensional real homogeneous Lorentz transformations ($x_0^2 - x_1^2 - x_3^2 =$ invariant) which is isomorphic to the little group of a spacelike fourvector.

22. Show that the matrices

$$W = \begin{pmatrix} \alpha & \beta \\ x\beta & \tilde\alpha \end{pmatrix}$$

form a group for any real x, and for $x = 1, 0$, and -1 one gets all three little groups of the Poincaré group with $\alpha\tilde\alpha - x\beta\tilde\beta = 1$.

23. Discuss the unitary representations of the three-dimensional Euclidian group E_3 (semidirect product of translations and rotations in three dimensions), in which the momenta **p** are diagonalized, by the same method of induced representations that we used for the Poincaré group and Euclidian group E_2. [Compare also A. S. Wightman, *Rev. Mod. Phys.*, **34**, 845 (1962), Sec. 3.]

24. Total Angular Momentum Representation. The Poincaré group has 10 infinitesimal generators, four momenta $\mathbf{P}_\mu$ and six generators $J_{\mu\nu}$ of the homogeneous Lorentz transformations. In constructing the S-matrix in this chapter we have used a representation in which $\mathbf{P}_\mu$ and a spin operator (defined in the text) are diagonalized; the states are labeled by the eigenvalues of these operators: $|k_\mu,s\rangle$. Now the angular momentum does not commute with all the $\mathbf{P}_\mu$ (spin-orbit coupling). One can, however, also represent the Poincaré group by diagonalizing other subgroups. Two such subgroups where angular momentum enters are: (1) diagonalize the homogeneous subgroup; (2) diagonalize energy P_0 and the three-dimensional Euclidian group E_3 (see above, Exercise 23). In the latter case the states will be labeled by energy, helicity (eigenvalue of the invariant $\mathbf{P} \cdot \mathbf{J}$), angular momentum, and the third component of the angular momentum.

In the scattering problems one is interested in the total angular momentum of two or more particles. This problem is implicitly solved in this book by constructing the invariant amplitudes and then performing partial wave projections (see, e.g., Chap. 12). Group theoretically the problem amounts to reducing the direct product of two irreducible representations according to the total J of the particles.

Transform the states of two particles $|k_1s_1,k_2s_2\rangle$ into the total angular momentum states $|JM\ldots\rangle$ and show that the S-matrix in this labeling has the transformation property

$$S_{MM'}^{JJ'} = \mathscr{D}_{MN}^J S_{NN'}^{JJ'} \mathscr{D}_{N'M'}^{J'\,\dagger},$$

as in Eq. (2.45′). Then, as in Eq. (2.46),

$$S_{MM'}^{JJ'} = S^J \delta^{JJ'} \delta_{MM'}.$$

[See also J. Werle, *Relativistic Theory of Reactions* (Amsterdam: North-Holland Publ. Co., 1966).]

CHAPTER 3

Transition Probability, Phase Space, and Unitarity

This chapter deals with the connection of the S-matrix or the amplitudes and the experimental quantities. In Sec. 3.1 the transition probabilities, cross section, and lifetime formulas are given. In Sec. 3.2 we define and evaluate the spin polarization. This is followed by a discussion of the unitarity condition with an invariant phase space factor, the optical theorem (Sec. 3.4) and, finally, in Sec. 3.5, the evaluation of the phase-space factors in terms of the center of mass quantities—i.e., total energy and momentum. These last formulas are important not only practically but also in the discussion of analytical properties of the amplitudes in terms of the total energy.

3.1 Cross Sections and Lifetimes

In this section we shall connect the probability W_{fi} with its actual measurement. How is any probability measured? By repeated measurements and by counting the relative frequency of occurrence of the event. To measure W_{fi} directly one has to measure for a large number of single events the final momenta of all particles. However, experiments are not performed on individual scattering events. One has usually a continuous beam of initial particles, some finite target area with a large number of scatters. Final momenta are measured in a stationary state. Most important of all, the experiments are done in ordinary space, not in momentum space, so that we must correlate position measurements to the momentum measurement.

We have defined $|R_{fi}|^2$ as the transition probability from the configuration i to the configuration f specified by momenta and other quantum numbers. But this is the probability over all time and over all space. In the calculation of the cross sections and lifetimes we need the probabilities per unit time and volume; only these are the measurable quantities for the usual experiments with continuous beams.

Let us exhibit the conservation of the total energy momentum, Eq. (2.42), explicitly. We define

$$R(f,i) = (2\pi)^4 \delta(P_i - P_f) G(f,i) = G(f,i) \int e^{i(P_i - P_f)x} \, dx. \qquad (3.1)$$

In calculating $|R|^2$ the square of the δ-function must be carefully defined: one of the δ-functions can be taken as the total volume of space V and total time T in which interaction takes place; in fact using the relation

$$\lim_{\substack{V \to \infty \\ T \to \infty}} \frac{1}{VT} \left[\int_{VT} e^{i(P_i - P_f)x} \, dx \right]^2 = (2\pi)^4 \delta(P_i - P_f)$$

we obtain the *transition probability per unit time and unit volume*

$$W_{if} = (2\pi)^4 \delta(P_i - P_f) |G(f,i)|^2. \qquad (3.2)$$

Because the momentum variables are continuous we calculate the probability per unit time and volume that the final momenta are in the range k_f and $k_f + dk_f$ and corresponding to definite values of spins, isospins, etc. This is obtained by multiplying Eq. (3.2) by the phase-space factors of the final particles (density of final states per unit energy interval). The invariant phase-space factor is given by

$$\rho = \prod_{f=1}^{N} \left[\frac{d^4 k_f}{(2\pi)^4} (2) 2\pi \delta(k_f^2 - m_f^2) \theta(k_f^0) \right], \qquad (3.3)$$

where N is the number of final particles.

It will be convenient to carry a factor $(2\pi)^n$ with a n-dimensional δ-function and a factor $(2\pi)^{-n}$ with an n-dimensional differential $d^n k$. The phase-space factor is actually a three-dimensional differential, for

$$\delta(k^{0^2} - \mathbf{k}^2 - m^2) = \delta(k^0 - \sqrt{\mathbf{k}^2 + m^2})/2k^0 \quad \text{(for positive energies),}$$

and k^0-integration can be done replacing everywhere k^0 by $\sqrt{\mathbf{k}^2 + m^2} = E$
Hence

$$\rho = \prod_{f=1}^{N} \left[\frac{d^3 k_f}{(2\pi)^3} \cdot \frac{1}{E_f} \right]. \qquad (3.4)$$

This equation shows that the factor (2) in Eq. (3.3) was introduced because of the invariant normalization: one particle per volume $1/E$. It is also at this point that the Planck constant $\hbar$ enters into the theory for dimensional reasons. Note that the number of states with one particle in the volume V is $d^3 k V/(2\pi\hbar)^3$.

Remark: If there are n identical particles among the N final state particles we have to divide the right-hand side of Eq. (3.4) by $(1/n!)$; the available phase space is now that much smaller.

The differential transition probability per unit time and volume with the final momenta in the interval dk_f is then

$$dW_{if} = (2\pi)^4 \delta(P_i - P_f)|G|^2 \prod_{f=1}^{N} \frac{d^4k_f}{(2\pi)^4} (2)2\pi\delta(k_f^2 - m_f^2)\theta(k_f^0). \quad (3.5)$$

For a single initial system the inverse of Eq. (3.5) is the *differential lifetime.*

For two initial systems and arbitrary final systems one measures the *differential cross sections* which are the ratio of dW_{if} and of the current density, i.e., the number of incoming particles per unit time and unit area. To obtain an invariant expression for the current density we first go to a special frame in which the two initial particles are moving towards each other. In that frame the current density is given by

$$j = \frac{v_1 + v_2}{V_1 V_2} = \frac{p_1 E_2 + p_2 E_1}{V_1 V_2 E_1 E_2}, \quad (3.6)$$

where v_i are the magnitudes of the velocities of the particles, $v = p/E$, p_i the magnitudes of the three-dimensional momenta, $p = |\mathbf{k}|$, and V_i, the normalization volume, $V = 1/E$. In the frame we are considering the numerator of Eq. (3.6) can be written as

$$p_1 E_2 + p_2 E_1 = [(k_1 \cdot k_2)^2 - m_1^2 m_2^2]^{1/2}.$$

Therefore the invariant current density in an arbitrary frame is

$$j \Rightarrow \mathscr{J} = [(k_1 \cdot k_2)^2 - m_1^2 m_2^2]. \quad (3.7)$$

We obtain then the differential cross section

$$d\sigma_{fi} = |G(f,i)|^2(2\pi)^4\delta(P_i - P_f)\frac{1}{\mathscr{J}} \prod_{f=1}^{N} \left\{\frac{d^4k_f}{(2\pi)^4} 2(2\pi)\delta(k_f^2 - m_f^2)\theta(k_f^0). \quad (3.8)\right.$$

Writing

$$\delta(P_i - P_f) = \delta(E_1 + E_2 - \sum_f E_f)\delta(\mathbf{k}_1 + \mathbf{k}_2 - \sum_f \mathbf{k}_f)$$

we can do one momentum integration:

$$d\sigma_{fi} = |G(f,i)|^2 2\pi\delta(E_1 + E_2 - \sum_f E_f)\frac{1}{\mathscr{J}} \prod_{f=1}^{N-1} \frac{d^3k_f}{(2\pi)^3} \frac{1}{E_f} \frac{1}{E_N}. \quad (3.9)$$

The remaining δ-function can be used to do one more integration, for example, over the magnitude of $\mathbf{k}_{N-1}$. Let $d^3k_{N-1} = p^2\, dp\, d\Omega$, $p = |\mathbf{k}_{N-1}|$; then

$$\delta\left\{E_1 + E_2 - \sum_{f=1}^{N-2} E_f - (p^2 + m_{N-1}^2)^{1/2}\right.$$

$$\left. - \left(m_N^2 + \left(\mathbf{k}_1 + \mathbf{k}_2 - \sum_{f=1}^{N-2} \mathbf{k}_f - \mathbf{k}_{N-1}\right)^2\right)^{1/2}\right\}$$

$$= \delta(p - \bar{p})\left/\left[\frac{p}{E_{N-1}} + \frac{p - |\mathbf{k}_1 + \mathbf{k}_2 - \sum_{f=1}^{N-2} \mathbf{k}_f|\cos\alpha}{E_N}\right],\right.$$

where α is the angle between $\mathbf{k}_{N-1}$ and $\left(\mathbf{k}_1 + \mathbf{k}_2 - \sum_f \mathbf{k}_f\right)$ and $\bar{p}$ the value of p determined by energy conservation. We have used the general formula

$$\delta\{f(x)\} = \sum_i \frac{\delta(x - a_i)}{|f'(a_i)|}, \quad f(a_i) = 0.$$

If we carry then the p-integration we obtain

$$d\sigma = |G|^2 \frac{1}{\mathscr{I}} \prod_{f=1}^{N} \left(\frac{1}{E_f}\right) \cdot \frac{pE_N E_{N-1}}{E_N + E_{N-1} - E_{N-1}|\mathbf{k}_1 + \mathbf{k}_2 - \sum_{f=1}^{N-2} \mathbf{k}_f| \frac{\cos \alpha}{p}}$$

$$\times \frac{d\Omega}{(2\pi)^2} \cdot \sum_{f=1}^{N-2} \frac{d^3 k_f}{(2\pi)^3}. \quad (3.10)$$

In particular for $N = 2$ and in the center-of-mass frame we find (with p' being the center-of-mass momenta of the initial particles)

$$d\sigma = |G|^2 \frac{1}{(E_1 + E_2)(E_3 + E_4)} \frac{p}{p'} \frac{d\Omega}{(2\pi)^2}, \quad (3.11)$$

which for elastic scattering becomes

$$d\sigma = |G|^2 \frac{1}{(E_1 + E_2)^2} \frac{d\Omega}{(2\pi)^2} = |F|^2 \, d\Omega, \quad (3.12)$$

where

$$F = G/2(E_1 + E_2).$$

The above formulas also hold if some of the particles have zero mass.

In nonrelativistic limit we get

$$d\sigma|_{NR} = |G|^2 \frac{d\Omega}{(2\pi)^2} \Big/ (m_1 + m_2),$$

so that for potential scattering in the Born approximation ($m \neq 0$)

$$|G|^2 = m^2 |V(\mathbf{p}' - \mathbf{p})|^2,$$

where $V(\mathbf{p}' - \mathbf{p})$ is the Fourier transform of the potential $V(r)$ which shows us the normalization of G. The normalization of G will be determined by unitarity or optical theorem.

The cross-section formulas above are for polarized particles. Sometimes one is interested in cross section averaged over the spin directions of the final particles in which case the above formulas have to be divided by the factor $\prod_f (2S_f + 1)$.

3.2   Polarization

The polarization is an important measurable quantity and compares the number of particles in various spin states. For example, if we consider one spin $\frac{1}{2}$ particle in the final configuration, we can measure the relative frequencies of events with spin up and with spin down. Hence, we define the *polarization P* by

$$P = \frac{\text{number of events } (m = \frac{1}{2}) - \text{number of events } (m = -\frac{1}{2})}{\text{total number of events}}.$$

It is convenient to define the polarization as a vector, **P**, so that one can look at spin in any direction. With respect to third component of spin, for example, and for an initially unpolarized beam, we have immediately from the above definitions

$$P_3 = \frac{\sum_i |R_{i\frac{1}{2}}|^2 - \sum_i |R_{i,-\frac{1}{2}}|^2}{\sum_{ij} |R_{ij}|^2} = \frac{\text{tr } (R^\dagger \sigma_3 R)}{\text{tr } (R^\dagger R)},$$

where the trace operation is in spin space alone. Thus, vectorially

$$\mathbf{P} = \frac{\text{tr } (R^\dagger \boldsymbol{\sigma} R)}{\text{tr } (R^\dagger R)}. \tag{3.13}$$

If the *initial* spin $\frac{1}{2}$ particle beam is itself polarized we have to introduce weight functions in the above equation for the initial states *i*. The result can be expressed as follows

$$\mathbf{P}_f = \frac{\text{tr } (R^\dagger \boldsymbol{\sigma} R) + \text{tr } (R^\dagger \boldsymbol{\sigma} R(\boldsymbol{\sigma} \cdot \mathbf{P}_i))}{\text{tr } (R^\dagger R) + \mathbf{P}_i \cdot \text{tr } (R \boldsymbol{\sigma} R^\dagger)}, \tag{3.14}$$

where **P**$_i$ is the initial polarization.

A whole family of polarization numbers can be defined in the case of higher spins and more than one particle with spin, which measure the relative number of particles in various spin states.

3.3   Unitarity

In this section we write the unitarity condition of Chap. 1 in a relativistically invariant form both for the *R*- and the *M*-amplitudes. The unitarity condition, Eq. (1.12), involves an integral over the parameters of the intermediate states, which must be chosen in an invariant way. Because the total linear momentum is conserved and the amplitudes are defined only on the mass shells we have the same invariant phase-space factors as in the calculation of differential probabilities:

$$R_{m\hat{n}}(K_f, K_i) + R_{nm}^*(K_i, K_f) = -\sum_j \int \left[\frac{dk_j}{(2\pi)^4} 2(2\pi)\delta(k_j^2 - m_j^2)\theta(k_j^0) \right]$$

$$\times R_{mf}(K_f, K_j) R_{ni}^*(K_i, K_j), \tag{3.15}$$

where $P = P_i = P_j$ is the sum of the initial or final momenta and the factor

$[(2\pi)^4\delta(P_i - P_f)]$ is included in the definition of R. In the second form of the unitarity condition the two R-functions on the right are replaced by

$$R^*(K_j, K_f)R(K_j, K_i).$$

The summation is over the spin, isospin, ... indices of the variables K_j and over the number of particles in the set K_j allowed by selection rules.

In matrix notation with respect to spinor indices we have

$$R(f,i) + R^\dagger(i,f) = -\sum_j \rho_j R(f,j) R^\dagger(i,j). \tag{3.16}$$

[Note that $R(i,f)$ has indices $R_{n\dot{n}}(i,f)$, then $R^\dagger = (R_{\dot{m}n})^* = R_{m\dot{n}}$ by Eq. (2.66).]

To write the unitarity for the M-functions we use Eq. (2.55) connecting the R- and M-amplitudes, i.e.,

$$R(f,i) = D^{0F^{-1}}M(f,i)D^{0S^{-1\dagger}},$$

[matrix notation is with respect to spinor indices]

$$R_{m\dot{n}} = D_m^{0Fr}M_{rs}D_{\dot{n}}^{0S\dagger\dot{s}}$$

and

$$R(i,f) = D^{0S}M(i,f)D^{0F\dagger}$$

or

$$R^\dagger(i,f) = D^{0F^{-1}}M^\dagger(i,f)D^{0S\dagger^{-1}}.$$

We insert these equations into Eq. (3.16) and multiply with D^{0F} on the left and with D^{0S} on the right and obtain

$$M(f,i) + M^\dagger(i,f) = -\sum \int \rho M(f,j)[D^{0J\dagger^{-1}}D^{0J^{-1}}]M^\dagger(i,j). \tag{3.17}$$

Now from its definition, Eq. (2.63),

$$D^{0J\dagger}D^{0J} = \prod_j D^{0S_j}[B^{-1\dagger}_{k_j\leftarrow p_j}B^{-1}_{k_j\leftarrow p_j}]$$

$$= \prod_j D^{0S_j}[B_{k_j\leftarrow p}B^\dagger_{k_j\leftarrow p_j}]^{-1}$$

$$= \prod_j D^{0S_j}\left(\frac{k_j\cdot\tilde{\sigma}}{m_j}\right).$$

Thus, with the spinor indices written out, we get

$$M_{m\dot{n}}(f,i) + M^*_{\dot{n}\dot{m}}(i,f) = -\sum_j \int \rho_j M_{m\dot{r}}(f,j)\prod_j\left[D^{0S_j}\left(\frac{k_j\cdot\tilde{\sigma}}{m_j}\right)\right]^{\dot{r}\dot{n}}M^*_{\dot{n}\dot{n}}(i,j). \tag{3.18}$$

Equation (3.18) is one of the most important equations of the whole theory. It will be the basis for determining the singularities of the amplitudes.

The left-hand side of Eq. (3.18) is a "generalized real part," "Re," of the

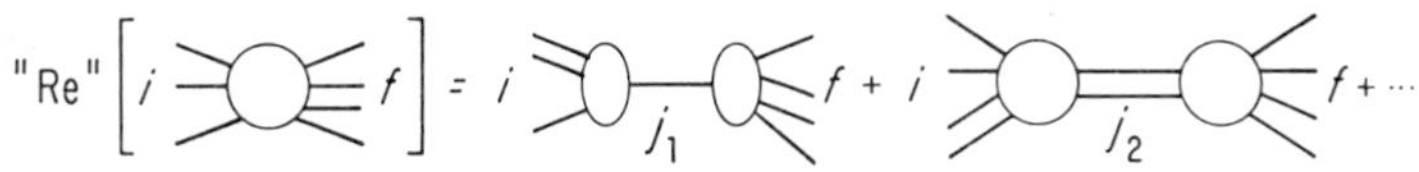

Figure 3.1

amplitude so that we can represent Eq. (3.18) diagrammatically as shown in Fig. 3.1. The right-hand side of the diagram indicates symbolically the sum of the amplitudes $M(i,j)$ and $M(j,f)$ in the manner indicated by Eq. (3.18). We recognize here a kind of perturbation theory connecting one amplitude to others which is, however, quite different than the field theoretical or the ordinary quantum-mechanical perturbation theory. The particles in the set j are all on the mass shell.

3.4   General Optical Theorem

If we compare Eq. (3.5) for the differential transition probability dW_{if} and the unitarity condition (3.15), written in terms of the reduced amplitudes G,

$$G_{m\bar{n}}(k_f;k_i) + G_{\bar{n}m}^*(k_i;k_f) = -\sum \int \rho G_{m\bar{r}}(k_f;k_j)G_{\bar{r}\bar{n}}^*(k_i;k_j)(2\pi)^4\delta(k_f - k_i),$$

(3.19)

with $\sum k_i = \sum k_j = \sum k_f = P$, we can get a relation between dW_{if} and the real part of $G(k;k)$:

$$2ReG_{m\bar{n}}(k_i;k_i) = -\sum_j \int dW_{ij} = -W_{i\,\text{total}}.$$

(3.20)

That is, the total transition probability per unit time and volume from a given initial state to *all* final states is equal twice the real part of the reduced amplitude for particles scattered into their initial values ("forward scattering amplitude"). If we divide the right-hand side with the initial "invariant current density $\mathscr{J}$" we get the "total cross section" (including, of course, all inelastic processes), and

$$2ReG_{m\bar{n}}(k_i;k_f) = -\frac{\mathscr{J}}{2}\,\sigma_{\text{total}}.$$

(3.21)

This is the general optical theorem. Special instances of this equation will be used in later chapters.

3.5   Phase-Space Factors in Terms of Total Energy

Let us now rewrite the unitarity condition in terms of the following variables; E = total center-of-mass energy of the incoming or final particles, P = total center-of-mass momentum, Γ and Ω the remaining energy (of subsystems) and angle variables, and Λ spin, isospin, and other quantum numbers. We set

$$G(k_f;k_i)|_{\text{c.o.m.}} = G(E)[(2\pi)^4\delta(E_f - E_i)\delta(\mathbf{P}_f)(2\pi)^4\delta(E_i - E)\delta(\mathbf{P}_i)]^{1/2} \quad (3.22)$$

where we have suppressed in $G(E)$ defined in Eq. (3.1) the (Ω,Γ,Λ) indices both for initial and final particles. In the center-of-mass system, $\mathbf{P} = 0$ and $G(E)$ does not depend on $\mathbf{P}$. We now insert Eq. (3.22) into the unitarity condition and introduce the Jacobian of the transformation into the new variables:

$$\prod_{j=1}^{N} \left\{ \frac{dk_j}{(2\pi)^4} 2(2\pi)\delta(k_j^2 - m_j^2) D^{0S_j}\left(\frac{k_j \cdot \tilde{\sigma}}{m_j}\right)\theta(k_j^0) \right\}$$

$$= \frac{dE}{2\pi} \frac{d\mathbf{P}}{(2\pi)^3} d\Omega \, d\Gamma \, d\Lambda \, \rho_N(E,\Omega,\Gamma,\Lambda). \quad (3.23)$$

This equation defines the N-particle phase space matrix ρ_N in the new variables $(E,\Omega,\Gamma,\Lambda)$. We then obtain

$$[G(E) + G^\dagger(E)][(2\pi)^4\delta(E_f - E_i)\delta(\mathbf{P}_f)(2\pi)^4\delta(E_i - E)\delta(\mathbf{P}_i)]^{1/2}$$

$$= -\sum_N \sum_\Lambda \int d\Omega \, d\Gamma \, G(E_j)\rho_N(E,\Omega,\Gamma,\Lambda)G^\dagger(E_j) \frac{dE \, d\mathbf{P}}{(2\pi)^4}$$

$$+ [(2\pi)^4\delta(E_f - E)\delta(\mathbf{P}_f)(2\pi)^4\delta(E_j - E)\delta(\mathbf{P}_i)$$

$$\times (2\pi)^4\delta(E_i - E)\delta(\mathbf{P}_i)(2\pi)^4\delta(E_j - E)\delta(\mathbf{P}_j)]^{1/2}$$

or

$$G(E) + G^\dagger(E) = -\sum_{N,\Lambda} \int d\Omega \, d\Gamma \, dE_j \, G(E_j)\rho_N G^\dagger(E_j)\delta(E_j - E), \quad (3.24)$$

or, finally, in matrix form with respect to Ω,Γ,Λ indices (continuous or discrete),

$$G(E) + G^\dagger(E) = -\sum_N G_{f,N}(E)\rho_N(E)G^\dagger_{i,N}(E). \quad (3.24')$$

The phase-space matrix ρ_N changes discontinuously at each new threshold. We evaluate the first two simple cases, and then the general case.

a. Single Spinless Particle Intermediate State

In the rest frame of the particle we have

$$\frac{dk}{(2\pi)^3} \frac{1}{E} = \frac{dE}{2\pi} \frac{d\mathbf{P}}{(2\pi)^3} \rho_1(E).$$

Hence

$$\rho_1(E) = \frac{2\pi}{E} \delta(E - m) = (2\pi)2m\delta(E^2 - m^2). \quad (3.25)$$

b. Two-Body Phase Space, No Spin

The new variables are $E,\mathbf{P}$ and two angle variables, the angles of the unit 3-momentum in the center-of-mass (c.o.m.) frame. We have then

$$\frac{d\mathbf{k}_1}{(2\pi)^3}\frac{d\mathbf{k}_2}{(2\pi)^3}\frac{1}{E_1E_2} = \frac{dE}{2\pi}\frac{d\mathbf{P}}{(2\pi)^3}\,d\Omega\,\rho_2(E,\Omega). \qquad (3.26)$$

In the center-of-mass frame: $k_1 = (E_1,-\mathbf{q})$, $k_2 = (E_2,\mathbf{q})$, $E = E_1 + E_2$ and $\mathbf{P} = \mathbf{k}_1 + \mathbf{k}_2 = 0$; Ω are angles of $\hat{\mathbf{q}}$. Because $d\mathbf{P} = d\mathbf{k}_1$ we obtain

$$\frac{q^2\,dq}{(2\pi)^3}\frac{1}{E_1E_2} = \frac{dE}{2\pi}\,\rho_2(E);$$

ρ_2 depends only on E in this case. We can express dE in terms of dq using

$$E = (q^2 + m_1^2)^{\frac12} + (q^2 + m_2^2)^{\frac12} = E_1 + E_2, \qquad (3.27)$$

i.e.,

$$dE = \frac{E}{E_1E_2}\,q\,dq.$$

Thus,

$$\rho_2(E) = \frac{1}{(2\pi)^2}\frac{q}{E}, \qquad (3.28)$$

or, if we express q in terms of E by Eq. (3.27), we get

$$\rho_2(E) = \frac{\theta[E^2 - (m_1 + m_2)^2]}{(2\pi)^2 2E^2}\,[E^4 - 2E^2(m_1^2 + m_2^2) + (m_1^2 - m_2^2)^2]^{\frac12}. \qquad (3.28')$$

In terms of the invariant quantity $s = E^2$ we have

$$\rho_2(s) = \frac{\theta[s - (m_1 + m_2)^2]}{(2\pi)^2 2s}\,[\{s - (m_1 + m_2)^2\}\{s - (m_1 - m_2)^2\}]^{\frac12}. \qquad (3.28'')$$

Equation (3.28″) simplifies greatly in the *equal-mass case*

$$\rho_2(s) = \left(\frac{1}{2\pi}\right)^2\left[\frac{s - 4m^2}{4s}\right]^{\frac12}\theta(s - 4m^2)$$

$$= \left(\frac{1}{2\pi}\right)^2\left[\frac{q^2}{4(q^2 + m^2)}\right]^{\frac12}\theta(q^2). \qquad (3.29)$$

c. N-Body Phase Space[1]

For the N-body phase space of spinless particles a suitable choice of variables generalizing the previous case is the following:

Total momentum $\mathbf{P}$, $M_1 = $ total energy of the particles 1 and 2 in their center-of-mass frame

$$M_1 = (m_1^2 + k_{11}^2)^{\frac12} + (m_2^2 + k_{11}^2)^{\frac12},$$

---

[1] N-body phase-space integrals have been already partly evaluated by W. Heisenberg, *Z. Physik.*, **120**, 513, 673 (1943). See also H. P. Stapp, UCRL–10261, App. A. J. M. Leblonc and F. Lurçat, *J. Math. Phys.*, **6**, 1564 (1965).

where k_{11} is the magnitude of the center-of-mass momentum, $k_1 = (E_1, \mathbf{k}_{11})$, $k_2 = (E_2, -\mathbf{k}_{11})$ in the c.o.m. frame; $M_2 =$ total energy of the particles 3 and (1–2) in the c.o.m. frame of the three

$$M_2 = (M_1^2 + k_{22}^2)^{\frac{1}{2}} + (m_3^2 + k_{22}^2)^{\frac{1}{2}},$$

where $k_3 = (E_3, \mathbf{k}_{22})$ in the new frame, and so on. Finally

$$M_{N-1} = (M_{N-2}^2 + k_{N-1,N-1}^2)^{\frac{1}{2}} + (m_N^2 + k_{N-1,N-1}^2)^{\frac{1}{2}} \equiv E.$$

We have then $(N-1)$ variables $M_1 \ldots M_{N-1}$, 3-momentum variables $\mathbf{P}$, and $2(N-1)$-angle variables of the vectors $\mathbf{k}_{11}$, $\mathbf{k}_{N-1,N-1}$—altogether $3N$ variables.

One can first transform the variables $(\mathbf{k}_1, \ldots \mathbf{k}_N)$ to the variables $(\mathbf{P}, \mathbf{k}_{11}, \ldots, \mathbf{k}_{N-1,N-1})$. Let J_1 be the Jacobian of this transformation. Then for spinless particles,

$$\prod_{i=1}^{N} \left(\frac{d^3 \mathbf{k}_i}{(2\pi)^3} \frac{1}{E_i} \right) = \prod_{i=1}^{N-1} \left(\frac{d^3 \mathbf{k}_{ii}}{(2\pi)^3} \frac{1}{E_i} \right) \frac{d\mathbf{P}}{(2\pi)^3} \cdot J_1$$

$$= \frac{dE}{2\pi} \frac{d\mathbf{P}}{(2\pi)^3} \, d\Omega \, d\Gamma \, \rho_N,$$

or, canceling the angular parts $d\Omega$ and $d\mathbf{P}$,

$$\prod_{i=1}^{N-1} \left(\frac{k_{ii}^2 \, dk_{ii}}{(2\pi)^3} \frac{1}{E_i} \right) J_1 = \frac{dE}{2\pi} d\Gamma \, \rho_N = \prod_{i=1}^{N-1} \left(\frac{dM_i}{2\pi} \right) \rho_N,$$

where we have chosen $d\Gamma = \prod_{i=1}^{N-2} \left(\dfrac{dM_i}{2\pi} \right)$. The Jacobian of the transformation from k_{ii}^2 to M_i is

$$J_2 = \frac{\partial(M_i)}{\partial(k_{ii}^2)} = \prod_{i=1}^{N-1} \frac{1}{2} \frac{\sqrt{k_{ii}^2 + m_i^2} + \sqrt{k_{ii}^2 + M_{i-1}^2}}{\sqrt{k_{ii}^2 + m_i^2} \sqrt{k_{ii}^2 + M_{i-1}^2}}.$$

The first Jacobian, on the other hand, is given by

$$J_1 = \left[\prod_{i=1}^{N-1} m_i^{\mathrm{red}} \right]^{-1} M_{N-1}^{-1}$$

where

$$m_i^{\mathrm{red}} = \frac{\sqrt{k_{jj}^2 + m_j^2} \sqrt{k_{jj}^2 + M_{j-1}^2}}{\sqrt{k_{jj}^2 + m_j^2} + \sqrt{k_{jj}^2 + M_{j-1}^2}}.$$

Collecting these results we have the simple result

$$\rho_N = \frac{1}{E} \prod_{j=1}^{N-1} \left(\frac{k_{jj}}{(2\pi)^2} \right). \tag{3.30}$$

At threshold ρ_N behaves as $E^{(3N-5)/2}$ (see Exercise 3). For $N = 2$ we obtain from Eq. (3.30)

$$\rho_2 = \frac{1}{E} \frac{k_{11}}{(2\pi)^2},$$

which is Eq. (3.27) again.

Problems and Further Developments

1. Show that the Lorentz transformation which takes two fourvectors k_1 and k_2 into their center-of-mass frame values (in which $k_1' = (E_1, \mathbf{q})$, $k_2' = (E_2, -\mathbf{q})$ is generated by A, where

$$A^{-1} = \sqrt{\frac{(k_1 + k_2) \cdot \sigma}{(E_1 + E_2)_{CM}}} \cdot U;$$

   A is a 2×2 unimodular matrix, U a unitary matrix.
2. Work out the details of N-body phase-space calculation.
3. Evaluate the threshold behavior of the N-body phase space.
4. What is the effect of the spin factors in Eq. (3.22) to ρ_N?
5. Evaluate explicitly ρ_3 and investigate the nature of the 3-body normal threshold singularity.
6. Discuss the phase-space factor ρ_3 in the variables of the Dalitz plot. (Compare Exercise 3, Chap. 6.)
7. Derive Eq. (3.14) in analogy to the derivation of Eq. (3.13).
8. Consider the amplitude R_{ij} in Eqs. (3.13) and (3.14) as a 2×2 matrix in spin space. Every 2×2 matrix can be written in the form $R_{ij} = g\delta_{ij} + ih(\boldsymbol{\sigma} \cdot \mathbf{n})_{ij}$, where $\mathbf{n}$ is a unit vector. Evaluate Eqs. (3.13) and (3.14) in terms of the scalar amplitudes g and h. [Compare Chap. 12, Eq. (12.4), and Sec. 12.3(a).]
9. Derive expressions for the lifetime of unstable particles decaying into two and three particles (see also Exercise 3, Chap. 6).

CHAPTER 4

Construction of Covariant Scattering Amplitudes

In this chapter we shall determine the most general form of the amplitudes satisfying the invariance principles in the form of suitable and well-defined basis functions multiplied with scalar coefficients. The problem with arbitrary spins and isospins is thus reduced to that of spinless particles with the difference that instead of one, one has a number of scalar amplitudes. The scalar coefficients are functions of the invariants formed out of momenta of the problem to which the analytic methods of later chapters will be applied. We treat the simpler case of isotopic spin amplitudes first.

4.1   Construction of Isotopic Spin Amplitudes

We saw in the previous chapter that the problem of construction of isotopic spin amplitudes $M^{I_1 I_2 \cdots}$ is that of finding the most general form of isotropic or invariant spinors of given rank and type. Before discussing the general form of these amplitudes, let us first treat some simple cases.

For the scattering of one $I = \frac{1}{2}$ and one $I = 0$ particle into again an $I = \frac{1}{2}$ and $I = 0$ particle, we have the equation

$$R^{\alpha_1}_{\alpha_3} = D^{\frac{1}{2}}_{\beta_3} D^{\frac{1}{2} \cdot \alpha_1}{}_{\beta_1} R^{\beta_1}_{\beta_3}, \tag{4.1}$$

or, in matrix notation, $R = D^{\frac{1}{2}} R D^{\frac{1}{2}\dagger}$. The unique solution of this equation, by Schur's lemma, and because D is unitary, is

$$R^{(\frac{1}{2},\frac{1}{2})\alpha_1}_{\alpha_3} = A \delta^{\alpha_1}_{\alpha_3}, \tag{4.2}$$

where A is a scalar amplitude in isotopic spin space; it will have spin indices, which will be discussed in the next section. The invariance under isotopic spin rotations has reduced the number of amplitudes from four to one.

The next case is $I_3 = I_4 = I_1 = I_2 = \frac{1}{2}$, scattering of two $I = \frac{1}{2}$ particles into two others. The transformation equation is

$$R^{\alpha_1\alpha_2}_{\alpha_3\alpha_4} = D^{\frac{1}{2}}_{\alpha_3\beta_3} D^{\frac{1}{2}}_{\alpha_4\beta_4} D^{\frac{1}{2}\,*\,\alpha_1}{}_{\beta_1} D^{\frac{1}{2}\,*\,\alpha_2}{}_{\beta_2} R^{\beta_1\beta_2}_{\beta_3\beta_4}. \tag{4.3}$$

The R-matrix with four indices has 16 components, but the invariance condition reduces it two, because the total isotopic spin has two values, 0 and 1. (See the general theorems below.) We can pair one D with one D^* as in Eq. (4.1) and, therefore, obtain immediately two solutions so that

$$R^{(\frac{1}{2}\frac{1}{2}\frac{1}{2}\frac{1}{2})\alpha_1\alpha_2}_{\alpha_3\alpha_4} = A\delta^{\alpha_1}_{\alpha_3}\delta^{\alpha_2}_{\alpha_4} + B\delta^{\alpha_2}_{\alpha_3}\delta^{\alpha_1}_{\alpha_4}, \tag{4.4}$$

where A and B are again isotopic scalars. We can also pair two D's and using the general identity (App. 3)

$$D(u)D(C)D^T(u) = D(C), \tag{4.5}$$

we see that $C_{\alpha_3\alpha_4}C^{-1\alpha_1\alpha_2}$ is also a solution of Eq. (4.3), but it can be shown easily that this is a linear combination of the two solutions in Eq. (4.4). Here C, C^{-1} as well as $D(C), D(C^{-1})$ are the lowering and raising spinor operators.

Quite generally, if all four I's are equal, we can immediately write three solutions

$$R^{(IIII)\alpha_1\alpha_2}_{\alpha_3\alpha_4} = A_1\delta^{\alpha_1}_{\alpha_3}\delta^{\alpha_2}_{\alpha_4} + A_2\delta^{\alpha_2}_{\alpha_3}\delta^{\alpha_1}_{\alpha_4} + A_3 D(C)_{\alpha_3\alpha_4}D(C^{-1})^{\alpha_1\alpha_2}. \tag{4.6}$$

For $I = 1$, Eq. (4.6) is the complete solution; if $I > 1$, we need more solutions.

Now we discuss the general I-spin case of two body scattering processes. The results will be easily generalizable to processes involving more than two particles. The transformation equation is now

$$R^{\alpha_1\alpha_2}_{\alpha_3\alpha_4} = D^{I_3}_{\alpha_3\beta_3} D^{I_4}_{\alpha_4\beta_4} D^{I_1\,*}{}_{\alpha_1\beta_1} D^{I_2\,*}{}_{\alpha_2\beta_2} R^{\beta_1\beta_2}_{\beta_3\beta_4}. \tag{4.7}$$

If we reduce the direct products $D^{I_3} \otimes D^{I_4}$ and $D^{I_1} \otimes D^{I_2}$ into their irreducible parts, using Eq. (A4.1) in App. 4, we find

$$R^{\alpha_1\alpha_2}_{\alpha_3\alpha_4} = \sum_I [I_3I_4I]^{\beta_3\beta_4}\{I_3I_4I\}^{\alpha}_{\alpha_3\alpha_4}D^I_{\alpha\beta} R^{\beta_1\beta_2}_{\beta_3\beta_4} \sum_{I'} \{I_1I_2I'\}^{\alpha_1\alpha_2}_{\alpha'}[I_1I_2I']^{\beta'}_{\beta_1\beta_2} D^{I'\,*}_{\alpha'\beta'}, \tag{4.8}$$

where the symbols [ ] and { } are Clebsch-Gordan coefficients (see App. 4 for their transformation properties). Or, with the unitarity condition of the Clebsch-Gordan coefficients (A4.2),

$$[I_3I_4I]^{\alpha_3\alpha_4}_{\alpha}[I_1I_2I']^{\alpha'}_{\alpha_1\alpha_2} R^{\alpha_1\alpha_2}_{\alpha_3\alpha_4} = D^I_{\alpha\beta} D^{I'\,*}_{\alpha'\beta'}[I_3I_4I]^{\beta_3\beta_4}_{\beta}[I_1I_2I']^{\beta'}_{\beta_1\beta_2} R^{\beta_1\beta_2}_{\beta_3\beta_4}.$$

Thus the quantities

$$R^{II'}_{\alpha'\alpha} \equiv [I_3I_4I]^{\alpha_3\alpha_4}_{\alpha}[I_1I_2I']^{\alpha'}_{\alpha_1\alpha_2} R^{\alpha_1\alpha_2}_{\alpha_3\alpha_4} \tag{4.9}$$

represent the amplitudes corresponding to *total isotopic spin* values and satisfy

$$R_\alpha^{II'}{}_{\alpha'} = D_{\alpha\beta}^I D^{I'}{}_{\alpha'}^{*}{}_{\beta'} R_\beta^{II'}{}_{\beta'} \tag{4.10}$$

or

$$R^{II'} = D^I R D^{I'\dagger},$$

which by Schur's lemma gives

$$R_\alpha^{II'}{}_{\alpha'} = R^I \delta^{II'} \delta_\alpha^{\alpha'} \tag{4.11}$$

and shows that the total isotopic spin I as well as the total isotopic spin components are conserved in the reaction. Furthermore, we have as many amplitudes as there are total I-values common to both the initial and final particles.

The inverse of Eq. (4.9), using (A4.3) and Eq. (4.11), is given by

$$R_{\beta_3\beta_4}^{\beta_1\beta_2} = \sum_I R^I \{I_3 I_4 I\}_{\beta_3\beta_4}^\gamma \{I_1 I_2 I\}_\gamma^{\beta_1\beta_2}; \quad \gamma = \text{fixed}. \tag{4.12}$$

We see from this equation [or from Eq. (4.8)] that the scalar coefficients $A, B, C, \ldots$ in R are related linearly to the amplitudes R^I, which are of equal number, and vice versa.

An isotropic spinor, by definition, transforms according to the D^0-representation. In Eq. (4.8), we have the sum of products of $D^I D^{I'*}$. These products contain D^0-representation only if D^I and $D^{I'}$ are equivalent, or $I = I'$, which is another way of proving Eq. (4.11) and arriving at the total number of linearly independent amplitudes.

Finally, we show how to obtain the arbitrary amplitude $R^{(I_1 I_2 I_3 I_4)}$ from the basic amplitude $R^{\frac{1}{2}\frac{1}{2}\frac{1}{2}\frac{1}{2}}$, given by Eq. (4.4), by a recursion method. For this purpose, we go back to Eq. (4.7) and split each D^{I_i} as follows:

$$D_{\alpha_i\beta_i}^{I_i\beta_i} = \sum_{\substack{n_i n_i \\ m_i' n_i'}} [L_i J_i I_i]_{\alpha_i}^{m_i n_i} \{L_i J_i I_i\}_{m_i' n_i'}^{\beta_i} D_{m_i}^{L_i m_i'} D_{n_i}^{J_i n_i'}, \quad (i = 1,2,3,4).$$

Bringing the factor $[\ ]_\alpha^{mn}$ to the left-hand side of Eq. (4.7) we see that the expression

$$\prod_{i=1}^{2} [L_i J_i I_i]_{\alpha_i}^{m_i n_i} \prod_{j=3}^{4} \{L_j J_j I_j\}_{m_j n_j}^{\alpha_j} R_{\alpha_3\alpha_4}^{\alpha_1\alpha_2}$$

is a product of two R-functions, namely

$$R_{m_3 m_4}^{m_1 m_2} R_{n_3 n_4}^{n_1 n_2}.$$

Consequently we have the recursion formla

$$R_{(\alpha)}^{(I)} \equiv R_{\alpha_3\alpha_4}^{I_3 I_4 I_1 I_2 \alpha_1 \alpha_2} = \prod_{i=3}^{4} [L_i J_i I_i]_{\alpha_i}^{m_i n_i} \prod_{j=1}^{2} \{L_j J_j I_j\}_{m_j n_j}^{\alpha_j} R_{m_3 m_4}^{(L)m_1 m_2} R_{n_3 n_4}^{(J)n_1 n_2}. \tag{4.13}$$

Now we are in a position to construct successively arbitrary amplitudes starting from Eq. (4.4). For example, for the scattering of $I = 1$ and $I_2 = \frac{1}{2}$ particles, we find [1]

$$R^{(1\frac{1}{2}\,1\,\frac{1}{2})}_{\alpha_3\alpha_4\,\alpha_1\alpha_2} = A\delta^{\alpha_1}_{\alpha_3}\delta^{\alpha_2}_{\alpha_4} + B(-1)^{\alpha_3}\varepsilon^{\alpha_1}_{-\alpha_3\,n}\rho^{n\alpha_2}_{\alpha_4}, \qquad (4.14)$$

where ε is the completely antisymmetric tensor and ρ^n $(n = 1,0,-1)$ are the three "spherical" Pauli matrices

$$\rho^1 = -\frac{1}{\sqrt{2}}(\sigma_1 + i\sigma_2); \quad \rho^0 = \sigma_3; \quad \rho^{-1} = \frac{1}{\sqrt{2}}(\sigma_1 - i\sigma_2). \qquad (4.15)$$

For other examples, see Table 4–1. Isospin amplitudes for production processes can be constructed in a similar way but are much more involved.[2]

Table 4–1

Isospin Amplitudes for Two-Body Scattering Processes

I_1	I_2	I_3	I_4	AMPLITUDES $M^{\alpha_3\alpha_4}_{\alpha_1\alpha_2}$
$\frac{1}{2}$	$\frac{1}{2}$	$\frac{1}{2}$	$\frac{1}{2}$	$A\delta^{\alpha_3}_{\alpha_1}\delta^{\alpha_4}_{\alpha_2} + B\delta^{\alpha_4}_{\alpha_1}\delta^{\alpha_2}_{\alpha_3}$
1	$\frac{1}{2}$	1	$\frac{1}{2}$	$A\delta^{\alpha_3}_{\alpha_1}\delta^{\alpha_4}_{\alpha_2} + B(-1)^{\alpha_1}\varepsilon_{-\alpha_1}{}^{\alpha_3}{}_n\rho^{n\alpha_4}_{\alpha_2}$
1	1	1	1	$A\delta^{\alpha_3}_{\alpha_1}\delta^{\alpha_4}_{\alpha_2} + B\delta^{\alpha_4}_{\alpha_1}\delta^{\alpha_3}_{\alpha_2} + C(-1)^{\alpha_1+\alpha_3}\delta_{\alpha_1,-\alpha_2}\delta^{\alpha_3,-\alpha_4}$
$\frac{1}{2}$	$\frac{3}{2}$	$\frac{1}{2}$	$\frac{3}{2}$	$A\delta^{\alpha_3}_{\alpha_1}\delta^{\alpha_4}_{\alpha_2} + B\rho^{n\alpha_3}_{\alpha_1}\Gamma^{\alpha_4}_{n\alpha_2}$
1	$\frac{3}{2}$	1	$\frac{3}{2}$	$A\delta^{\alpha_3}_{\alpha_1}\delta^{\alpha_4}_{\alpha_2} + BT^{\alpha_3\alpha_4}_{\alpha_2;\alpha_1} + CT^{\alpha_3\alpha_4}_{\alpha_1\alpha_2;}$
$\frac{3}{2}$	$\frac{3}{2}$	$\frac{3}{2}$	$\frac{3}{2}$	$A\delta^{\alpha_3}_{\alpha_1}\delta^{\alpha_4}_{\alpha_2} + B\delta^{\alpha_4}_{\alpha_2}\delta^{\alpha_3}_{\alpha_2} + C(-1)^n\Gamma^{n\alpha_3}_{\alpha_1}\Gamma^{-n\alpha_4}_{\alpha_2} + D(-1)^n\Gamma^{n\alpha_4}_{\alpha_1}\Gamma^{-n\alpha_3}_{\alpha_2}$

$$\rho^1 = -\frac{1}{\sqrt{2}}(\sigma_1 + i\sigma_2), \quad \rho^0 = \sigma_3, \quad \rho^{-1} = \frac{1}{\sqrt{2}}(\sigma_1 - i\sigma_2)$$

$$\Gamma^1 = \sqrt{2}\rho^1 \otimes \rho^{-1} + \sqrt{3}I \otimes \rho^1$$
$$\Gamma^0 = 2\rho^0 \otimes I + I \otimes \rho^0$$
$$\Gamma^{-1} = -\sqrt{2}\rho^{-1} \otimes \rho^1 + \sqrt{3}I \otimes \rho^{-1}$$

$$T^{\alpha_3\alpha_4}_{\alpha_2;\alpha_1} = \{1\,\tfrac{1}{2}\,\tfrac{3}{2}\}^{\alpha_3 n}_{\alpha_2}\{1\,\tfrac{1}{2}\,\tfrac{3}{2}\}^{\alpha_4}_{\alpha_1 n}.$$

4.2   Construction of Spin Amplitudes; Massive Particles

According to our discussion in Chap. 2, we first construct the spinorial M-amplitudes. It is then easy to evaluate the R-amplitudes. We begin again with the simplest cases.

[1] A. O. Barut and B. C. Unal, *Nuovo Cimento*, **28**, 112 (1963); A. Kotansky and K. Zalewski, *Acta Phys. Polon.*, **26**, 117 (1964).
[2] See A. O. Barut and Y. Leung, *Phys. Rev.*, **138**, B1119 (1965).

For the scattering of a spin 0 and spin $\frac{1}{2}$ particle the fundamental equation is

$$M_{m_3 \dot{m}_1}(K) = D^{0\frac{1}{2}}_{m_3 n_3} D^{0\frac{1}{2}\ast}_{\dot{m}_1 \dot{n}_1} M_{n_3 \dot{n}_1}(\Lambda^{-1}K), \qquad (4.16)$$

or, because $D^{(0\frac{1}{2})}(A) = A$, in matrix notation,

$$M(K) = AM(\Lambda^{-1}K)A^\dagger. \qquad (4.16')$$

Because the total spin is not conserved, we have four linearly independent amplitudes. Mathematically, A is not unitary and we cannot use Schur's lemma the way we did in the case of isospin. If we compare Eq. (4.16') with

$$Ak^\mu \sigma_\mu A^\dagger = (\Lambda k)^\mu \sigma_\mu, \qquad (4.17)$$

which connects 2×2 unimodular matrices A to Lorentz transformations (App. 3), where k is an arbitrary fourvector, we see that we can put

$$M_{m_3 \dot{m}_1}(K) = f^\mu(K)\sigma_{\mu m_3 \dot{m}_1}. \qquad (4.18)$$

This equation simply says that the 2×2 matrix M is a linear combination of the four Pauli matrices. The coefficients $f^\mu(K)$ are fourvector functions of the momenta. Choosing a basis in the fourvector space, $v^\mu_{(i)}$, we have

$$f^\mu(K) = \sum_{i=1}^{4} A_i(K)v^\mu_i, \qquad (4.19)$$

where $A^{(i)}(K)$ are the scalar amplitudes. Thus the final form of the amplitude is

$$M = \sum_{i=1}^{4} A_i(K)v^\mu_i \sigma_\mu. \qquad (4.20)$$

There is an arbitrariness in the choice of the basis vectors $v^\mu_{(i)}$. One may choose, e.g., the three physical momentum vectors k_1, k_2, k_3 (k_4 is no longer linearly independent by energy-momentum conservation) and the skew product $\varepsilon_{\mu\nu\lambda\rho}k_1^\nu k_2^\lambda k_3^\rho$, or linear combinations of these. (Note that there are degenerate cases such as forward scattering, or decay of one particle into two, etc., where not even three physical vectors are linearly independent. See Chaps. 5 and 6).

Let us now assume that we have both Lorentz-invariance and isotopic spin invariance and let the particles have $I = 1$ and $I = \frac{1}{2}$ (e.g., π-N scattering). Then combining (4.20) and (4.14) we have in total eight amplitudes $A_i^{(\pm)}$ which are now scalars in both spin and isospin spaces:

$$M = \sum_{i=1}^{4} [A_i^{(+)}I + A_i^{(-)}\varepsilon \cdot \rho]v_i \cdot \sigma. \qquad (4.21)$$

Here $I = \delta^{\alpha_1}_{\alpha_3}\delta^{\alpha_2}_{\alpha_4}$ and $\varepsilon \cdot \rho = (-1)^{\alpha_2}\varepsilon^{\alpha_2}_{-\alpha_4 n}\rho^{n\alpha_1}_{\alpha_3}$ are operators in isospin space. Finally the R-amplitude for this case is given by

$$R = \sum_{i=1}^{4} (A_i^{(+)}\cdot I + A_i^{(-)}\varepsilon \cdot \rho)U_3^{-1}\sqrt{\frac{k_3 \cdot \tilde{\sigma}}{m_3}}\, v_i \cdot \sigma \sqrt{\frac{k_1 \cdot \tilde{\sigma}}{m_1}}\, U_1$$

$$= \sum_{i=1}^{4} (A_i^{(+)}\cdot I + A_i^{(-)}\varepsilon \cdot \rho)R_i, \qquad (4.22)$$

where R_i are the basis functions for the R-amplitudes. Here we have taken the particles k_3 and k_1 to be the spin $\frac{1}{2}$ particles, and k_2 and k_4 to be the spin zero particles:

$$R_i = U_3^{-1}\sqrt{\frac{k_3 \cdot \tilde{\sigma}}{m_3}}\, v_i \cdot \sigma \sqrt{\frac{k_1 \cdot \tilde{\sigma}}{m_1}}\, U_1. \qquad (4.23)$$

Next we consider the scattering of two spin $\frac{1}{2}$ particles. The amplitude $M_{m_3 m_4 m_1 m_2}$ has now 16 linearly independent elements. The transformation equation is now

$$M(K) = A \otimes AM(\Lambda^{-1}K)(A \otimes A)^{\dagger}. \qquad (4.24)$$

We can now use the solution (4.18) twice and obtain, for example,

$$M_{m_3 m_4 \tilde{m}_1 \tilde{m}_2} = f^{\mu}(K)\sigma_{\mu m_3 \tilde{m}_1}g^{\nu}(K)\sigma_{\nu m_4 \tilde{m}_2}, \qquad (4.25)$$

or, with Eq. (4.19),

$$M = \sum_{i,j=1}^{4} A_{ij}(v_i \cdot \sigma) \otimes (v_j \cdot \sigma). \qquad (4.26)$$

Other solutions of Eq. (4.24) can also be found immediately, e.g.,

$$f^{\mu}\sigma_{\mu m_3 \tilde{m}_2}g^{\nu}\sigma_{\nu m_4 \tilde{m}_1} \qquad \text{or} \qquad C_{m_3 m_4}C_{\tilde{m}_1 \tilde{m}_2},$$

but these solutions are the linear combinations of the 16 basis vectors in Eq. (4.25).

It is not necessary to write the solution of Eq. (4.24) as a product of terms as in Eq. (4.25). If $\rho_{\mu\nu}$ are any set of sixteen 4×4 matrices satisfying

$$A \otimes A\rho_{\mu\nu}(A \otimes A)^{\dagger} = \Lambda^{\sigma}_{\mu}\Lambda^{\lambda}_{\nu}\rho_{\sigma\lambda}, \qquad (4.27)$$

then we have the solutions

$$M(K) = \sum_{i=1}^{16} A_i T^{\mu\nu}\rho_{\mu\nu} \qquad (4.28)$$

where $T^{\mu\nu}_{(i)}$ are any linearly independent set of tensors of rank 2 in the momentum space.

Because the Clebsch-Gordan series formulas in Appendix 4 also holds for the representation $D^{0S}(A)$ we can immediately translate the results of the previous section to general spin case.

First we define amplitudes belonging to total spin S' and S of the initial and final particles:

$$M^{SS'}_{m\dot{m}} = [S_3 S_4 S]^{m_3 m_4}_m [S_1 S_2 S']^{\dot{m}_1 \dot{m}_2}_{\dot{m}} M^{S_3 S_4 S_1 S_2}_{m_3 m_4 \dot{m}_1 \dot{m}_2}, \tag{4.29}$$

which satisfy

$$M^{SS'}(K) = D^{0S} M(\Lambda^{-1} K) D^{0S'\dagger}. \tag{4.30}$$

Because of the appearance of $(\Lambda^{-1}K)$ on the right side, in contrast to Eq. (3.10), the total spin S is, in general, not conserved.

For $S = S'$ the solution Eq. (4.30) is

$$M^{SS'}(K) = D^{0S}\left(\sum_i A_i v_i \cdot \sigma\right). \tag{4.31}$$

Because

$$\sum_{\substack{S' = S_1 + S_2 \\ S = S_3 + S_4}}^{\substack{|S_3 - S_4| \\ |S_1 - S_2|}} (2S + 1)(2S' + 1) = \prod_{i=1}^{4} (2S_i + 1) \tag{4.32}$$

the number of independent amplitudes obtained from Eq. (4.30) is the same as obtained from $M^{S_3 S_4 S_1 S_2}$.

Furthermore, we have again the analog of the recursion formula (4.13) to calculate higher spin amplitudes from the lower ones:

$$M^{S_3 S_4 S_1 S_2}_{m_3 m_4 \dot{m}_1 \dot{m}_2} \equiv M^{(S)}_{(m)} = \left[\prod_{i=1}^{4} [J_i L_i S_i]^{n_i r_i}_{m_i}\right] M^{(J)}_{(n)} M^{(L)}_{(r)}. \tag{4.33}$$

The general solution of Eq. (4.30) can be given in terms of the matrices generalizing the Pauli σ-matrices, which are solutions of Eq. (4.16′). The rectangular ρ-matrices have all the properties of σ-matrices and satisfy the equation

$$D^{0S}(A)\rho^{(SS')}_{(\mu)} D^{0S'}(A)^{\dagger} = \Lambda^{(\nu)}_{(\mu)} \rho^{(SS')}_{(\nu)}, \tag{4.34}$$

where $(\mu),(\nu)$ stand for a set of tensor indices and $\Lambda^{(\nu)}_{(\mu)}$ is a direct product of Lorentz transformations, one for each tensor index in (μ); $\rho^{(\frac{1}{2}\frac{1}{2})}_\mu = \sigma_\mu$. We have then

$$M^{SS'}(K) = \sum_i A_i T^{(\mu)}_{(i)} \rho^{(SS')}_{(\mu)}, \tag{4.35}$$

where $A^{(i)}(SS')$ are the scalar amplitudes belonging to total spin and $T^{(\mu)}_{(i)}$ a tensor basis.

The ρ-matrices are built up successively from the Pauli matrices by a Clebsch-Gordan series. For example, if $S = S' = 1$, and we expand D^{01} and $D^{01\dagger}$ in Eq. (4.34) and use Eq. (4.17) twice, we obtain

$$\rho^{\mu\nu}(SS')_{\alpha\dot{\alpha}} = [\tfrac{1}{2}\tfrac{1}{2} S]^{\beta\gamma}_{\alpha}[\tfrac{1}{2}\tfrac{1}{2} S']^{\dot{\beta}\dot{\gamma}}_{\dot{\alpha}} \sigma^{\mu}_{\beta\dot{\beta}} \sigma^{\nu}_{\gamma\dot{\gamma}}. \tag{4.36}$$

Thus we see that the amplitudes for higher spins can be built up from those of spin $\frac{1}{2}$ alone with the help of the above generalized spin matrices.

The general formulas need not be given here,[3] rather we shall give important specific cases in the physical applications as we go along.

Even in the case of more than four particles we can always express the total amplitude in the form

$$M^{(S)}(K) = \sum_i A_i Y_i^{(S)}(k_1, \ldots, k_n), \tag{4.37}$$

where the Y_i are the set of linearly independent spinorial basis functions constructed essentially from terms of the form $v^\mu \sigma_\mu, T^{\mu\nu} \rho_{\mu\nu}, \ldots$, and A_i are scalar amplitudes.

There are three important considerations to be made in the actual choice of the basis functions Y_i:

(1) Discrete Transformations. The spinor basis functions should have definite parities under the discrete transformations of parity P, charge conjugation C, and time reversal T, in order to discuss the full Lorentz group. The next chapter will be devoted to this question.

(2) Unitarity. The basis functions should be so chosen that the unitarity condition takes the simplest possible form. For the applications this is a most important point. In general, the scalar amplitudes A_i will not satisfy uncoupled unitarity condition. The problem is to find those combinations of the amplitudes in which the unitarity condition uncouples as much as possible. It is then convenient to start from the unitarity condition for one and two particle intermediate states and let these conditions determine the amplitudes (Part II deals with these applications). A general a priori discussion of the construction of amplitudes may be academic, if it does not take into account the diagonalization of the basis functions entering the unitarity equation.

(3) Kinematical Singularities. The expansion of the amplitudes in the form (4.37) should not introduce additional singularities in the scalar coefficients A_i. At certain values of the momenta the functions Y_i, or combinations of Y_i, can vanish. This will happen when the momenta are not all linearly independent (i.e., forward and backward scatterings in all channels in the case of the two-body problem). In this case A_i, or combinations of A_i, could develop poles at such points without M being singular. Because the whole method of dispersion relations relies on the analyticity of the amplitudes with singularities that have definite physical meaning, such additional *kinematical singularities* due to the expansion (4.37) must be avoided.

[3] For further properties of $\rho_{\mu\nu}$-matrices and amplitudes, see A. O. Barut, I. Muzinich, and D. Williams, *Phys. Rev.*, **130**, 442 (1963); D. Williams, in Lectures in Theoretical Physics, Vol. VIIa (Boulder, Colo.: U. of Colorado Press, 1965). The problem of covariant amplitudes has also been discussed in a different form by H. Joos, *Fortschr. der Physik*, **10**, 65 (1962), and by K. Hepp, *Helv. Phys. Acta*, **36**, 355 (1963); **37**, 55 (1964).

In this connection it is of importance to consider also the five fundamental spinor-tensors of a *pair* of spin $\frac{1}{2}$ particles, which have definite parities under the discrete transformations P, C, and T. These are the tensorial solutions of Eq. (4.16′) and are shown both in two-component and four-component forms in Table 4–2. The connection between two- and four-component spinors is discussed in App. 5. [See Eqs. (A5.11) and (A5.12).]

Table 4–2

Spinorial "Currents" of Two Spin $\frac{1}{2}$ Particles of Momenta k and k′

	AMPLITUDE M IN TWO-COMPONENT FORM	AMPLITUDE R IN FOUR-COMPONENT FORM
S	$(k' + k)\cdot\sigma$	$\bar{u}(k')u(k)$
V	$\sigma^\mu + k'\cdot\sigma\tilde{\sigma}^\mu k\cdot\sigma$	$\bar{u}(k')\gamma_\mu u(k)$
A	$\sigma^\mu - k'\cdot\sigma\tilde{\sigma}^\mu k\cdot\sigma$	$\bar{u}(k')\gamma_\nu\gamma_5 u(k)$ (4.38)
T	$k'\cdot\sigma(\tilde{\sigma}^\mu\sigma^\nu - \tilde{\sigma}^\nu\sigma^\mu) + (\sigma^\mu\tilde{\sigma}^\nu - \sigma^\nu\tilde{\sigma}^\mu)k\cdot\sigma$	$\bar{u}(k')\gamma_{\mu\nu}u(k)$
P	$(k' - k)\cdot\sigma$	$\bar{u}(k')\gamma_5 u(k)$
		$\gamma_{\mu\nu} = \frac{1}{2}(\gamma_\mu\gamma_\nu - \gamma_\nu\gamma_\mu)$

In Table 4–2, S, V, A, T, P refer to the transformation property (as scalar, vector, axial vector, tensor, and prendoscalar), e.g.,

$$AT_{\mu\nu}(k',k)A^\dagger = \Lambda_\mu^\sigma\Lambda_\nu^\rho T_{\sigma\rho}(k',k),\qquad(4.39)$$

and similarly for the others. The transformation properties under inversions (i.e., the distinction between S and P, or between V and A) is discussed in the next chapter. Each of the basis function has one dotted and one undotted index corresponding to the third component of spin of the outgoing and ingoing spin $\frac{1}{2}$ particles. We may refer to these forms as *currents* because they connect one outgoing and one ingoing particle.

From the above *currents* we can construct the amplitudes by contraction, either with fourvectors and tensors:

$$v^\mu V_\mu,\ t^{\mu\nu}T_{\mu\nu},\ \dots,$$

or with other "currents." For example, for the scattering of two spin $\frac{1}{2}$ particles we have the two currents shown in Fig. 4.1, and the amplitudes

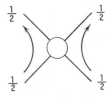

Figure 4.1 Pairs of fermions connected by the arrow give a contribution to the amplitude shown in Table 4–2.

can be constructed by a direct product in the spinor space:

$$S_1 \otimes S_2; \quad V_1^\mu \otimes V_{2\mu}; \quad A_1^\mu \otimes A_{2\mu}; \quad T_1^{\mu\nu} \otimes T_{2\mu\nu}; \quad P_1 \otimes P_2.$$

These are actually the amplitudes that one uses. For example, for the nucleon-nucleon problem, explicitly:

$$M = \sum_{i=1}^{5} A_i Y_i,$$

$$Y_1 = \frac{1}{4m^4} (k_3 + k_1) \cdot \sigma \otimes (k_4 + k_2) \cdot \sigma$$

$$Y_2 = -\frac{1}{8} \frac{1}{4m^4} [k_3 \cdot \sigma(\tilde\sigma^\mu \sigma^\nu - \tilde\sigma^\nu \sigma^\mu) + (\sigma^\mu \tilde\sigma^\nu - \sigma^\nu \tilde\sigma^\mu)k_1 \cdot \sigma]$$

$$\otimes [k_4 \cdot \sigma(\tilde\sigma_\mu \sigma_\nu - \tilde\sigma_\nu \sigma_\mu) + (\sigma_\mu \tilde\sigma_\nu - \sigma_\nu \tilde\sigma_\mu)k_2 \cdot \sigma]$$

$$Y_3 = -\frac{1}{4m^4} [(m^2 \sigma^\mu - k_3 \cdot \sigma\tilde\sigma^\mu k_1 \cdot \sigma) \otimes (m^2 \sigma_\mu - k_4 \cdot \sigma\tilde\sigma_\mu k_2 \cdot \sigma)$$

$$Y_4 = \frac{1}{4m^4} (m^2 \sigma^\mu + k_3 \cdot \sigma\tilde\sigma^\mu k_1 \cdot \sigma) \otimes (m^2 \sigma_\mu + k_4 \cdot \sigma\tilde\sigma_\mu k_2 \cdot \sigma)$$

$$Y_5 = \frac{1}{4m^4} (k_3 - k_2) \cdot \sigma \otimes (k_4 - k_2) \cdot \sigma.$$

(See Exercise 8, Chap. 5.)

4.3   Direct Construction of Helicity Amplitudes

In Chapter 2 we defined the helicity amplitudes H by the special choice of the rotation matrices U in $B_{k \leftarrow p} = \sqrt{k \cdot \sigma / m} \, U$. Having constructed the spinorial amplitudes M, the actual amplitudes R or H can be obtained by the connection (2.50). It is also possible to construct the basis for the helicity amplitudes (or R) directly and it is remarkable that they only involve the matrices $D(B_{k \leftarrow p})$.

For a pair of spin $\frac{1}{2}$ particles of momenta k_3 and k_1, the invariance equation of the helicity amplitudes is (with B written short for $B_{k \leftarrow p}$ and with $q = \Lambda^{-1}k$)

$$H(K) = B^{-1}(k_3)AB(q_3)H(q)B^\dagger(q_3)A^\dagger B^{-1\dagger}(k_1). \tag{4.40}$$

We can easily verify that this equation admits the following solutions:

$$\begin{aligned} H_1 &= B^{-1}(k_3)B(k_1), \\ H_2 &= B^\dagger(k_3)B^{-1\dagger}(k_1), \end{aligned} \tag{4.41}$$

and, if there are other independent fourvectors n in the problem,

$$\begin{aligned} H_3 &= B^{-1}(k_3)B(n)B^\dagger(n)B^{-1\dagger}(k_1), \\ H_4 &= B^\dagger(k_3)B^{-1\dagger}(n)B^{-1}(n)B(k_1). \end{aligned} \tag{4.42}$$

The helicity forms of the five fundamental "currents" of Table 4–2, Eq. (4.39), are given in Table 4–3.

Table 4–3

Helicity "Currents" of Two Spin $\frac{1}{2}$ Particles

$$B(k) \equiv B_{k \leftarrow p} = \sqrt{\frac{k \cdot \sigma}{m}}\, U$$

S	$B^{-1}(k')B(k)$
V	$B^{-1}(k')\sigma^{\mu}B^{-1\dagger}(k) + B^{\dagger}(k')\tilde{\sigma}^{\mu}B(k)$
A	$B^{-1}(k')\sigma^{\mu}B^{-1\dagger}(k) - B^{\dagger}(k')\tilde{\sigma}^{\mu}B(k)$
T	$B^{-1}(k')[\sigma^{\mu}\tilde{\sigma}^{\nu} - \sigma^{\nu}\tilde{\sigma}^{\mu}]B(k) + B^{\dagger}(k')[\tilde{\sigma}^{\mu}\sigma^{\nu} - \tilde{\sigma}^{\nu}\sigma^{\mu}]B^{-1\dagger}(k)$
P	$B^{\dagger}(k')B^{-1\dagger}(k)$

$$(4.43)$$

Again from these basic forms the helicity amplitudes can be constructed by contraction, as before.

4.4   Gauge Invariance and Amplitudes for Photon Processes

So far we have considered the amplitudes for massive particles only. We have seen in Chap. 2 that for massless particles the representations of the Lorentz group are quite different in that we have always one spin state (two, if parity is conserved), instead of $(2S + 1)$ spin states for massive particles of spin S. Therefore we have to give a separate discussion of photon and neutrino amplitudes.

Consider first the simple process shown Fig. 4.2, with particles 1, 2, 3

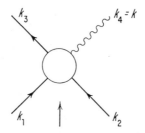

Figure 4.2   Labeling of momenta in a process involving one photon.

being spinless and massive particles and particle 4 a photon of momentum k (i.e., photoproduction of pions on pions). If the photon had a rest mass the transformation property of the amplitude would be

$$M(K) = D^{01}(A)M(\Lambda^{-1}K). \tag{4.44}$$

The amplitude M has now one spinor index. The solution of this equation can be written as

$$M_m = \sum_i A_i v_{\mu}^i \varepsilon_m^{\mu}(k), \tag{4.45}$$

where the fourvector ε_μ is orthogonal to k:

$$\varepsilon^\mu k_\mu = 0, \quad k^2 \neq 0. \tag{4.46}$$

Thus there are three such linearly independent spacelike ε-vectors corresponding to the three directions of polarization of the spin 1 massive particle. (The spinor index m takes the values $1, 0, -1$.) In (4.45), A^i are scalar amplitudes and v_i four linearly independent fourvectors. The polarization vector ε is defined by

$$D^{01}(A)_\mu \varepsilon(\Lambda^{-1}k) = \Lambda^\nu_\mu \varepsilon_\nu(k), \tag{4.47}$$

so that Eq. (4.45) satisfies Eq. (4.44), as can be verified. We shall now obtain an explicit expression for the polarization vector. For this purpose we replace $D^{01}(A)$ in (4.47) by

$$D^{01}(A)^n_m = [\tfrac{1}{2}\tfrac{1}{2}1]^{\alpha\beta}_m \{\tfrac{1}{2}\tfrac{1}{2}1\}^n_{\gamma\delta} A^\gamma_\alpha A^\delta_\beta$$

and obtain

$$A^\gamma_\alpha \{\tfrac{1}{2}\tfrac{1}{2}1\}^n_{\gamma\delta} \varepsilon^\mu_n(\Lambda^{-1}k) A^\delta_\beta = \Lambda^\mu_\nu \{\tfrac{1}{2}\tfrac{1}{2}1\}^m_{\alpha\beta} \varepsilon^\nu_m(k).$$

This equation shows that the product of ε and the Clebsch-Gordan coefficient transform exactly like $\sigma^\mu_{\alpha\beta}(k)$—the Pauli spinors with two undotted indices. On the other hand, we have

$$\sigma^\mu_{\alpha\beta}(k) = \sigma_{\gamma\beta} G^{T\beta}_{\hat\beta} = \sigma^\mu \frac{k \cdot \tilde\sigma}{m} C,$$

where the metric spinor G is given by

$$G = \frac{k \cdot \sigma}{m} C^{-1}, \quad G_m^{\;\dot i} = \left(\frac{k \cdot \sigma}{m}\right)_{m\dot m} C^{-1\dot m \dot i}.$$

Consequently we can put (up to a scalar multiplicative factor on the right)

$$\{\tfrac{1}{2}\tfrac{1}{2}1\}^n_{\alpha\beta} \varepsilon^\mu_n(k) = \frac{1}{\sqrt{2}} (k \cdot \sigma \tilde\sigma^\mu C^{-1})_{\alpha\beta}$$

(the factor $\tfrac{1}{2}$ is for normalization purposes) or, finally,

$$\varepsilon^\mu_n(k) = [\tfrac{1}{2}\tfrac{1}{2}1]^{\alpha\beta}_n \frac{1}{\sqrt{2}} (\sigma^\mu k \cdot \tilde\sigma C)_{\alpha\beta}. \tag{4.48}$$

Similarly,

$$\varepsilon^\mu_{\dot n}(k) = [\tfrac{1}{2}\tfrac{1}{2}1]^{\dot\alpha\dot\beta}_{\dot n} \frac{1}{\sqrt{2}} (C k \cdot \tilde\sigma \sigma^\mu)_{\dot\alpha\dot\beta}. \tag{4.48'}$$

Indeed, we can verify that the orthogonality relations (4.46) are satisfied, for

$$k^\mu \varepsilon^n_\mu = \text{tr} \{[\tfrac{1}{2}\tfrac{1}{2}1]^n C^{-1}\} = 0.$$

In the rest frame of the spin 1 particle we obtain the vectors

$$\varepsilon_1^\mu = \frac{1}{\sqrt{2}}\, \sigma_{\frac{1}{2},-\frac{1}{2}}^\mu = \frac{-1}{\sqrt{2}}\begin{pmatrix} 0 \\ 1 \\ -i \\ 0 \end{pmatrix}, \quad \varepsilon_{-1}^\mu = \frac{1}{\sqrt{2}}\begin{pmatrix} 0 \\ 1 \\ i \\ 0 \end{pmatrix}, \quad \varepsilon_0^\mu = \begin{pmatrix} 0 \\ 0 \\ 0 \\ -1 \end{pmatrix} \tag{4.49}$$

$$k = (m,0,0,0).$$

so that ε_0 is in the z-direction, $\varepsilon_1 - \varepsilon_{-1}$ in the x-direction, and $\varepsilon_1 + \varepsilon_{-1}$ in the y-direction.

We now make the photon mass zero. The condition $k^2 = 0$ has two effects:

(a) If $\varepsilon \cdot k = 0$ and $k^2 = 0$, then there are in general only two linearly independent polarization vectors, because there are only two linearly independent spacelike vectors orthogonal to a lightlike vector.

(b) If we had chosen $\varepsilon' = \varepsilon + \lambda k$ we have still

$$\varepsilon' \cdot k = 0,$$

so that ε is determined up to an additive term λk. For $k^2 \neq 0$ we did not have this freedom. Consequently, the amplitudes (4.45) in the case of photons must be invariant under the transformation

$$\varepsilon \to \varepsilon + \lambda k. \tag{4.50}$$

This is the form of *gauge invariance* in our formulation.

If we keep the definition (4.48) even for massless case we obtain in the frame where $k = (1001)$, for example, only one direction of polarization (the other will be obtained under a parity transformation):

$$\varepsilon_1^\mu = \frac{-1}{\sqrt{2}}\begin{pmatrix} 0 \\ 1 \\ -i \\ 0 \end{pmatrix}, \quad \varepsilon_0^\mu = \frac{1}{\sqrt{2}} k^\mu = \begin{pmatrix} 1 \\ 0 \\ 0 \\ 1 \end{pmatrix}\frac{1}{\sqrt{2}}, \quad \varepsilon_{-1}^\mu = 0. \tag{4.49'}$$

Let us now go back to our amplitude, Eq. (4.45). The condition $k^2 = 0$, or equivalently Eq. (4.50), gives

$$\sum_i A_i v_\mu^i k^\mu = 0. \tag{4.51}$$

This condition restricts the number of linearly independent scalar amplitudes to two. To see this simply let us choose, e.g., $v_1 = k$, $v_2 = k_1$, $v_3 = k_2$, and $v_4 = [kk_1k_2]$. We have then from Eq. (4.51)

$$A_2 k_1 \cdot k + A_3 k_2 \cdot k = 0,$$

so that A_3 can be expressed in terms of A_2 and A_1 and does not appear at all. Hence

$$M = A[(k_1 \cdot \varepsilon)(k \cdot k_2) - (k_2 \cdot \varepsilon)(k \cdot k_1)] + B\varepsilon^\mu(k)\varepsilon_{\mu\nu\lambda\rho}k^\nu k_1^\lambda k_2^\rho, \quad (4.52)$$

and we have two scalar amplitudes under proper Lorentz transformations.

Next we· consider the two-photon process shown Fig. 4.3 (Compton

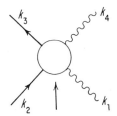

Figure 4.3 Labeling of momenta in a process with two photons.

effect of a scalar particle). Again we start with nonzero masses. The solution of the transformation equation

$$M(K) = D^{01}(A)M(\Lambda^{-1}K)D^{01}(A)^\dagger \quad (4.53)$$

can be written in the form

$$M_{m_3 \dot{m}_1} = \varepsilon^\mu_{\dot{m}_3}(k_3)T_{\mu\nu}\varepsilon^\nu_{\dot{m}_1}(k_1) \quad (4.54)$$

because

$$D^{01}(A)\varepsilon^\mu_m(k) = \Lambda^\mu_\nu \varepsilon^\nu(\Lambda^{-1}k); \quad \varepsilon^\mu_{\dot{m}}(k)D^{01}(A)^\dagger = \Lambda^\mu_\nu \varepsilon^\nu_{\dot{m}}(\Lambda^{-1}k)$$

with

$$\varepsilon(k_3) \cdot k_3 = 0, \quad \varepsilon(k_1) \cdot k_1 = 0,$$

and the problem is characterized by nine amplitudes.

Now again we make $k_1^2 = k_3^2 = 0$ and use the invariance under the transformation $\varepsilon \to \varepsilon + \lambda k$ and obtain [$\varepsilon_1 \equiv \varepsilon_1(k_1)$, $\varepsilon_3 \equiv \varepsilon_3(k_3)$]

$$\lambda_1 \varepsilon_3^\mu T_{\mu\nu}k_1^\nu + \lambda_3 k_3^\mu T_{\mu\nu}\varepsilon_1^\nu + \lambda_1\lambda_3 k_3^\mu T_{\mu\nu}k_1^\nu = 0. \quad (4.55)$$

If we choose the tensor $T_{\mu\nu}$ such that

$$T_{\mu\nu}k_1^\nu = 0 \quad \text{and} \quad k_3^\mu T_{\mu\nu} = 0, \quad (4.56)$$

we can satisfy the condition (4.55) independent of ε_1 and ε_3. Now let

$$T_{\mu\nu} = \sum_{ij} A_{ij}v_\mu^i v_\nu^j. \quad (4.57)$$

We will show that the conditions (4.55) reduce the nine amplitudes further to four. Equation (4.57) inserted in Eq. (4.56) gives

$$\sum A_{ij}v_\mu^i v_\nu^j k_3^\mu = 0, \quad \sum A_{ij}v_\mu^i v_\nu^j k_1^\nu = 0.$$

We choose $v^1 = k_1$ and $v^2 = k_3$; then

$$A_{1j}v_\nu^j(k_1 \cdot k_3) + A_{3j}v_\nu^j(v_3 \cdot k_3) + A_{4j}v_\nu^j(v_4 \cdot k_3) = 0,$$
$$A_{i2}v_\mu^i(k_1 \cdot k_3) + A_{i3}v_\mu^i(v_3 \cdot k_1) + A_{i4}v_\mu^i(v_4 \cdot k_1) = 0.$$

In the nondegenerate case (i.e., not at the boundary of the physical region) we can always choose v^3 and v^4 orthogonal to both k_1 and k_3. For example, by Gramm-Schmidt orthogonalization,

$$v^3 = z - k_1 \frac{k_3 \cdot z}{k_1 \cdot k_3} - k_3 \frac{k_1 \cdot z}{k_1 \cdot k_3},$$

$$v^4 = [v^3 k_1 k_3]; \quad z = \alpha k_2 + \beta k_4.$$

Clearly, then,

$$v^3 \cdot k_1 = v^3 \cdot k_3 = v^4 \cdot k_3 = v^4 \cdot v^3 = 0.$$

Consequently, because $(k_1 \cdot k_3) \neq 0$,

$$A_{1j}v^j = 0 \quad \text{and} \quad A_{i2}v^i = 0;$$

and because v^j are linearly independent we have finally

$$A_{1j} = 0 \quad \text{and} \quad A_{i2} = 0.$$

This makes seven of the sixteen amplitudes A_{ij} = zero. Furthermore in forming

$$M = \varepsilon_3^\mu T_{\mu\nu}\varepsilon_1^\nu,$$

with the conditions $\varepsilon(k_3) \cdot k_3 = 0$ and $\varepsilon(k_1) \cdot k_1 = 0$, we see that five other amplitudes do not contribute, and we are left with four terms:

$$M = A_{33}\varepsilon_3 \cdot v^3 \varepsilon_1 \cdot v^3 + A_{34}\varepsilon_3 \cdot v^3 \varepsilon_1 \cdot v^4 + A_{43}\varepsilon_3 \cdot v^4 \varepsilon_1 \cdot v^3 + A_{44}\varepsilon_3 \cdot v^4 \varepsilon_1 \cdot v^4$$

$$= \varepsilon_3^\mu \varepsilon_1^\nu \sum_{i=1}^{4} A_i M_{\mu\nu}^i, \tag{4.58}$$

where

$$M_i^{\mu\nu} = (v_3^\mu v_3^\nu, \ v_3^\mu v_4^\nu, \ v_4^\mu v_3^\nu, \ v_4^\mu v_4^\nu).$$

As we shall explain in the next section, the amplitudes A_{33} and A_{44} have the same sign under the parity transformation and A_{34} and A_{43} have the same sign but opposite to the first pair, so that under parity conservation the number of scalar amplitudes is two.

For the amplitudes of the Compton scattering of a spin $\frac{1}{2}$ particle, we refer to Chap. 13.

4.5 Amplitudes for Neutrino Processes

Finally we shall discuss the amplitudes when one or more of the particles are massless fermions. We saw in Chap. 2 that the spinor index of a massless particle must transform like a nullspinor, which puts a restriction on the amplitude given by Eq. (2.57) or (2.58). We construct therefore the amplitudes as though the particles all were massive, and then impose the condition of masslessness afterwards; this reduces the number of amplitudes considerably.

As an example, consider the scattering of a spin 0 and a spin $\frac{1}{2}$ particle into again a spin 0 and spin $\frac{1}{2}$ particle. We have in general the four amplitudes

$$M = A_1(k_3 + k_1)\cdot\sigma + A_2(k_3 - k_1)\cdot\sigma + A_3(n\cdot\sigma + k_3\cdot\sigma n\cdot\tilde{\sigma}k_1\cdot\sigma)$$
$$+ A_4(n\cdot\sigma - k_3\cdot\sigma n\cdot\tilde{\sigma}k_1\cdot\sigma), \quad n = k_2 + k_4.$$

We shall see in the next chapter that in this choice each basis function has definite parity. Now if both of the fermions of momenta k_3 and k_1 are massless we have from Eq. (2.58) the two conditions

$$\begin{aligned}(k_3\cdot\tilde{\sigma})M &= 0, \quad k_3^2 = 0, \\ M(k_1\cdot\tilde{\sigma}) &= 0, \quad k_1^2 = 0,\end{aligned} \qquad (4.59)$$

or

$$(A_1 - A_2)k_3\cdot\tilde{\sigma}k_1\cdot\sigma + (A_3 + A_4)k_3\cdot\tilde{\sigma}n\cdot\sigma = 0,$$
$$(A_1 + A_2)k_3\cdot\sigma k_1\cdot\tilde{\sigma} + (A_3 + A_4)n\cdot\sigma k_1\cdot\tilde{\sigma} = 0.$$

The vectors k_3, k_1, and n being independent, we must have

$$A_1 \pm A_2 = 0, \qquad A_3 + A_4 = 0,$$

or $A_1 = 0$, $A_2 = 0$, $A_3 = -A_4$. Hence the only amplitude that survives is

$$M = Ak_3\cdot\sigma n\cdot\tilde{\sigma}k_1\cdot\sigma.$$

If only one of the fermions is massless we have only one of the above conditions so that the number of the amplitudes is two:

$$M = A_1 k_3\cdot\sigma + A_2 k_3\cdot\sigma n\cdot\tilde{\sigma}k_1\cdot\sigma.$$

For interactions of the type spin $\frac{1}{2}$ + spin $\frac{1}{2} \to$ spin $\frac{1}{2}$ + ν (e.g., β-decay) the 16 amplitudes (if time reversal and parity are not conserved!) will be reduced by condition (4.59) for the neutrino to 15 or 14. But empirically, the weak interactions of the type $n \to p + e + \nu$, $\mu \to e + \nu + \bar{\nu}$ have a much simpler structure than that. [See Sec. 10.2(c).] The simplicity is due partly to assumed T-invariance, partly to neglect of those amplitudes that vanish at very low energies, and partly to new principles found to be valid in weak interactions at low energies. [See Sec. 10.3(e).]

Problems and Further Developments

1. Consider the decay of a particle of isospin I into two and three particles. Find the amplitudes and the restrictions imposed on the isospin of decay particles. Show that the S-matrix of the vertex in isospin space is given by the Clebsch-Gordan coefficients, or the $3j$-symbols.

2. Show that the amplitude in Eq. (4.4) can also be written as

$$R^{\frac{1}{2}\frac{1}{2}\frac{1}{2}\frac{1}{2}} = A'I \otimes I + B'\sigma \otimes \sigma.$$

Find the relation between the A, B-amplitudes and the A', B'-amplitudes.

3. Consider the amplitude $R^{(1111)}$ given by Eq. (4.6). Here the indices α_i run from $+1$ to -1. Using the unitary matrix

$$U_{\alpha\beta} = \frac{1}{\sqrt{2}} \begin{pmatrix} -1 & -i & 0 \\ 0 & 0 & \sqrt{2} \\ 1 & -i & 0 \end{pmatrix},$$

where β runs 1, 2, 3, transform $R^{(1111)}$ into the new indices.

4. Prove the reduction formula given in App. 4, Eq. (A4.1), and the formulas (App. 4, Eqs. A4.2 and A4.3).

5. Prove Eqs. (A4.7), (A4.8), and (A4.9) in App. 4.

6. Obtain the amplitudes R^I from $R^{(1111)}$ using Eqs. (4.6) and (4.9).

7. Derive Eq. (4.14) using Eq. (4.13) and Eqs. (4.4) and (4.6).

8. Do Problems (4) and (5) when D^I are replaced by $D^{(0l)}$; in other words, show that the same Clebsch-Gordan series (A4.1) holds also for $D^{0l_1} \otimes D^{0l_2}$.

9. Construct all isotropic tensors T^{ijk} under orthogonal transformations (indices 1, 2, 3, or 1, 0, -1) and isotropic tensors $T^{\mu\nu\lambda\sigma}$ (indices 0, 1, 2, 3) under homogeneous Lorentz transformations.

10. Inserting Eq. (4.26) into Eq. (4.29), calculate M^{11}, M^{10}, M^{00}.

11. Prove Eq. (4.32).

12. Consider a general amplitude $R^{\alpha_3\cdots}_{\alpha_1\cdots}$, the remaining isospin indices being suppressed. Show that the linear combination $\sum_\alpha R^{\alpha_1\cdots}_{\alpha_3\cdots}$ can be constructed as though the particles 1 and 3 had isospin zero. This result is true for any unitary symmetry group. In particular, show that

$$\sum_\alpha R^{\alpha\beta_2}_{\alpha\beta_1} = \text{const.} \ \delta^{\beta_2}_{\beta_1}.$$

   (*Hint:* Use in Eq. (4.7) or, in its generalization, the unitarity condition $\sum_\alpha D^\gamma_\alpha D^{*\rho}_\alpha = \delta^{\gamma\rho}$.)

13. As a further extension of Fig. 4.2 construct the amplitudes for a process of the type $K^- + p \rightarrow \Lambda + \omega$ (i.e., spin $0 + $ spin $\frac{1}{2} \rightarrow$ spin $\frac{1}{2} + $ spin 1).

14. Construct a theory of invariant amplitudes under the Euclidian group E_3 (three-dimensional rotations and translations)—see Chap. 2, Exercise 23. These are the nonrelativistic counterparts of our covariant amplitudes. Indicate a passage from relativistic to nonrelativistic amplitudes.

CHAPTER 5

Discrete Symmetry Transformations and Analytic Continuation

5.1 Discrete Symmetry Operations

So far we have considered continuous symmetry transformations, the 2×2 special unitary group for isospin, and the quantum mechanical restricted Lorentz group for spin. A number of discrete groups, such as parity, particle-antiparticle conjugation, time reversal, various inversions, and their combinations also play an important role in the classification of particles and their interactions.

These discrete groups have two elements because a repeated application of the transformation gives back the identity. The group is commutative, its representations are direct products of one-dimensional representations, one for each particle. These representations are phase factors η. Thus, according to our general discussion, in Sec. 2.1, of the invariance principles, we obtain for all such discrete transformations, considered separately, the equation

$$R(\alpha'_f, \alpha'_i) = \eta R(\alpha_f, \alpha_i) = \prod_{f,i} \eta_f \eta_i^{-1} R(\alpha_f, \alpha_i), \tag{5.1}$$

where α' are the transformed quantities to be specified in each case. As before, if the final particle transforms according to the representation η_f, the initial particle transforms according to conjugate representation η_i^{-1}. The total η must be ± 1; the individual η's in general need not be. Equation (5.1) places a restriction on the amplitude and expresses the physical condition that the process is invariant under the transformation considered. Of course, Eq. (5.1) is not true for any process; e.g., the weak interactions do not conserve parity. The validity and also the physical interpretation of abstract discrete transformations must be considered for each interaction separately. The implication of the invariance, Eq. (5.1), on the M-amplitudes is as follows: From the connection between the two amplitudes, Eq. (2.50), we have (with $U = 1$)

$$M(\alpha'_f,\alpha'_i) = \prod_f D^{0S_f}\left(\sqrt{\frac{k'_f \cdot \sigma}{m_f}}\right) R(\alpha'_f,\alpha'_i) \prod_i D^{0S_i^\dagger}\left(\sqrt{\frac{k'_i \cdot \sigma}{m_i}}\right)$$

$$= \eta \prod_f D^{0S_f}(\alpha') R(\alpha_f,\alpha_i) \prod_i D^{0S_i^\dagger}(\alpha'). \tag{5.2}$$

If we define a new quantity M' by

$$M'(\alpha) = \prod_f D^{0S_f}(\alpha) D^{0S_f^{-1}}(\alpha') M(\alpha') \prod_i D^{0S_i^{\dagger -1}}(\alpha') D^{0S_i^\dagger}(\alpha), \tag{5.3}$$

then clearly the condition of invariance is

$$M'(\alpha_f,\alpha_i) = \eta M(\alpha_f,\alpha_i). \tag{5.4}$$

In addition to Eq. (5.1) we shall also discuss the so-called antiunitary representations of the discrete groups. These arise naturally when time reversal is considered, and they involve an interchange of incoming and outgoing particles.

5.2   Parity

This is the transformation in which the spatial parts of the momenta are measured in a reflected coordinate frame:

$$\alpha' \equiv \alpha^P = \{k^0_j, -\mathbf{k}_j\}. \tag{5.5}$$

Energy as well as spin indices m_j and isospin indices α_i are unchanged. To conserve energy and momentum the transformation must be made on *all* particles. Because now

$$k' \cdot \sigma \equiv k^P \cdot \sigma = k \cdot \tilde{\sigma}, \tag{5.6}$$

we obtain from Eq. (5.3)

$$M^P(\alpha_f,\alpha_i) = \prod_f D^{0S_f}\left(\frac{k \cdot \sigma}{m}\right) M(\alpha'_f,\alpha'_i) \prod_i D^{0S_i^\dagger}\left(\frac{k \cdot \sigma}{m}\right) \tag{5.7}$$

and

$$M^P(\alpha_f,\alpha_i) = \eta^P M(\alpha_f,\alpha_i); \quad \eta^P = \prod \eta^P_f \eta^{P-1}_i. \tag{5.8}$$

Note that the arguments of D are now $\dfrac{k \cdot \sigma}{m}$ and not $\left(\dfrac{k \cdot \sigma}{m}\right)^{1/2}$.

Let us consider, as an example, the spin 0-spin $\frac{1}{2}$ case. Then, from Eq. (5.7),

$$M^P(K) = \frac{k_3 \cdot \sigma}{m_3} M(K^P) \frac{k_1 \cdot \sigma}{m_1}.$$

We found in the previous chapter that

$$M(K) = \sum_i A_i v^i_\mu \cdot \sigma^\mu.$$

Hence

$$M(K^P) = \sum_i A_i v^i_\mu \tilde{\sigma}^\mu.$$

We see now that not every basis $v \cdot \sigma$ is parity invariant. For example, a term $M = k_1 \cdot \sigma$ is not, while $M = (k_1 + k_3) \cdot \sigma$ is. If we symmetrize or anti-symmetrize we see that the forms

$$v^i \cdot \sigma + \frac{k_3 \cdot \sigma}{m_3} v^i \cdot \tilde{\sigma} \frac{k_1 \cdot \sigma}{m_1}$$

have the parity $\eta^P = +1$, and the terms

$$v^i \cdot \sigma - \frac{k_3 \cdot \sigma}{m_3} v^i \cdot \tilde{\sigma} \frac{k_1 \cdot \sigma}{m_1}$$

have the parity $\eta^P = -1$. If we choose, e.g.,

$$v^{(1)} = \frac{k_1}{m_1}, \qquad v^{(2)} = \frac{k_2}{m_2}, \qquad v^{(3)} = \frac{k_3}{m_3},$$

and

$$v^{(4)}_\mu = [k_1 k_2 k_3]_\mu = \varepsilon_{\mu\nu\lambda\rho} k^\nu_1 k^\lambda_2 k^\rho_3,$$

we find the following four basis functions with definite signs of η_P:

$$Y^1 = \left(\frac{k_1}{m_1} + \frac{k_3}{m_3} \right) \cdot \sigma, \qquad\qquad \eta^P = +1$$

$$Y^2 = \left(\frac{k_1}{m_1} - \frac{k_3}{m_3} \right) \cdot \sigma, \qquad\qquad \eta^P = -1$$

$$\bar{Y}^3 = \frac{k_2}{m_2} \cdot \sigma + \frac{k_3 \cdot \sigma}{m_3} \frac{k_2 \cdot \tilde{\sigma}}{m_2} \frac{k_1 \cdot \sigma}{m_1}, \qquad \eta^P = +1$$

$$\bar{Y}^4 = \frac{k_2}{m_2} \cdot \sigma - \frac{k_3 \cdot \sigma}{m_3} \frac{k_2 \cdot \tilde{\sigma}}{m_2} \frac{k_1 \cdot \sigma}{m_1}, \qquad \eta^P = -1$$

(5.9)

Because of the identity

$$\frac{k_1 \cdot \sigma}{m_1} \frac{k_2 \cdot \tilde{\sigma}}{m_2} \frac{k_3 \cdot \sigma}{m_3} = i \begin{bmatrix} k_1 & k_2 & k_3 \\ m_1 & m_2 & m_3 \end{bmatrix} \cdot \sigma + \frac{k_1 \cdot \sigma}{m_1} \frac{k_2 \cdot k_3}{m_2 m_3}$$

$$- \frac{k_2 \cdot \sigma}{m_2} \frac{k_1 \cdot k_3}{m_1 m_3} + \frac{k_3 \cdot \sigma}{m_3} \frac{k_1 \cdot k_2}{m_1 m_2}, \quad (5.10)$$

which follows from the relation

$$\sigma^\mu \tilde{\sigma}^\lambda \sigma^\nu = i\varepsilon^{\rho\mu\lambda\nu} \sigma_\rho + \sigma^\mu g^{\lambda\nu} - \sigma^\lambda g^{\mu\nu} + \sigma^\nu g^{\lambda\mu}, \quad (5.10')$$

the remaining terms are linear combinations of the four above ones. We can also choose instead of $\bar{Y}^3$, $\bar{Y}^4$, the more symmetric combinations

$$Y^3 = n \cdot \sigma + \frac{k_3 \cdot \sigma}{m_3} n \cdot \tilde{\sigma} \frac{k_1 \cdot \sigma}{m_1}, \qquad \eta^P = +1$$

$$Y^4 = n \cdot \sigma - \frac{k_3 \cdot \sigma}{m_3} n \cdot \tilde{\sigma} \frac{k_1 \cdot \sigma}{m_1}, \qquad \eta^P = -1$$

(5.11)

where

$$\eta = \frac{k_2}{m_2} + \frac{k_4}{m_4}.$$

In a similar way we can verify using Eqs. (5.7) and (5.8) that the fundamental spinorial "currents" given in Table 4–2, Eq. (4.38) have the indicated parities: $+1$ for S, A, T and -1 for V and P. (See Exercise 4.)

We shall denote the phases n_f^P, n_i^P the *intrinsic parity of the particle* and the phase η^P, in Eq. (5.8), the *intrinsic parity of the process*. Clearly η^P depends on the type and the number of the particles, i.e., on the type of process considered. Thus, the intrinsic parities occur from the beginning but we do not know yet what intrinsic parity to assign to what particle, or whether they are unique.

If the amplitude has a definite parity (i.e., if parity is conserved), it follows immediately from Eq. (5.1) that if the initial and final particles are the same the intrinsic parity of the process is plus one (the no-scattering part of the S-matrix has also parity plus one). Furthermore, the intrinsic parity of a process does not change if we add (or subtract) the same particle to initial and final configurations.

The assignment of intrinsic parities to the particles is, in general, *not unique.*[1] If there are additive conservation laws, energy momentum, charge, etc., denoted by q_j, then together with η_j, also $\eta'_j = \eta_j \exp(iq_j a)$ is also an intrinsic parity, for all a, for

$$\prod_{i,f} \eta'_f \eta'^{-1}_i = \prod_{i,f} \eta_f \eta^{-1}_i \exp\left[i\left(\sum_f q_f - \sum_i q_i\right)a\right] = \prod_{i,f} \eta_f \eta^{-1}_i. \quad (5.11)$$

The actual intrinsic parity assignments will be discussed in Chap. 10.

Parity Transformation of the Polarization Vector

Under the parity transformation, the two basis functions in Eq. (4.52) transform differently. The time component of the skew product $[kk_1k_2]$ changes sign, the space components do not, just the opposite of the vector k. Hence under parity conservation we can take any one of the two terms in Eq. (4.52). The polarization vector $\varepsilon(k)$ transforms under parity into

$$\varepsilon^{P\mu}_n(k) = [\tfrac{1}{2}\tfrac{1}{2} 1]^{\alpha\beta}_n \frac{1}{\sqrt{2}} (\tilde{\sigma}^\mu k \cdot \sigma C)_{\alpha\beta}, \quad (5.12)$$

[1] See in this connection G. C. Wick, A. S. Wightman, and E. P. Wigner, *Phys. Rev.,* **88**, 101 (1952). We have introduced intrinsic parities quite naturally from the beginning. A different point of view is taken by H. P. Stapp, *Phys. Rev.,* **128**, 1963 (1962), where he shows the construction of a set of intrinsic parities a posteriori from the total parity of the process.

and in the special frame of Eq. (4.49′) we obtain the other direction of polarization, as we have expected:

$$\varepsilon_1^{P\mu} = 0, \quad \varepsilon_0^{P\mu} = \frac{1}{\sqrt{2}} k^\mu, \quad \varepsilon_{-1}^{P\mu} = \frac{1}{\sqrt{2}} \begin{pmatrix} 0 \\ 1 \\ -i \\ 0 \end{pmatrix}. \tag{5.13}$$

The question of the intrinsic parity of the antiparticles will be discussed after we introduce the concept of antiparticle in the next section.

5.3   Time Reversal and Antiparticles

The time-reversal operation changes the sign of the energy: $k^0 \to -k^0$. How are we going to interpret a negative energy physically, since we have defined particles always to have positive energies $k_i^0 > 0$, $k_i^2 = m_i^2$?

We will show in this section that as far as the transformations properties are concerned the amplitude of a process, with the sign of the energy momentum vectors reversed, can be interpreted as the amplitude of a related process in which these particles have been changed from ingoing to outgoing particles, or vice versa, with their additive quantum numbers and their third components of spin and isospin also reversed.

Consider for simplicity of writing the transformation PT; $k^\mu \to -k^\mu$, on one outgoing particle of momentum k_3, for example. We shall first discover the interpretation of the new amplitude $R(-k_3, k_4, \ldots, k_1 k_2)$ and then consider the restrictions imposed on it by the time-reversal invariance. For this purpose we go back to the transformation properties of the amplitude. Under translations, particle 3 contributes now a factor $\exp(-ik_3 a)$ just as an ingoing particle. Hence in order to conserve the total energy-momentum conservation we have to interpret k_3 as an ingoing particle of positive energy momentum. The physical region of the new momenta is of course different. The relation $\sum_f k_f + k_3 = \sum_i k_i$ goes over into $\sum_f k_f = \sum_i k_i + k_3$.

What about its spin and isospin? The particle 3 with isotopic spin I_3 transforms according to D^{I_3}. In order to interpret it as an ingoing particle we have to transform D^{I_3} into $D^{I_3\dagger}$. This can be done by the relation

$$D^I(u)_\alpha^\beta = (-1)^{\alpha-\beta} D^{I*}(u)_{-\beta}^{-\alpha}, \tag{5.14}$$

which follows from the equivalence relation $D^I = D^{I*}(C) D^I D^I(C^{-1})$ (see App. 3). The same relations hold for spin

$$D^S(A')_m^n = (-1)^{m-n} D^{S*}(A')_{-n}^{-m}. \tag{5.14′}$$

It is convenient to consider Eqs. (5.14) and (5.14′) as transformations, changing the undotted indices into dotted ones, and vice versa:

$$D_m^{S_n} = D^S(C)_m^{\dot{m}} D_{\dot{m}}^{S*\dot{n}} D^S(C^{-1})_{\dot{n}}^n, \tag{5.14″}$$

with the understanding that the numerical value of a dotted index is the negative of the undotted one, and vice versa.

Thus in order to interpret the particle of momentum $-k_3$ as an ingoing particle of momentum k_3 we have to change the spin and isospin indices into their negatives. From the amplitude

$$R_{\substack{m_3 m_4 \dots;\, \dot{m}_1 \dot{m}_2 \dots \\ \alpha_3 \alpha_4 \dots;\, \dot{\alpha}_1 \dot{\alpha}_2 \dots}}(-k_3 k_4 \dots;\, k_1 k_2 \dots),$$

which we cannot interpret physically, we obtain thus a physically interpretable amplitude

$$R_{\substack{m_4 \dots;\, m_3 \dot{m}_1 \dot{m}_2 \dots \\ \alpha_4 \dots;\, \alpha_3 \dot{\alpha}_1 \dot{\alpha}_2 \dots}}(k_4 \dots;\, k_3 k_1 k_2 \dots)$$

as shown schematically in Fig. 5.1a,

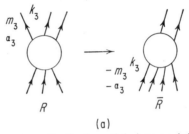

(a)

Figure 5.1a   Changing of a final particle into an initial antiparticle.

We now define the particle with the same mass, spin, and isospin, but opposite spin and isospin *components*, as the *antiparticle* of the original particle.[2] It is clear that if there are more additive conservation laws the sign of the corresponding quantum numbers for the antiparticles have to be reversed; because $e^{iaq} = e^{-ia(-q)}$, an outgoing particle of additive quantum numbers q becomes an ingoing particle (transforming according to conjugate representation $\exp(-iaq')$, with $q' = -q$).

Let us now consider the change of sign on all momenta. In order, therefore, that the change of sign of energy momentum vector will take us from one physically interpretable amplitude to another we must also reverse the signs of all additive quantum numbers—in other words, make from an outgoing particle an incoming antiparticle. We further change on both sides of the equation the signs of k_f, k_i, q_f, and q_i, and obtain the following equation:

$$\left[\prod_i D^{S_i}(C^{-1}) D^{I_i}(C^{-1}) R^T(-k_f, -k_i) \prod_f D^{S_f}(C) D^{I_f}(C) \right]$$

$$= e^{(\Sigma k_i - \Sigma k_f)a} e^{(\Sigma q_i - \Sigma q_f)\lambda} \prod_i D^{S_i}(A'(-k)) D^{I_i}(u)$$

$$\times \left[\prod_i D^{S_i}(C^{-1}) D^{I_i}(C^{-1}) R^T(-\Lambda^{-1} k_f, -\Lambda^{-1} k_i) \prod_f D^{S_f}(C) D^{I_f}(C) \right]$$

$$\times \prod_f D^{S_f\dagger}(A'(-k)) D^{I_f\dagger}(u). \tag{5.15}$$

---

[2] We recall that the concept of antiparticles occurred first in connection with the Dirac equation. Its basis there and here lies in the time-reversal operation.

This equation, when compared with Eq. (2.40), shows that the expression in square bracket transforms exactly like an amplitude $\bar{R}(k_i,k_f)$ in which anti-particles i are outgoing and antiparticles f are incoming. We therefore write

$$\bar{R}(k_i,k_f) = \eta \prod_i D^{S_i}(C^{-1})D^{I_i}(C^{-1})R^T(-k_f,-k_i)\prod_f D^{S_f}(C)D^{I_f}(C), \quad (5.16)$$

and see that, conversely, if in the amplitude $\bar{R}(k_i,k_f)$ the k's take negative values, it describes the new physical process on the right, namely the so-called *CPT-equivalent process*. Consequently one process would be the analytic continuation of the other if we could show that R and $\bar{R}$ are the same function. Then we would have the relation

$$R(-k_f,-k_i) = \eta \prod_f D^{S_f}(C^{-1})D^{I_f}(C^{-1})R^T(k_i,k_f)\prod_i D^{S_i}(C)D^{I_i}(C) \quad (5.17)$$

(see Sec. 5). In terms of indices, a particle in the final configuration has an undotted index; the antiparticle has a dotted index. In the initial configuration it is the other way around: the particle has a dotted index; the antiparticle an undotted one.

Because of the change of sign of additive quantum numbers and of the third component of spin and isospin (particle—antiparticle conjugation) and the change of initial and final configurations to which we we were led automatically, the transformation (5.15) or (5.16) is actually the so-called *CPT-transformation*. To obtain T alone we have to change once more the signs of the quantum numbers to compensate the change occurring by the reversal of initial and final particles and operate with P. These transformations will be formulated in the next section.

5.4 The Discrete Transformations CPT, C, T

The amplitudes $R(k_f,k_i)$ are defined, to begin with, for positive values of the energies k_f^0 and k_i^0. We look now at the CPT-transformation in a different way and ask if we can interpret $R(k_f,k_i)$ in any way if the arguments take negative values. This would correspond to the analytic continuation of the amplitude along the negative axes of energies and momenta. The analyticity assumptions are, we shall see, most easily introduced by means of CPT-transformation.

We assume, for the time being, all particles to be distinguishable and start from the transformation law:

$$R(k_f,k_i) = e^{i(\Sigma k_f - \Sigma k_i)a}e^{i(\Sigma q_f - \Sigma q_i)\lambda}$$

$$\times \prod_f \{D^{S_f}(A_f')D^{I_f}(u)\}R(\Lambda^{-1}k_f,\Lambda^{-1}k_i)\prod_i \{D^{S_i\dagger}(A_i')D^{I_i\dagger}(u)\},$$

where q is the set of additive quantum numbers. Using Eq. (5.14) we transform all D's into D^* and all $D^\dagger$'s into D^T. In order to correctly interpret

k_i as outgoing and k_f as ingoing particles we further see that the transformation

$$R(k_f,k_i) \rightarrow R(-k_f,-k_i) \tag{5.18}$$

can now be given a precise meaning by the right-hand side of Eq. (5.17). In terms of the dotted and undotted indices explained in the previous section, the condition of CPT invariance can be written as

$$\text{CPT}: \; R_{m_f \dot{m}_i \alpha_f \dot{\alpha}_i}(k_f,k_i) = \eta \bar{R}_{\dot{m}_i m_f \dot{\alpha}_i \alpha_f}(k_i,k_f) = \eta R_{m_f \dot{m}_i \alpha_f \dot{\alpha}_i}(-k_f,-k_i), \tag{5.19}$$

which consists of dotting all the indices (particle-antiparticle) and changing initial and final configurations. Here m_f and m_i represent the set of final and initial indices collectively.

The particle-antiparticle conjugation affects only the indices and changes dotted and undotted indices, but does not change the initial state into final state. The requirement of C-invariance is

$$\text{C}: \; R_{\substack{m_f \dot{m}_i \\ \alpha_f \dot{\alpha}_i}}(k_f,k_i) = \eta^{\text{C}} R_{\substack{\dot{m}_f m_i \\ \dot{\alpha}_f \alpha_i}}(k_f,k_i). \tag{5.20}$$

Thus combining Eqs. (5.19) and (5.20) we have the requirement of PT-invariance

$$\text{PT}: \; R_{\substack{m_f \dot{m}_i \\ \alpha_f \dot{\alpha}_i}}(k_f,k_i) = \eta^{\text{PT}} R_{\substack{\dot{m}_f m_i \\ \dot{\alpha}_f \alpha_i}}(-k_f,-k_i), \tag{5.21}$$

which simply changes initial and final configurations. Finally, using P, we get the requirement of T-invariance:

$$\text{T}: \; R_{\substack{m_f \dot{m}_i \\ \alpha_f \dot{\alpha}_i}}(k_f,k_i) = \eta^{\text{T}} R_{\substack{\dot{m}_f m_i \\ \dot{\alpha}_f \alpha_i}}(-k_f^0,\mathbf{k}_f; -k_i^0,\mathbf{k}_i). \tag{5.22}$$

Equations (5.20), (5.21), and (5.22) must be satisfied if a process is invariant under charge conjugation, parity, and time reversal.

Transformation of Indices in the Spinorial Amplitudes

We shall now derive the equations corresponding to Eqs. (5.19)–(5.22) for the M-amplitudes, which are the quantities we construct first. The M-amplitudes have spinor indices with respect to Lorentz group whereas the spinor indices of the R-amplitudes are with respect to the rotation group. The operators that change dotted indices into undotted ones, and vice versa, are different from those in Eq. (5.13); in particular we know that now these two types of indices belong to inequivalent representations.

Let us write Eq. (5.19) out explicitly[3]:

$$R(k_f,k_i) = \eta \prod_f D^{s_f}(C^{-1}) \bar{R}^{\text{T}}(k_i,k_f) \prod_i D^{s_i}(C), \tag{5.23}$$

---

[3] We do not need, from here on, to carry the isospin indices as they are the same for both M- and R-amplitudes.

and insert, on both sides, R in terms of M-amplitudes:

$$R(k_f,k_i) = \prod_f D^{0S_f}(B^{-1}_{k \to p})M(k_f,k_i) \prod_i D^{0S_i}(B^{t-1}_{k \to p}). \qquad (5.24)$$

We then obtain

$$M(k_f,k_i) = \eta \prod_f D^{0S_f}(BC^{-1}B^{-1*})\bar{M}^T(k_i,k_f) \prod_i D^{0S_i}(BC^{-1}B^{-1*})^\dagger. \quad (5.25)$$

Here, the quantity $BC^{-1}B^{-1*}$ has a simple form

$$G \equiv BC^{-1}B^{-1*} = \sqrt{\frac{k \cdot \sigma}{m}} \, UC^{-1}U^{-1*}\left(\sqrt{\frac{k \cdot \sigma}{m}}\right)^{T-1} = \sqrt{\frac{k \cdot \sigma}{m}} \, C^{-1} \sqrt{\frac{k \cdot \tilde{\sigma}^T}{m}}$$

$$= \frac{k \cdot \sigma}{m} C^{-1} = C^{-1} \frac{k \cdot \tilde{\sigma}^T}{m}, \qquad (5.26)$$

where we have used Eq. (12) in App. 3.[4]

The quantities $D^{0S}(BC^{-1}B^{-1*})$ are just the mixed spinors changing undotted indices into dotted ones, and vice versa, for $D^{0S}(BC^{-1}B^{-1*})^\dagger$. This follows from the identity

$$A = \frac{k \cdot \sigma}{m} C^{-1}A^*C \frac{(\Lambda^{-1}k) \cdot \tilde{\sigma}}{m} = G(k)A^*G^{-1}(\Lambda^{-1}k) \qquad (5.27)$$

and, by group property,

$$D^{0S}(A) = D^{0S}\left(\frac{k \cdot \sigma}{m} C^{-1}\right)D^{0S*}(A)D^{0S}\left(C \frac{\Lambda^{-1}k \cdot \tilde{\sigma}}{m}\right). \qquad (5.27')$$

Or, more directly, if we write Eq. (5.13) for $A' = B^{-1}_{k \to p}AB_{q \to p}$, change $D^S \to D^{0S}$, and expand, we obtain Eq. (5.27'). In terms of indices

$$D^{0S}(A)_m{}^n = D^{0S}\{G(k)\}_m{}^{\dot{m}}D^{0S*}(A)_{\dot{m}}{}^{\dot{n}}D^{0S}\{G^{-1}(\Lambda^{-1}k)\}_{\dot{n}}{}^n. \qquad (5.27'')$$

We shall write simply again G instead of $D^{0S}(G)$.

We now know how to define M-amplitudes in which dotted and undotted indices are changed. Consequently the CPT, Eq. (5.25), can be written as

$$\text{CPT:}\ M_{m_f \dot{m}_i}(k_f,k_i) = \eta M_{\dot{m}_i m_f}(k_i,k_f)$$
$$= \eta M_{m_f \dot{m}_i}(-k_f,-k_i). \qquad (5.28)$$

[4] We have the relations:

$$G^T = C \frac{k \cdot \sigma^T}{m} = \frac{k \cdot \tilde{\sigma}}{m} C; \qquad G^{-1} = C \frac{k \cdot \tilde{\sigma}}{m} = \frac{k \cdot \sigma^T}{m} C$$

and

$$G^\dagger = C \frac{k \cdot \sigma}{m} = \frac{k \cdot \tilde{\sigma}^T}{m} C;$$

hence

$$G^{T\dagger} = -G^{-1} \qquad \text{or} \qquad G = -G^{T\dagger-1} = -G^{*-1}.$$

These mixed spinor indices are as follows:

$$G:\ G_m{}^{\dot{t}}; \qquad G^T:\ G^{\dot{t}}{}_m; \qquad G^{-1}:\ G_{\dot{s}}{}^n; \qquad G^{-1T}:\ G^n{}_{\dot{t}}.$$

This equation is formally the same as Eq. (5.19), as it should be, for the physical interpretation of dotted and undotted indices is the same, although the indices on M are mathematically quite different than the indices on R. In a similar way we have

$$C: \quad M_{m_f \dot{m}_i}(k_f,k_i) = \eta^C M_{\dot{m}_f m_i}(k_f,k_i) = \eta^C G_f^{-1} M_{n_f \dot{n}_i} G_i^T \tag{5.29}$$

$$PT: \quad M_{m_f \dot{m}_i}(k_f,k_i) = \eta^{PT} M_{m_i \dot{m}_f}(k_i,k_f) = \eta^{PT} M_{\dot{m}_f m_i}(-k_f,-k_i) \tag{5.30}$$

$$T: \quad M_{m_f \dot{m}_i}(k_f,k_i) = \eta^T M_{m_i \dot{m}_f}(k_i^0,-\mathbf{k};\, k_f^0,-\mathbf{k}_f)$$
$$= \eta^T M_{\dot{m}_f m_i}(-k_f^0,\mathbf{k}_f;\, -k_i^0,\mathbf{k}_i). \tag{5.31}$$

To obtain, in terms of the M-amplitude, the analog of Eq. (5.16) we cannot simply express both sides of Eq. (5.16) in terms of M, using Eq. (5.24), because the k's on the right-hand side are negative and in Eq. (5.24) $B = \sqrt{\dfrac{k \cdot \sigma}{m}}\, U$ is not defined for negative k. Instead, we follow the steps (5.14)– (5.16) from the beginning for the M-amplitudes. The transformation law is

$$M(k_f,k_i) = e^{i(\Sigma k_f - \Sigma k_i)a} e^{i(\Sigma q_f - \Sigma q_i)\lambda} \prod_f D^{0S_f}(A) M(\Lambda^{-1}k_f, \Lambda^{-1}k_i) \prod_i D^{0S_i^\dagger}(A).$$

Using, this time, Eq. (5.27), we transform all D^{0S_f} into $D^{0S_f^*}$ and all D^{0S_i} into $D^{0S_i^T}$, change the signs of k's and q's, and obtain finally

$$\bar{M}(k_f,k_i) = \eta \prod_f D^{0S_f}\{G(-k)\} M^T(-k_i,-k_f) \prod_i D^{0S_i}\{G^\dagger(-\Lambda^{-1}k)\}, \tag{5.32}$$

which, when compared with Eq. (5.25), again shows how the CPT-equivalent process is obtained from the original process by changing the momenta to their negative values.

Because the amplitudes can be expanded in the form of Eq. (4.37), where the basis functions Y_i carry the transformation property of M, it is sufficient to consider the transformation properties of the basis functions Y_i under C, PT, T,... in order to verify or formulate the invariance requirement under these transformations.

As an example, consider the basis given by Eqs. (5.9) and (5.11). The parities of these basis functions under C, T, and PT are as follows:

	C	T	PT	
Y^1:	+1	+1	+1	
Y^2:	+1	−1	+1	(5.33)
Y^3:	+1	+1	+1	
Y^4:	−1	+1	−1	

To see how the above table is evaluated consider the original amplitude to have the indices

$$M_{m_f \dot{m}_i}(k_f,k_i).$$

The related amplitudes are then

Under C: $M_{\check{m}_f m_i}(k_f, k_i),$

Under CPT: $M_{\check{m}_f m_i}(k_i, k_f),$

Under PT: $M_{m_i \check{m}_f}(k_i, k_f).$

These amplitudes can then be related to the original one by the mixed tensors G. We obtain, e.g., under C,

$$M_{m_f \check{m}_i} = \eta G^{\check{n}_f}_{m_f} M_{\check{n}_f n_i} G^{n_i}_{\check{m}_i}$$
$$= \eta G M^{\mathrm{T}} G^{-1^{\mathrm{T}}}.$$

Consequently for the basis functions Y_1 and Y_2 we get

$$(k_3 \pm k_1) \cdot \sigma = \eta C^{-1} k_3 \cdot \tilde{\sigma}^T [(k_1 \pm k_3)\sigma^T] k_1 \cdot \tilde{\sigma}^T C^{-1}$$
$$= \eta(k_3 \pm k_1) \cdot \sigma;$$

hence $\eta = +1$ for both. Similarly for Y_3 and Y_4 we get

$$(n \cdot \sigma \pm k_3 \cdot \sigma n \cdot \tilde{\sigma} k_1 \cdot \sigma) = \eta C^{-1} k_3 \cdot \tilde{\sigma}^T (n \cdot \sigma^T \pm k_3 \cdot \sigma^T n \cdot \tilde{\sigma}^T k_1 \sigma^T) k_1 \cdot \tilde{\sigma}^T C^{-1}$$
$$= \eta C^{-1} k_3 \cdot \tilde{\sigma}^T n \cdot \sigma^T k_1 \cdot \tilde{\sigma}^T C^{-1} \pm C^{-1} n \cdot \tilde{\sigma}^T C^{-1}$$
$$= \pm \eta (n \cdot \sigma \pm k_3 \cdot \sigma n \cdot \tilde{\sigma} k_1 \cdot \sigma);$$

hence $\eta = \pm 1$.

The connection of the amplitudes under PT is

$$M_{m_f \check{m}_i}(f, i) = \eta G^{\check{n}_f}_{m_f} M_{m_i \check{m}_f}(i, f) G^{n_i}_{\check{m}_i}$$
$$= \eta G M^{\mathrm{T}}(i, f) G^{-1^{\mathrm{T}}},$$

which gives of course the same result as C. From this it follows that all basis functions of a given process have the same + parity under CPT. The T-transformation follows from the P-parities of Sec. 2 and the PT.

Any basis system $\{Y_i\}$ that one can construct is automatically CPT-invariant. However, this is not yet the CPT theorem; it is discussed in the next section.

Summary

The net result of these considerations is simply the following: If we have a set of definite spinorial basis functions $Y_i (k_1, \ldots, k, \ldots, k_n)$ for a process, then these functions are also the proper basis functions for all the related *antiparticle processes* in their respective physical ranges. For example, if the reaction $1 + 2 \rightarrow 3 + 4$ is described by the basis functions $Y_i(k_3 k_4, k_1 k_2)$, we can write these as $Y_i\{-(-k_3), k_4; k_1, -(-k_2)\}$ and if the momenta $(-k_3) = k_3'$ and $(-k_2) = k_2'$ are physical, they describe the reaction $1 + \bar{3} \rightarrow \bar{2} + 4$, in the range where $-k_3' + k_4 = k_1 - k_2'$, or $k_1 + k_3' = k_2' + k_4$, which is precisely the conservation law for the new process.

It should be emphasized that this result is independent of the analyticity assumption or independent of the validity of CPT-invariance. However we cannot say anything at the moment how the scalar amplitudes A_i of various antiparticle processes are related to each other.

It is sometimes convenient to start with a situation where all momenta are ingoing and distinguish various antiparticle processes whether k or $(-k)$ is physical. This "*all in*" *formalism* is however not necessary; one can start with any process and reach all other antiparticle processes from there.

5.5   CPT Theorem and Analyticity

Among all possible antiparticle processes there is a particular one in which all $(-k_i)$ are physical. This is the *CPT-equivalent reaction*—all outgoing particles are changed into ingoing antiparticles, and vice versa. For a reaction and its CPT-equivalent one we note the following characteristic properties:

   (a) the physical regions are the same,
   (b) the arguments of the scalar amplitudes A_i are the same,
   (c) the basis functions satisfy either

$$Y_i(-K) = Y_i(K), \qquad \text{for all } i,$$

or

$$Y_i(-K) = -Y_i(K), \qquad \text{for all } i. \qquad (5.34)$$

The last equation follows from the fact that the basis functions Y_i are polynomials in k's made up of factors of the type $(k \cdot \sigma)$, $(k \cdot \varepsilon)$, etc., and that for a given process all Y_i have either an even power of k or an odd power of k.

The *CPT theorem* states that a reaction and its CPT equivalent reaction occur with the same probability. Relativistic invariance brings us very close to the CPT theorem but CPT does not follow from relativistic invariance alone. (Note that in field theory also one needs local commutativity postulates in addition to relativistic invariance.) A natural physical postulate, which we may call the *uniqueness principle* to the effect that there is a unique set of scalar amplitudes defined over a given physical region (determined by the masses), is sufficient, together with Eq. (5.34), to guarantee the CPT theorem. We see this from the above properties (a), (b), and (c). The basis functions of antiparticle processes being polynomials are clearly analytic continuation of each other. The scalar amplitudes of these processes defined over disjoint regions can be combined into one over-all function, and the above principle tells us that when we come back to the same physical region (i.e., CPT-equivalent process) the function coincides with the original function. Thus analyticity (in the real) follows. Conversely, it is clearly possible to derive CPT from the stronger assumption of analyticity in the real (or minimal analyticity), which says that all amplitudes of the $\frac{1}{2}(2^n - 2)$ crossed channels are in fact analytic continuations of each other.[5] Because of the above

---

[5] For a proof of CPT theorem in field theory, see G. Lüders, *Ann. Phys.*, **2**, 1 (1957), R. Jost, *Helv. Phys. Acta*, **30**, 409 (1957). For a proof of CPT from the postulate of analyticity see H. P. Stapp, *Phys. Rev.*, **125**, 2139 (1962). We have not assumed the analyticity as a postulate rather a heuristic principle that the quantum numbers determine the S-matrix uniquely, which leads to analyticity.

properties (a), (b), and (c) it is sufficient to require analyticity of the scalar amplitudes.

The following question now arises: Can we talk about analytic continuation in the real without going into the complex plane? Analyticity in the real is characterized by Taylor expansion. For some functions the analytic continuation in the real is defined, but the amplitudes we are dealing with have singularities (in particular branch points for physical values of momenta). In that case the analytic continuation in the real cannot be nicely defined. For example, $\sqrt{x}$ cannot be expanded in a Taylor series around $x = 0$, nor can $e^{-1/x}$ around $x = 0$, etc.

Thus we are led to analytic continuation for complex k. "Minimal analyticity" may not be quite meaningful without some analyticity in the complex. And if we say that there is some analytic continuation of M into the complex region, including the various real physical regions of the crossed channels, then there is no need for a principle of minimal analyticity—it follows immediately. Thus the amplitudes of the form

$$M = \sum_i A_i(s, t, \dots) Y_i$$

can be considered automatically as covariant amplitudes under complex Lorentz transformations Λ, $(\Lambda^T G \Lambda = G)$, because Y_i transform correctly and $s, t, \dots$ are invariant. The complex Lorentz group has still two parts, Λ_+ and Λ_-, and a dependence on (sign k^0) cannot be excluded without analyticity or CPT invariance.

Assuming that there are no natural boundaries around the physical region so that some analytic continuation is possible, we shall give in Chap. 7 a prescription for making an explicit analytic continuation and see what singularities we encounter by this process.

Connection with the Complex Lorentz Transformations

Finally we discuss the connection of analyticity and CPT theorem with the complex Lorentz transformations:

The basis functions Y_i can immediately be continued to complex values of k and they are covariant functions under complex Lorentz group ($\Lambda^T G \Lambda = G$, Λ complex), because the basic elements $k \cdot \sigma$ satisfies the relation (App. 2)

$$Ak \cdot \sigma B^\dagger = \{\Lambda(A,B)k\} \cdot \sigma, \tag{5.35}$$

where $\Lambda(A,B)$ is an element of the complex Lorentz group, which is isomorphic to the direct product of two unimodular groups. The scalar functions A_i are also scalars under complex Lorentz group. Consequently if they have an analytic continuation (e.g., no natural boundary on the real axis) the S-matrix and the fundamental invariance equations can be continued analytically to complex Lorentz transformations. Within the complex transformations the element $\Lambda = -I$ is continuously connected with the identity element $\Lambda = +I$; hence taking $\Lambda = -I$ in Eq. (2.51) we obtain the CPT theorem.

Thus we see by this process that by analytic continuation of the real covariant functions of fourvectors, we obtain analytic covariant functions; covariant under the complex, connected Lorentz group[6] (Hall-Wightmann lemma).

Schematically we have the following situation:

Real proper Lorentz group $\longrightarrow$ Real regular covariant functions
$\downarrow$ $\Downarrow$
Complex Lorentz group $\longrightarrow$ Analytic covariant functions
$(L^T G L = G)$

Existence of Antiparticles

We know now how to construct the basis functions for the amplitudes of antiparticle processes. Furthermore, it was deduced that if the scalar amplitudes are analytic functions, the amplitudes of the antiparticle processes are analytic continuations of the particle processes, for two analytic functions coinciding in the physical region of one process must also coincide in the physical regions of the crossed processes. One question, however, still remains: Why do the antiparticles, which were introduced from the transformation properties of the amplitudes, actually exist in the laboratory? The amplitudes could be analytic functions, yet the antiparticles need not exist.

If the particles did not possess any internal quantum numbers at all, but only the quantum numbers of the Poincaré group, then antiparticle processes correspond to particle processes with different spin orientations; there would be no way of distinguishing particles from antiparticles. With the internal quantum numbers present having the values $+q$ and $-q$, the Hilbert space of states is the representation space of Poincaré group plus other groups giving rise to these quantum numbers. Because the S-matrix is defined between the states of the representations of the symmetry groups, antiparticle processes must exist, for by a transformation of the group one can pass from the particle states to antiparticle states. This reasoning puts the question of the existence of antiparticles into the nature of the symmetry groups for additive quantum numbers. These groups must be such that states with both positive and negative quantum numbers exist.

An argument of a different type is the following: consider a larger process in which a particle A gives rise to a pole in the physical region of the over-all process (see the unitarity diagram shown in Fig. 5.1b). By an analytic

[6] D. Hall and A. S. Wightmann, *Kel. Dansk Videnskap. Selskab. Mat.-fys.*, **31**, no. 5 (1957); R. Jost, *Theoretical Physics in the Twentieth Century* (New York: Wiley, 1960), For a generalization of this theorem to arbitrary domains, see H. P. Stapp, UCRL Report 10843 (Berkeley: U. of California Press, 1964); R. Minkowski, D. N. Williams, and R. Seiler, in *Symposium on the Lorentz Group*, Lectures in Theoretical Physics, Vol. VIIa (Boulder, Colo.: U. of Colorado Press, 1965).

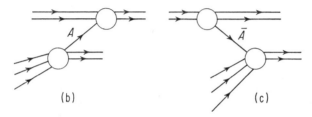

(b)   (c)

Figures 5.1*b* and 5.1*c* Changing of a particle A into antiparticle $\bar{A}$ by an analytic continuation of a larger process.

continuation we can pass to the situation shown in Fig. 5.1*c*, which again corresponds to a pole in the over-all amplitude.[7] But the particle has now become an antiparticle just as was the case in Fig. 5.1*a*. Thus analyticity implies the existence of both situations in Figs. 5.1*b* and 5.1*c*, hence the existence of antiparticle processes as subdiagrams. But this argument does not tell us why nonzero quantum numbers should exist. It is, however, interesting that the analyticity implies that together with a state of quantum number q, there must be also a state with the additive quantum number $-q$.

5.6   Crossing Relations

We have seen that the so-called CPT-equivalent reaction (i.e., particles → antiparticles, initial configuration → final configuration) is related to the original reaction by analytic continuation in all momenta. The procedure we have followed in the previous section is quite general. We can change a single initial particle, for example, to a final antiparticle (see Fig. 5.1*a*), or any number of them in any direction. We obtain in this way a whole family of amplitudes[8] related to each other by analytic continuation. The basis functions are given by $Y_i(\cdots -k \cdots)$ in which only those particles which are exchanged have a minus sign associated with them. These are then the general so-called crossing relations. The relation of the scalar amplitudes between the crossed channels depends whether we use new basis functions $\bar{Y}_i$ for the crossed channels, or the above analytically continued basis functions.

As an example, consider the two-body reaction

$$a + b \to c + d. \tag{5.36}$$

The two reactions

$$a + \bar{c} \to \bar{b} + d,$$
$$a + \bar{d} \to c + \bar{b}, \tag{5.37}$$

---

[7] For details of this analytic continuation see D. Olive, *Phys. Rev.*, **135**, B745 (1964) and H. P. Stapp, in International Seminar on High Energy Physics, Trieste, International Atomic Energy Agency, Vienna, 1965.

[8] The actual number is $\frac{1}{2}(2^n - 2)$, including decay reactions.

where the bar denotes the antiparticle and the three CPT-equivalent reactions to these, namely

$$\bar{c} + \bar{d} \to \bar{a} + \bar{b}, \quad b + \bar{d} \to \bar{a} + c, \quad \bar{c} + b \to \bar{a} + d,$$

give us altogether six processes related to each other by analytic continuation. If we choose a different basis on the direct and crossed channel, we can relate these bases to each other by analytic continuation. For example, for the process $a + \bar{c} \to \bar{b} + d$ we obtain:

$$\begin{aligned}
\overline{M}_{m_c m_d \dot{m}_a \dot{m}_b}(k_c k_d, k_a k_b) &= \eta D^{0S_c}\{G(-k_c)\} M^T(-k_b, k_d; k_a, -k_c) D^{0S_b}\{G^\dagger(-\Lambda^{-1} k_b)\} \\
&= \eta M_{\dot{m}_b m_d \dot{m}_a m_c}(-k_b, k_d; k_a, -k_c). \tag{5.38}
\end{aligned}$$

In particular we obtain the so-called *crossing matrices* if we write both sides of Eq. (5.38) in terms of the scalar amplitudes and basis functions:

$$\sum_i A_i Y_i = \sum_j \overline{A}_j \overline{Y}_j \tag{5.39}$$

and express $\overline{A}_j$ in terms of the A_i:

$$\overline{A}_j = \sum_j \beta_{ji} A_i, \tag{5.40}$$

if

$$Y_i = \sum_j \beta_{ji} \overline{Y}_j. \tag{5.41}$$

Then β is the crossing matrix relating the scalar amplitudes in two channels.

If we do not choose new bases $\overline{Y}$ in the crossed channels, but use the ones obtained from the original basis by the change of sign of momenta, then the same amplitudes A_i also describe the crossed processes, as we have seen in the previous section. For example, if $Y(k_3 k_4, k_1 k_2)$ is a basis for $1 + 2 \to 3 + 4$, then $Y(-k_3, k_4; -k_1, k_2)$ is a basis for $3 + 2 \to \bar{1} + 4$, etc. This is the more straightforward and simple procedure and will be adopted here. (See Chaps. 12 and 13.)

Crossing Relations in Isospin

We wish now to see explicitly how the isotopic spin amplitudes of different channels are related to each other. These formulas will allow us later on to calculate the effect of a particle pole in one channel, e.g., to the other crossed channels.

Consider a two-body amplitude $M(K)$ and the amplitude $M(K')$ obtained when particles 2 and 3, e.g., are interchanged; the argument K' means that the momenta k_2 and k_3 have been interchanged. Using Eq. (5.14), these two amplitudes can be made formally to transform in the same way. Then from the principle of analytic continuation we obtain the relation

$$M^{I_3 \alpha_3, I_4 \alpha_4}_{I_1 \alpha_1, I_2 \alpha_2}(K) = (-1)^{-I_2 + I_3 - \alpha_2 - \alpha_3} M^{I_2 - \alpha_2, I_4 \alpha_4}_{I_1 \alpha_1, I_3 - \alpha_3}(K').$$

To find the relations of total isospin amplitudes, we expand both sides of this equation according to Eq. (4.12). Then the two total isospin amplitudes are related by

$$M^I(K) = \sum_{I'} \alpha^{II'} M^{I'}(K')$$

where the so-called crossing matrix $\alpha^{II'}$ is given by

$$\alpha^{II'} = (-1)^{-I_2+I_3-\alpha_2-\alpha_3}[I_1I_2I]_m^{\alpha_1\alpha_2}[I_3I_4I]_{\alpha_3\alpha_4}^m[I_1I_3I']_n^{\alpha_1-\alpha_3}[I_2I_4I']_{-\alpha_2\alpha_4}^n$$

$$\equiv (2I'+1)(-1)^{I+I'-I_2-I_3}\begin{Bmatrix} I & I_1 & I_2 \\ I' & I_4 & I_3 \end{Bmatrix},$$

where $\begin{Bmatrix} a\,b\,c \\ d\,e\,f \end{Bmatrix}$ is Wigner's $6-j$ symbol. The numerical values of some useful crossing matrices are shown below:[9]

Process	$\alpha^{II'}(s \leftrightarrow u)$	$\alpha^{II'}(s \leftrightarrow t)$	$\alpha^{II'}(t \leftrightarrow u)$
$\tfrac{1}{2}\tfrac{1}{2} \to \tfrac{1}{2}\tfrac{1}{2}$	$\dfrac{1}{2}\begin{pmatrix} -1 & 3 \\ 1 & 1 \end{pmatrix}$	$\dfrac{1}{2}\begin{pmatrix} 1 & 3 \\ 1 & -1 \end{pmatrix}$	$\dfrac{1}{2}\begin{pmatrix} -1 & 0 \\ 0 & 1 \end{pmatrix}$
$\tfrac{1}{2}1 \to \tfrac{1}{2}1$	$\dfrac{1}{3}\begin{pmatrix} -1 & 4 \\ 2 & 1 \end{pmatrix}$	$\begin{pmatrix} \dfrac{1}{\sqrt{6}} & -1 \\ \dfrac{1}{\sqrt{6}} & -\dfrac{1}{2} \end{pmatrix}$	$\begin{pmatrix} \dfrac{1}{\sqrt{6}} & -1 \\ \dfrac{1}{\sqrt{6}} & -\dfrac{1}{2} \end{pmatrix}$
$\tfrac{1}{2}\tfrac{3}{2} \to \tfrac{1}{2}\tfrac{3}{2}$	$\dfrac{1}{4}\begin{pmatrix} 1 & -5 \\ -3 & -1 \end{pmatrix}$	$-\dfrac{1}{2\sqrt{2}}\begin{pmatrix} 1 & -\sqrt{5} \\ 1 & \tfrac{3}{5}\sqrt{5} \end{pmatrix}$	
$11 \to 11$		$\begin{bmatrix} \dfrac{1}{3} & 1 & \dfrac{5}{3} \\ \dfrac{1}{3} & \dfrac{1}{2} & -\dfrac{5}{6} \\ \dfrac{1}{3} & -\dfrac{1}{2} & \dfrac{1}{6} \end{bmatrix}$	
$1\tfrac{3}{2} \to 1\tfrac{3}{2}$	$\begin{bmatrix} \dfrac{1}{6} & -\dfrac{2}{5} & \dfrac{3}{2} \\ -\dfrac{1}{3} & \dfrac{11}{15} & \dfrac{3}{5} \\ \dfrac{1}{2} & \dfrac{2}{5} & \dfrac{1}{10} \end{bmatrix}$	$-\begin{bmatrix} \dfrac{\sqrt{3}}{6} & \dfrac{\sqrt{10}}{4} & \dfrac{5\sqrt{6}}{12} \\ \dfrac{\sqrt{3}}{6} & \dfrac{\sqrt{10}}{10} & -\dfrac{\sqrt{6}}{3} \\ \dfrac{\sqrt{3}}{6} & \dfrac{3\sqrt{10}}{20} & \dfrac{\sqrt{6}}{12} \end{bmatrix}$	

[9] A. O. Barut and B. C. Unal, *Nuovo Cimento*, **28**, 112 (1963), P. Carruthers and J. P. Krisch, *Ann. Phys.*, **33**, 1 (1965), C. N. Yang, *J. Math. Phys.*, **4**, 52 (1963), L. L. Foldy and R. F. Peierls, *Phys. Rev.*, **130**, 1585 (1963). For production amplitudes see A. O. Barut and Y. C. Leung, *Phys. Rev.*, **138**, B1119 (1965), A. Kotansky and K. Zalewsky, *Acta Phys. Polon.*, **26**, 117 (1964).

$$\tfrac{3}{2}\tfrac{3}{2} \to \tfrac{3}{2}\tfrac{3}{2} \quad -\frac{1}{20}\begin{bmatrix} -5 & 15 & -25 & 35 \\ 5 & -11 & 5 & 21 \\ -5 & 3 & 15 & 7 \\ 5 & 9 & 5 & 1 \end{bmatrix}, \quad -\frac{1}{20}\begin{bmatrix} -5 & -15 & -25 & -35 \\ -5 & -11 & -5 & 21 \\ -5 & -3 & 15 & -7 \\ -5 & 9 & -5 & 1 \end{bmatrix}$$

5.7 Intrinsic Parity of a Particle-Antiparticle Pair

Having defined the antiparticles we go back to the question of *intrinsic parity* of a particle-antiparticle pair. We have seen that if we add the same particle to the initial and final configuration with momenta k_1 and k_3 the parity of the reaction does not change. Now we can continue one particle to the other side of the reaction and obtain a particle-antiparticle pair. If the original basis functions were $Y_i(k_1 k_3 \ldots)$, the basis functions for the process containing particle-antiparticle pair is $Y_i(-k_1 k_3, \ldots)$ or $Y_i(k_1 - k_3, \ldots)$. Using Eqs. (5.7) and (5.8) we can easily see the parities of the new bases with respect to the old one. Suppose the particles we are adding have spin $\frac{1}{2}$, then the part of the basis functions depending on k_1 and k_3 are given by Eqs. (5.9). If we change $k_3 \to -k_3$ or $k_1 \to -k_1$ we see immediately that the parity n_P changes sign. Thus a fermion-antifermion pair has negative parity.

Problems and Further Developments

1. Show that the scattering of two spinless particles into two other spinless particles always conserves parity. What about the decay of a spinless particle into three spinless particles?

2. For the scattering of a spin $\frac{1}{2}$ (k_1) and spin 0 (k_2) particles into a spin $\frac{1}{2}$ (k_3) and spin 0 (k_4) particles show that

$$k_4 \cdot \sigma + k_3 \cdot \sigma k_4 \cdot \tilde{\sigma} k_1 \cdot \sigma = k_2 \cdot \sigma + k_3 \cdot \sigma k_2 \cdot \tilde{\sigma} k_1 \cdot \sigma,$$
$$k_4 \cdot \sigma - k_3 \cdot \sigma k_4 \cdot \tilde{\sigma} k_1 \cdot \sigma = 2 Y^2 + \bar{Y}^4,$$

   where Y^2 and $\bar{Y}^4$ are given by Eq. (5.9).

3. Prove the identity (5.10) and show that

$$a \cdot \sigma b \cdot \tilde{\sigma} c \cdot \sigma = (c \cdot \sigma b \cdot \tilde{\sigma} a \cdot \sigma)^*.$$

4. Prove the parities of "currents" given in Table 4–2, Eq. (4.38).

5. Prove the identity (5.27) directly.

6. Prove the relations (5.33).

7. Construct parity conserving amplitudes for the photoproduction process, $\gamma + N \to N + \pi$; and for the photodisintegration of deuteron, $\gamma + d \to N + N$.

8. Show that the sixteen amplitudes of the scattering of two spin $\frac{1}{2}$ particles (e.g., *N-N* scattering) reduce to ten under C-invariance alone, to eight under P-invariance alone, to six under P and T, or C and P (or C and T), finally to five in the equal mass case (identical particles).

CHAPTER 6

Scalar Amplitudes and
Invariant Momentum Products

We determined the M-amplitudes in Chap. 4 in the form

$$M = \sum_i A_i Y_i(K), \qquad (6.1)$$

where $Y_i(K)$ are well-defined basis functions which depend as polynomials on the momentum components k^μ; typically we have the products of terms of the form $k^\mu \sigma_\mu$. The coefficients A^i are scalars both in spin and isotopic spin space satisfying

$$A_i(K) = A_i(\Lambda^{-1}K). \qquad (6.2)$$

Any such scalar analytic function of momenta is a function of a finite number of invariants formed out of momenta,[1] such as the scalar product $k_i \cdot k_j$ (and skew products $[k, \ldots, k_n]$ if nonproper transformations are included). A dependence on sign (k^0) is not excluded by T-invariance but is excluded by CPT-invariance, or uniqueness principle as we have discussed in the previous chapter. More generally, a complex valued function of n fourvectors satisfying Eq. (6.2) and analytic in the domain D: $-\infty < Rek_\mu < +\infty$, $(Imk_\mu)^2 > 0$, $Imk_\mu^0 > 0$ (i.e., the so-called forward light cone), is a function of the scalar products $k_i \cdot k_j$, and is analytic over the whole domain of these scalar products when the k_i vary over the tube domain.[2]

Let n be the total number of initial and final particles so that M is a function of n fourvectors, or of $4n$ real variables. The number of linearly independent

---

[1] This is due to an application of the so-called *First Main Theorem* of the theory of invariants: "All invariants are expressible in terms of a finite number among them." See, for example, H. Weyl, *Classical Groups* (Princeton, N.J.: Princeton U. P., 1939), Chap. 2.

[2] This is the Hall-Wightman theorem. See D. Hall and A. S. Wightman, *Kgl. Dansk Vrdensk. Selsk. Mat. fys.*, **31**, no. 5 (1957). See also Ref. 6, Chap. 5.

invariant products is equal to the number of independent momentum variables. Now the $4n$ momentum components are not all independent; we have n mass-shell relations, $k_i^2 = m^2$, and ten components may be fixed arbitrarily due to the ten parameters of the inhomogeneous Lorentz group (four conditions for translations or energy momentum conservation $\sum k_f = \sum k_i$, six for homogeneous Lorentz transformations). Thus the total number of independent variables is

$$3n - 10, \quad \text{if} \quad n \geqslant 4. \tag{6.3}$$

For $n = 3$, all scalar products are determined by the masses, the domain over which the amplitude is defined is just a point. It is convenient, however, to keep, with $(n - 1)$ independent fourvectors, the $(n - 1)(n - 2)/2$ scalar products as argument of the amplitude although not all of these are linearly independent.

The three-body process with $k_3 = k_1 + k_2$ is physical only if

$$m_3 \geqslant m_1 + m_2. \tag{6.4}$$

This follows from the Schwarz inequality for two timelike vectors:

$$(k_1 k_2)^2 \geqslant k_1^2 k_2^2.$$

In choosing the invariant variables it is important to select them in such a way that they are also meaningful for the other crossed processes. For example, for the simplest process with four particles of physical momenta $k_1 \dots k_4$, a standard and convenient choice consists of the following variables:

$$\begin{aligned} s &= (k_1 + k_2)^2, \\ t &= (k_1 - k_3)^2, \\ u &= (k_1 - k_4)^2. \end{aligned} \tag{6.5}$$

To see the meaning of these variables we have to distinguish between scattering and decay processes. For scattering processes with k_1, k_2 incoming, k_3, k_4 outgoing momenta, s is the square of the total energy in the center-of-mass frame of incoming or outgoing particles:

$$\begin{aligned} s &= (E_1 + E_2)^2 = (E_3 + E_4)^2 \quad \text{in c.o.m. frame.} \\ &= \{\sqrt{q_s^2 + m_1^2} + \sqrt{q_s^2 + m_2^2}\}^2. \end{aligned} \tag{6.6}$$

The variables t and u are momentum-transfer variables; in the c.o.m. frame of the two incoming particles

$$\begin{aligned} t &= m_1^2 + m_3^2 - 2(q_s^2 + m_1^2)^{1/2}(q_s'^2 + m_3^2)^{1/2} + 2q_s q_s' \cos \theta_s, \\ u &= m_1^2 + m_4^2 - 2(q_s^2 + m_1^2)^{1/2}(q_s'^2 + m_4^2)^{1/2} - 2q_s q_s' \cos \theta_s, \end{aligned} \tag{6.7}$$

where q_s and q_s' are the c.o.m. momenta and θ_s the scattering angle in the so-called s-channel.[3]

---

[3] For equal-mass elastic scattering we get $s = 4(q^2 + m^2)$, $t = -2q^2(1 - \cos \theta)$, $u = -2q^2(1 + \cos \theta)$.

The usefulness of the variables (6.5) can now be seen if we go to the crossed reaction $1 + \bar{3} \to \bar{2} + 4$, for which k_1 and $-k_3$ are incoming particles and t has the meaning of the square of the total energy in the center-of-mass frame of particles 1 and $\bar{3}$ (or $\bar{2}$ and 4) and s and u are momentum-transfer variables. Similarly, for the reaction $1 + \bar{4} \to \bar{2} + 3$, u is the square of the total energy in the center-of-mass frame of particles 1, and $\bar{4}$, s, and t are momentum-transfer variables. For the CPT-equivalent reaction not only is the meaning of the variables s, t, u the same as the original reaction but also these variables have numerically the same values. The scalar amplitudes simultaneously describe at the same point the two CPT-equivalent reactions.

The variables s, t, u are not independent, and we have the relation

$$s + t + u = k_1^2 + 2k_1k_2 + k_2^2 + k_1^2 - 2k_1k_2 + k_3^2 + k_1^2 - 2k_1k_4 + k_4^2$$

$$= \sum_{i=1}^{4} k_i^2 + 2k_1(k_1 + k_2 - k_3 - k_4) \tag{6.8}$$

$$= \sum_{i=1}^{4} m_i^2.$$

It will be convenient, for reasons of symmetry, to consider the scalar amplitudes as functions of the three invariants, A_i (s,t,u), and keep the relation (6.8) in mind.

For the reaction

$$1 \to \bar{2} + 3 + 4$$

and the three other possible decay reactions, all three variables s, t, u are momentum-transfer variables.

The *physical region* of a reaction in the momentum space is the product of $(n - 1)$ mass-shell hyperboloids, $k_i^2 = m_i^2$, $k_i^0 > 0$. To see the range of analytic continuation in the variables s, t, u, ..., we have to express the physical region in terms of these scalar variables. For the four-particle processes we use for this purpose the so-called trilinear coordinates in the plane, measuring the coordinates s, t, u by the distances from the sides of an equilateral triangle (Fig. 6.1).

The coordinates s, t, u of any point P always satisfy the relation $s + t + u = \sum m_i^2 = h$, $h =$ the height of the triangle. (In the example in Fig. 6.1 the coordinate u is negative.)

The *physical regions* of the various channels can be characterized by the conditions

$$q = \sqrt{q^2} > 0 \quad \text{and} \quad -1 \leqslant \cos \theta \leqslant +1, \tag{6.9}$$

in the c.o.m. system of the particular reaction, for scattering, and for decay by

$$q_i > 0, \quad i = 2, 3, 4 \quad \text{(the three decay products).} \tag{6.10}$$

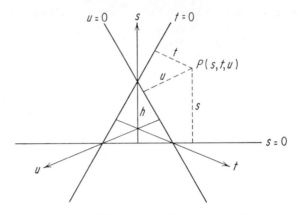

Figure 6.1   Trilinear coordinates in the plane.

If we apply Eq. (6.9) to the elastic scattering of two equal mass particles we immediately find the following shaded physical regions (Fig. 6.2).

The boundaries of the physical regions are very simple in this case. In the general case we have the conditions

$$k_i \cdot k_j > m_i m_j, \tag{6.11}$$

for we can go to a frame $k_i : (m_i 000)$; then $k_i \cdot k_j = m_i E_j > m_i m_j$. Now the condition that $\cos \theta = \pm 1$ means that we are in a degenerate case and do not

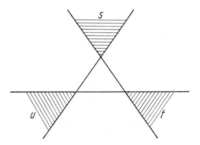

Figure 6.2   Physical regions of the scattering of two equal-mass particles.

have three linearly independent fourvectors. The *boundary of the physical region* is always characterized by the fact that the $(n - 1)$ fourvectors become linearly dependent. In the case $n = 4$ the condition that three fourvectors are linearly dependent, is expressed by

$$\Delta = \begin{vmatrix} k_1^2 & k_1 \cdot k_2 & k_1 \cdot k_3 \\ k_2 \cdot k_1 & k_2^2 & k_2 \cdot k_3 \\ k_3 \cdot k_1 & k_3 \cdot k_2 & k_3^2 \end{vmatrix} = 0. \tag{6.12}$$

If we express the scalar products in terms of the invariants, Eq. (6.12) becomes [4]

$$stu = \alpha s - \beta t + \gamma u, \tag{6.13}$$

where

$$\alpha = \frac{1}{h}(m_1^2 m_2^2 - m_3^2 m_4^2)(m_1^2 + m_2^2 - m_3^2 - m_4^2),$$

$$\beta = \frac{1}{h}(m_1^2 m_3^2 - m_2^2 m_4^2)(m_1^2 + m_3^2 - m_2^2 - m_4^2),$$

$$\gamma = \frac{1}{h}(m_1^2 m_4^2 - m_2^2 m_3^2)(m_1^2 + m_4^2 - m_2^2 - m_3^2).$$

The physical region itself is given by $\Delta > 0$ which is bounded by the cubic curve (6.13) whose asymptotes are $s = 0$, $t = 0$, and $u = 0$; the curve intersects the asymptotes on the line

$$\alpha s + \beta t + \gamma u = 0.$$

Specifically, we have the following relations in the three channels and in each case the boundary of the physical region is obtained by putting $\cos \theta = \pm 1$ [i.e., the three sections of the curve, Eq. (6.13)].

s-channel:

$$t = \frac{1}{2}\left\{h - s - \frac{1}{s}(m_1^2 - m_2^2)(m_3^2 - m_4^2)\right\}$$

$$+ \frac{\cos \theta_s}{2s}\{s^2 - 2s(m_1^2 + m_2^2) + (m_1^2 - m_2^2)^2\}^{\frac{1}{2}}$$

$$\times \{s^2 - 2s(m_3^2 + m_4^2) + (m_3^2 - m_4^2)^2\}^{\frac{1}{2}}$$

$$s_{\min} = (m_1 + m_2)^2. \tag{6.14}$$

t-channel:

$$u = \frac{1}{2}\left\{h - t - \frac{1}{s}(m_1^2 - m_3^2)(m_2^2 - m_4^2)\right\}$$

$$+ \frac{\cos \theta_t}{2t}\{t^2 - 2t(m_2^2 + m_4^2) + (m_2^2 - m_4^2)^2\}^{\frac{1}{2}}$$

$$\times \{t^2 - 2t(m_1^2 + m_3^2) + (m_1^2 - m_3^2)^2\}^{\frac{1}{2}}$$

$$t_{\min} = (m_1 + m_3)^2. \tag{6.15}$$

u-channel:

$$s = \frac{1}{2}\left\{h - u - \frac{1}{u}(m_1^2 - m_4^2)(m_2^2 - m_3^2)\right\}$$

$$+ \frac{\cos \theta_u}{2u}\{u^2 - 2u(m_1^2 + m_4^2) + (m_1^2 - m_4^2)^2\}^{\frac{1}{2}}$$

$$\times \{u^2 - 2u(m_2^2 + m_3^2) + (m_2^2 - m_3^2)^2\}^{\frac{1}{2}}$$

$$u_{\min} = (m_1 + m_4)^2. \tag{6.16}$$

[4] See also T. W. B. Kibble, *Phys. Rev.*, **117**, 1159 (1960).

For the decay processes we can use:

s-channel equation for $m_1 > m_2 + m_3 + m_4$ or $m_2 > m_1 + m_3 + m_4$,
t-channel equation for $m_3 > m_1 + m_2 + m_4$,
u-channel equation for $m_4 > m_1 + m_2 + m_3$.

A number of numerical examples of important typical processes is shown in Figs. 6.3–6.7.

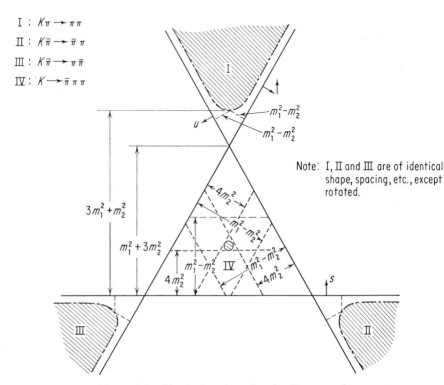

I : $K\pi \longrightarrow \pi\pi$

II : $K\bar{\pi} \longrightarrow \bar{\pi}\pi$

III : $K\bar{\pi} \longrightarrow \pi\bar{\pi}$

IV : $K \longrightarrow \bar{\pi}\pi\pi$

Note: I, II and III are of identical shape, spacing, etc., except rotated.

Figure 6.3 Physical regions for the $K\pi$-scattering.

The condition for the decay $1 \rightarrow \bar{2} + 3 + 4$ in terms of the masses is $m_1 > m_2 + m_3 + m_4$. In the rest frame of the decaying particle, where $k_1 = (m_1, 0)$, $-k_2 = (E_2, q_2)$, $k_3 = (E_3, q_3)$, $k_4 = (E_4, q_4)$, we have

$$s = m_1^2 + m_2^2 - 2m_1(q_2^2 + m_2^2)^{1/2},$$
$$t = m_1^2 + m_3^2 - 2m_1(q_3^2 + m_3^2)^{1/2}, \qquad (6.17)$$
$$u = m_1^2 + m_4^2 - 2m_1[(q_2 + q_3)^2 + m_4^2]^{1/2},$$

so that the physical region of this decay is bounded by the six lines:

$$s = (m_1 - m_2)^2, \qquad s = (m_3 + m_4)^2,$$
$$t = (m_1 - m_3)^2, \qquad t = (m_2 + m_4)^2, \qquad (6.18)$$
$$u = (m_1 - m_4)^2, \qquad u = (m_2 + m_3)^2.$$

A plot of this kind is actually used in the experimental analysis of the decay, the so-called *Dalitz plot.*[5] Consider, e.g., the decay $K^- \rightarrow \pi^+ + \pi^- + \pi^-$; then s is the square of energy of two π^- in their center-of-mass frame and t and u are the square of the two $\pi^+\pi^-$ pairs in their center-of-mass frames (see Exercise 3).

We have obtained distinct physical regions for the distinct processes associated with the same variables s, t, and u. One can, of course, always combine different functions defined in different regions into a single function

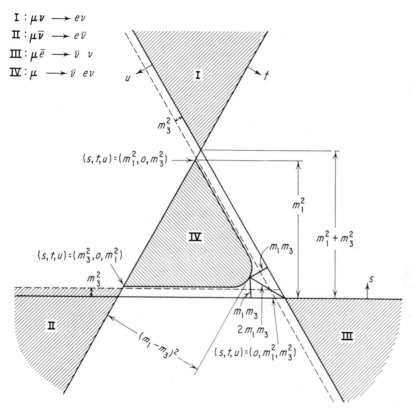

$$\mathrm{I}: \mu\nu \longrightarrow e\nu$$
$$\mathrm{II}: \mu\bar{\nu} \longrightarrow e\bar{\nu}$$
$$\mathrm{III}: \mu\bar{e} \longrightarrow \bar{\nu}\,\nu$$
$$\mathrm{IV}: \mu \longrightarrow \bar{\nu}\,e\nu$$

Figure 6.4 Physical regions for the $\mu\nu$-$e\nu$-scattering.

defined over the combined domain. However, if the function is analytic in some domain, then the knowledge of the function in one domain determines it everywhere. This is of course a very powerful statement. We want, therefore, to see if the analytic continuation of the amplitudes from one physical process

[5] R. H. Dalitz, *Phil. Mag.*, **44**, 1068 (1952). The variables used in the Dalitz plot are actually different from those in Eq. (6.18), but they can be transformed into these, or vice versa (see Exercise 3.)

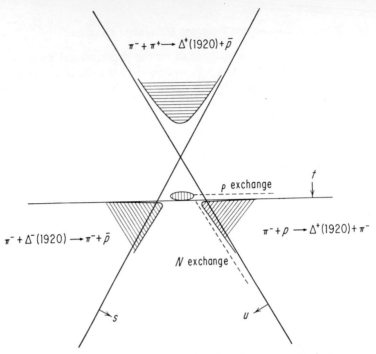

Figure 6.5 Physical regions for the $\pi\Delta \to \pi p$ scattering.

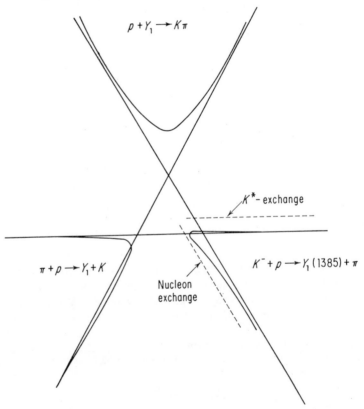

Figure 6.6 Physical regions for the $\pi p \to \Sigma K$ scattering.

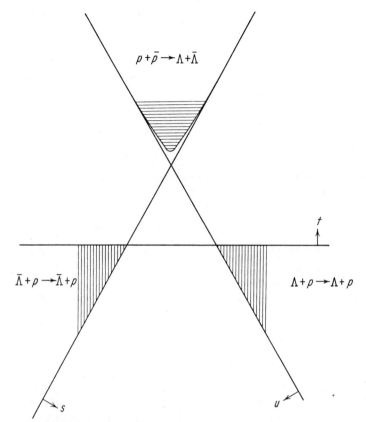

Figure 6.7 Physical regions for the Λp scattering.

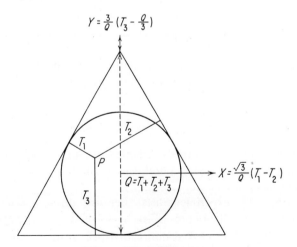

Figure 6.8 Dalitz plot.

to another can be extended to *analyticity of the amplitudes* in some domain in the complex planes. By writing the amplitudes in the form

$$M = \sum A_i(s, t, u, \ldots) Y_i(K) \tag{6.19}$$

it is clear that because the basis functions $Y_i(K)$ are polynomials in the components of the momenta they can be immediately considered as analytic functions. We recall that if some of the k's in Eq. (6.19) take negative values then $Y_i(K)$ at these new points form a basis of the new process, and $A_i(s, t, \ldots)$ is defined on the physical region of the new process.

In the next chapter we shall define an explicit analytic continuation of the scalar amplitude (6.19) and shall determine what singularities we are led to by this continuation.

Problems and Further Developments

1. Evaluate the physical regions in the s, t, u variables for the following systems: $N\pi \rightarrow N\pi$, $K\pi \rightarrow \pi\pi$, $\mu\nu \rightarrow e\nu$. Note that for the last two cases decays are energetically possible.

2. Consider a process with n (ingoing) particles; choose three unit vectors (velocities) k_1/m_1, k_2/m_2, k_3/m_3. Then show that among the scalars

$$s_{ij} = \left(\frac{k_i}{m_i} - \frac{k_j}{m_j} \right)^2$$

the following $(3n - 9)$: s_{12}, s_{23}, s_{31} and s_{1i}, s_{2i}, s_{3i} $(i = 4, \ldots, n - 1)$ have only one linear relation among them so that they give $3n - 10$ independent scalar invariants. [F. Rohrlich, Nucl. Phys. **67**, 659 (1965).]

3. *Dalitz plot for* $K^- \rightarrow \pi^+ \pi^- \pi^-$. From Eqs. (3.5) and (3.4) the decay rate (written, e.g., in the rest frame of K) is

$$\Gamma = \frac{2\pi}{h} V^2 \int \frac{d^3k_1 \, d^3k_2 \, d^3k_3}{(2\pi h)^6} \frac{\delta\left(\sum_i \mathbf{k}_i \right) \delta\left(m_K c^2 - \sum_i E_i \right)}{E_1 E_2 E_3} |G|^2;$$

G depends on two variables which we choose to be E_1 and E_2. Integrate over $\mathbf{k}_3$ and the angles of $\mathbf{k}_1$ and $\mathbf{k}_2$, then using $2E_3 \, dE_3 = 2c^2 k_1 k_2 \, d(\cos \theta)$, θ angle between $\mathbf{k}_1$ and $\mathbf{k}_2$, show that one obtains simply

$$\Gamma = \frac{2\pi}{h} \frac{V^2}{(2\pi h)^6} \cdot \frac{8\pi^2}{c^6} \int dE_1 \, dE_2 \, |G(E_1, E_2)|^2.$$

The important feature of these variables is that the weight function in the distribution is just 1, giving a uniform distribution if $G(E_1, E_2)$ is a slowly varying function. One can also plot the kinetic energies T_i instead of E_i, as is done by experimentalists, because $dE_1 \, dE_2 = dT_1 \, dT_2$ $(E = T + m_\pi c^2)$ (Fig. 6.8). Express Γ in terms of the s, t, u variables. Show that if the pions are treated nonrelativistically, the condition $\sum \mathbf{k}_i = 0$ forces the points to lie inside a circle shown in Fig. 6.8.

CHAPTER 7

Analytic Continuation and the
Singularities of the S-Matrix

"I shall find a way or make one."

We saw in the previous chapter how the CPT theorem and the concept of antiparticle are related to the analytic continuation of the amplitude from the physical region of one channel to the physical region of other channels. We also saw that this continuation must be made in general through a complex region.

In this chapter we shall define an analytic continuation procedure through unitarity and determine the singularities required by the unitarity condition. The physical significance of this process is that all the singularities of the S-matrix can be interpreted physically as particles, thresholds of new channels, resonances, and so on. Clearly an analytic function without any singularities (including at infinity) is a constant and does not carry any information; the information is in the singularities; and analytic functions are in principle determined by their singularities. Because the amplitudes are physically determined by the existence of particles and resonances, it becomes understandable why the singularities should acquire physical meanings. In this sense the theory of functions of complex variables plays the role not of a mathematical tool, but of a fundamental description of nature inseparable from physics, similar to the role played by linear operators and their eigenvalues in quantum theory. The physics is, so to speak, reflected in the collection of complex planes.

Another remarkable feature which we want to emphasize is that the unphysical regions of momenta acquire physical meaning through related processes. For example, a scattering experiment is done in the range of total energy E and scattering angle θ given by

$$E \geqslant E_{\text{threshold}}, \ -1 \leqslant \cos \theta \leqslant +1.$$

If we knew the amplitude in this range in all mathematical exactitude we

93

would know the analytic function everywhere. This is impossible. However, a different experiment done with antiparticles yields information on the amplitude outside the above region. This is the important point to be utilized in all the practical applications.

The *postulate* that we make now (in addition to the quantum postulates of Chap. 1) is that the S-matrix does not have any natural boundary just on the physical real axis so that we can make an analytic continuation. This postulate will be made more precise a little later when we define the so-called physical sheet.

The mathematical postulate of analyticity cannot be directly translated into physical terms except through crossed channels and the fact that analytic continuation to the crossed channels must be made through the complex domains. The postulate is true in Schrödinger theory and in perturbation theory where the analyticity in some cases can be related to the causality that there is no scattering before the incoming waves has reached the scatterer. However, there is no rigorous formulation of causality in relativistic theories and its connection with the analyticity. We shall take the analyticity as a working hypothesis, verify it by its consequences a posteriori, and interpret it physically by the processes in crossed channels.

7.1   The Definition of Analytic Continuation

Suppose we wish to discuss the analyticity in total energy E of the scattering amplitude $M(E)$, and fix the remaining variables which we therefore suppress in the following discussion. Let us write the unitarity condition Eq. (3.24) for

$$E_+ = E + i\varepsilon,$$

i.e., we approach the physical values of E from above in the complex E-plane,

$$M(E_+) + M^*(E_+) = -\sum_N \int d\Omega_N M_{f,N}(E_+)\rho_N M_{i,N}^*(E_+). \qquad (7.1)$$

If $M(E_+)$ is holomorphic in some domain G of the E-plane, then $M^*(E_+)$ is, in general, *not* analytic there. But we can use, e.g., the Schwartz reflection principle (see App. 6) to define an analytic continuation. Let

$$M'(E) \equiv -\{M(E^*)\}^*, \qquad (7.2)$$

then if $M(E)$ is analytic in G, $M'(E)$ is analytic in G^*—the domain G reflected through the real axis. We then have with $E_- = E - i\varepsilon$,

$$M'(E_-) = -\{M(E_+)\}^*; \qquad (7.3)$$

hence the unitarity becomes

$$M(E_+) - M'(E_-) = \sum_N \int d\Omega_N M(E_+)\rho_N(E_+)M'(E_-). \qquad (7.4)$$

The unitarity is now written in terms of two distinct analytic functions M and M'.

Suppose now that there is a portion A of the real E-axis where M is holomorphic and $M(E) = M'(E) = -\{M(E)\}^*$ on A, i.e., $M(E)$ is pure imaginary on A, then M and M' are analytic continuations of each other, i.e., there exists a function $\overline{M}$ holomorphic in the union of G and G^* such that

$$\overline{M}(E) = \begin{cases} M(E) & \text{for} \quad E \in G, \\ M'(E) & \text{for} \quad E \in G^*. \end{cases}$$

We can then write the unitarity in the form of an analytic equation

$$\overline{M}(E_+) - \overline{M}(E_-) = \sum_N \int d\Omega_N \overline{M}(E_+) \rho_N(E_+) \overline{M}(E_-). \tag{7.5}$$

On the left of Eq. (7.5) we have now the discontinuity of the new analytic function $\overline{M}$ across the real E-axis.

In the following Section we examine if the reality condition on M holds and determine the simplest singularities of $\overline{M}(E)$.

7.2   Normal Threshold Singularities

The unitarity condition expressing the conservation of the total probability in the presence of competing processes is valid in the physical range of E. This is clear from the θ-functions occurring in the phase-space factor. [See Eq. (3.29), for example.] Let us consider a case where the lowest intermediate state is a two-body state. Then below $E < (m_1 + m_2)$, the right-hand side of Eq. (7.5) vanishes, hence

$$\overline{M}(E_+) - \overline{M}(E_-) = 0 \quad \text{for} \quad E < (m_1 + m_2). \tag{7.6}$$

The function $\overline{M}(E)$ cannot be holomorphic in the whole E-plane for it would be then identically zero by Eq. (7.6). The point $E = (m_1 + m_2)$ must be a singular point. Indeed $\rho_2(E)$ contains a square root-type branch point at this value of E. From Eq. (7.5) we see that $\overline{M}(E)$ must have also a square root-type branch point.

Similarly, at each new threshold corresponding to 3, 4, 5, . . . particles in the intermediate state a new ρ_N term appears discontinuously, and, consequently $\overline{M}(E)$ must have branch points at these values of energy. These are the so-called *normal threshold singularities*.[1]

In addition there are, under certain conditions, anomalous threshold branch points not directly connected with the number of particles in the intermediate state (see Sec. 7.5). Thus $\overline{M}(E)$ is a multivalued function with branch points as shown in Fig. 7.1.

---

[1] These threshold singularities have been known for a long time. Heisenberg pointed out the singular character of the S-matrix. See in particular R. J. Eden, *Proc. Roy. Soc.*, A, **210**, 388 (1952). The square root singularity at the two-body normal threshold has been investigated in detail in W. Zimmermann, *Nuovo Cimento*, **21**, 249 (1961).

The two M-functions in Eq. (7.5) refer to different points E_+ and E_-. These points are actually very far from each other. The points continuously connected to E_- lie in another sheet obtained counterclockwise from E_-. If we introduce now the function $\overline{M}^{\mathrm{II}}(E)$ defined on the *second sheet*, counterclockwise, we can write

$$\overline{M}^{\mathrm{I}}(E) - \overline{M}^{\mathrm{II}}(E) = \sum_N \int d\Omega_N \overline{M}^{\mathrm{I}}_{f,N}(E)\rho_N(E)\overline{M}^{\mathrm{II}}_{i,N}(E). \tag{7.7}$$

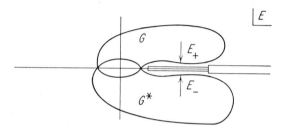

Figure 7.1   Definition of analytic continuation using Schwarz reflection principle.

Now all the arguments are the same, namely, $E = E_+$. Once we have introduced the branch point we can delete the θ-function in the unitarity equation.

The discussion in the variable $s = E^2$ is similar. There is a normal threshold branch point at $s = (m_1 + m_2)^2$. And we can write

$$\overline{M}(s_+) - \overline{M}(s_-) = \sum_N \int d\Omega_N \overline{M}_{f,N}(s_+)\rho_N(s)\overline{M}_{i,N}(s_-)$$

or

$$\overline{M}^{\mathrm{I}}(s) - \overline{M}^{\mathrm{II}}(s) = \sum_N \int d\Omega_N \overline{M}^{\mathrm{I}}_{f,N}(s)\rho_N(s)\overline{M}^{\mathrm{II}}_{i,N}(s).$$

In the future we shall always talk about the analytically continued amplitudes and drop the bar on M.

7.3   Contribution of One- and Two-Body Intermediate States to Unitarity

The first two terms of Eq. (7.1) for spinless particles of equal mass on the intermediate state now become

$$M(E) + M^\dagger(E) = -\frac{2\pi}{E}\,\delta(E - \mu)M_{f,1}(E)M^\dagger_{i,1}(E)$$

$$-\left(\frac{1}{2\pi}\right)^2\left\{\frac{s - 4m^2}{4s}\right\}^{\frac{1}{2}} \int d\Omega\, M_{f,2}(E)M^\dagger_{i,2}(E)\dots \tag{7.8}$$

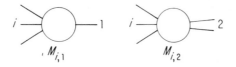

Figure 7.2   The amplitudes $M_{i,1}$ and $M_{i,2}$ entering in Eq. (7.8).

where $M_{i,1}$, $M_{i,2}$ are amplitudes from initial state to one and two particles, respectively (Fig. 7.2), similarly for $M_{f,1}$, $M_{f,2}$. The integration $d\Omega = d^3\mathbf{n}$ is over the angles of $\mathbf{q} = \mathbf{n}q$, the center-of-mass momentum of the two intermediate particles. The amplitudes $M_{i,2}$, $M_{f,2}$ also depend on these angles.

The unitarity condition connects the original amplitude $M(E)$ to other simpler amplitudes $M_{i,1}$, $M_{f,2}$, etc. This is one basis of approximations to be discussed in the next chapter to determine the scattering amplitude. Unitarity alone is, however, not enough, because on the left of Eq. (7.8) we have the combination $M + M^\dagger$, rather than M itself. But we shall see that Eq. (7.8) can be solved approximately for analytic functions. We discuss therefore in detail the analytic continuation of the unitarity equation.

a. "Elastic Unitarity"

We now study the form of the unitarity in detail in the special case of the elastic scattering of two equal-mass spinless particles with the same two particles in the intermediate state. In this case the amplitudes occurring on both sides of the unitarity are the same. We have then from Eqs. (3.12) and (3.24')

$$S = 1 + R = 1 + G(2\pi)^4\, \delta(P_i - P_f), \tag{7.9}$$

$$d\sigma = |G|^2\, \frac{1}{E^2}\, \frac{d\Omega}{(2\pi)^2}, \tag{7.10}$$

$$G(E,\theta) + G^*(E,\theta) = -\left(\frac{1}{2\pi}\right)^2\left[\frac{s - 4m^2}{4s}\right]^{1/2}\int d^3\mathbf{n}\, G(E,\theta')G^*(E,\theta''), \tag{7.11}$$

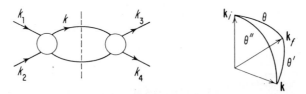

Figure 7.3   Center-of-mass momenta of the initial, intermediate and final states.

where the angles θ, θ', θ'' are as shown. We have the following kinematical relations (Fig. 7.3)

c.o.m. frame: $k_1 = (E,\mathbf{k}_1)$; $k_3 = (E,\mathbf{k}_f)$; $E = (E,\mathbf{k})$,

$$z = \cos\theta = \mathbf{k}_i\cdot\mathbf{k}_f; \quad z' = \cos\theta' = \mathbf{k}\cdot\mathbf{k}_f; \quad z'' = \cos\theta'' = \mathbf{k}\cdot\mathbf{k}_i,$$

$$z' = zz'' + (1 - z^2)^{1/2}(1 - z''^2)^{1/2}\cos\varphi,$$

where $\varphi = $ azimuth angle of n or k.

In the variables (E,z) (taking, say, $\mathbf{k}_i$ in the z-direction) we have

$$G(E,z) + G^*(E,z) = \lambda \int d\varphi\, dz''\, G(E,z')G^*(E,z''),$$

$$\lambda = -(1/2\pi^2)[(s - 4m^2)/4s]^{1/2},$$

or

$$G(E,z) + G^*(E,z) = \lambda \int d\varphi\, dz'\, dz''\, \delta(z' - zz'' - (1 - z^2)^{1/2}(1 - z''^2)^{1/2}\cos\varphi)$$
$$\times\, G(E,z')G^*(E,z'').$$

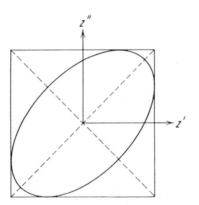

Figure 7.4   Region of integration in Eq. (7.12).

We can do the φ-integration first and obtain[2]

$$G(E,z) + G^*(E,z) \doteq 2\lambda \int_{-1}^{1} dz' \int_{-1}^{1} dz'' \frac{G(E,z')G^*(E,z'')}{[K(z,z',z'')]^{1/2}}\,\theta(K) \tag{7.12}$$

where
$$K(z,z',z'') = 1 - z^2 - z'^2 - z''^2 + 2zz'z''. \tag{7.13}$$

Due to the $\theta(K)$ factor in Eq. (7.12) the integration is actually over an ellipse, $-K \leqslant 0$, rather than a square (Fig. 7.4) with semi-major axis:

$$R = (1 + z)^{1/2}, \quad r = (1 - z)^{1/2}.$$

[2] Note that
$$\int_0^{2\pi} d\varphi\,\delta[z' - zz'' - (1 - z^2)^{1/2}(1 - z''^2)^{1/2}\cos\varphi] = 2\int_{-1}^{+1} \frac{dy}{\sqrt{1 - y^2}} \frac{\delta(y - y_0)}{\sqrt{1 - z^2}\,\sqrt{1 - z''^2}}.$$

where
$$y_0 = (z'' - zz'')/\sqrt{(1 - z^2)(1 - z''^2)}.$$

If we let

$$y = \frac{1}{\sqrt{2}}(z' + z''), \quad x = \frac{1}{\sqrt{2}}(z' - z''),$$

then

$$\frac{x^2}{1-z} + \frac{y^2}{1+z} = 1$$

is equivalent to $K = 0$.

Equation (7.12) can also be written in the form

$$G(E,z) + G^*(E,z) = 2\lambda \int_{-1}^{+1} dz' \int_{z_-''}^{z_+''} dz'' \frac{G(E,z')G^*(E,z'')}{\sqrt{K(z,z',z'')}} \tag{7.14}$$

where

$$z_+'' = zz' \pm [(1 - z^2)(1 - z'^2)]^{\frac{1}{2}}.$$

Finally, in terms of the variable $t = -2q^2(1 - z)$ or $z = 1 + t/2q^2$,

$$K(z,z',z'') \equiv K(q^2; t, t', t'')$$

$$= -\frac{1}{(4q)^4}\left[t^2 + t'^2 + t''^2 - 2(tt' + tt'' + t't'') - \frac{tt't''}{q^2}\right],$$

and

$$G(s,t) + G^*(s,t) = 2\lambda \int_{-4q^2}^{0} dt' \int_{-4q^2}^{0} dt'' \, G(s,t')G^*(s,t'') \frac{\theta(K')}{2q^2\sqrt{K'}}, \tag{7.15}$$

where

$$K' = -(t^2 + t'^2 + t''^2) + 2(tt' + tt'' + t't'') + \frac{tt't''}{q^2}.$$

For the left-hand side of the unitarity we shall also frequently use

$$G = iA,$$
$$G + G^* = iA - iA^* = -2ImA,$$

so that in terms of A,

$$ImA(E,\theta) = -\frac{\lambda}{2}\int d\Omega \, A(E,\theta')A^*(E,\theta''), \tag{7.16}$$

and so on, for the other forms of the unitarity.

Finally we also give a nonrelativistic normalization of the amplitude. Let

$$G(E,\theta) = 4\pi i f(E,\theta)$$

we get

$$Imf(E, \hat{\mathbf{n}}_f \cdot \hat{\mathbf{n}}_i) = \frac{1}{4\pi}\sqrt{\frac{k^2}{k^2 + m^2}}\int d\hat{\mathbf{n}} f(E, \hat{\mathbf{n}}_f \cdot \hat{\mathbf{n}})f^*(E, \hat{\mathbf{n}} \cdot \hat{\mathbf{n}}_i), \tag{7.17}$$

where $\hat{\mathbf{n}}_f$, $\hat{\mathbf{n}}_i$, and $\hat{\mathbf{n}}$ are the unit vectors in the direction of $\mathbf{k}_f$, $\mathbf{k}_i$, and $\mathbf{k}$. The nonrelativistic limit of the factor in front of the integral is just $k/4\pi$.

b. Partial-Wave Amplitudes

The unitarity equation for the two-body intermediate state can be written in a much more convenient way if we use partial-wave amplitudes. The equation involving an integral will split into infinitely many algebraic equations. Also many practical problems involve one or few angular-momentum states.

Any function of an angle θ can be expanded in a Legendre series:

$$A(E,\theta) = \sum_{\ell=0}^{\infty} (2\ell + 1)A_\ell(E)P_\ell(\cos \theta), \qquad (7.18)$$

which converges in an ellipse in the $\cos \theta$-plane (see later). The inverse of Eq. (7.18) is

$$A_\ell(E) = \frac{1}{2} \int_{-1}^{+1} dz\, A(E,\theta)P_\ell(z); \quad z = \cos \theta. \qquad (7.18')$$

Let us insert Eq. (7.18) on both sides of the unitarity Eq. (7.16):

$$\sum_{\ell} (2\ell + 1)ImA_\ell(E)P_\ell(z) = -\frac{\lambda}{2} \sum_{\ell'\ell''} (2\ell' + 1)(2\ell'' + 1)$$

$$\times \int\int d\Omega''\, A_{\ell'}(E)A_{\ell''}^*(E)P_{\ell'}(z')P_{\ell''}(z''),$$

or

$$ImA_\ell(E) = -\frac{\lambda}{2} \sum_{\ell'\ell''} (2\ell' + 1)(2\ell'' + 1)A_{\ell'}(E)A_{\ell''}^*(E)$$

$$\times \frac{1}{2} \int\int\int d\varphi\, dz\, dz''\, P_{\ell'}(z')P_{\ell''}(z'')P_\ell(z). \qquad (7.19)$$

We express $P_{\ell'}(z' = zz'' + (1 - z^2)^{\frac{1}{2}}(1 - z''^2)^{\frac{1}{2}} \cos \varphi)$ in terms of the others by using the identity[3]

$$P_{\ell'}(\cos \theta \cos \theta'' + \sin \theta \sin \theta' \cos \varphi)$$

$$= P_{\ell'}(\cos \theta)P_{\ell'}(\cos \theta'')$$

$$+ 2 \sum_{m=1}^{\infty} \frac{\Gamma(\ell' - m + 1)}{\Gamma(\ell' + m + 1)} P_{\ell'}^m(\cos \theta)P_{\ell'}^m(\cos \theta'') \cos (m\varphi). \qquad (7.20)$$

$$0 < \theta < \pi, \quad 0 \leqslant \theta' < \pi, \quad \theta + \theta' < \pi, \quad \varphi \text{ real};$$

then the φ-integrals of $\cos (m\varphi)$ give zero. From the first term of Eq. (7.20) we get products of $P_\ell(z)P_{\ell'}(z)$ and $P_{\ell''}(z'')P_{\ell'}(z'')$ for which we use the orthogonality of the Legendre polynomials

$$\int_{-1}^{+1} P_\ell P_{\ell'}\, dz = \frac{2}{2\ell + 1} \delta_{\ell\ell'}$$

[3] E. W. Hobson, *The Theory of Spherical and Ellipsoidal Harmonics* (Cambridge: Oxford U. P., 1931), p. 371.

and obtain

$$ImA_\ell(E) = -\lambda 2\pi |A_\ell(E)|^2, \tag{7.21}$$

$$\ell = 0, 1, 2, \ldots; \quad -\lambda = (1/2\pi)^2[(s - 4m^2)/4s]^{1/2}.$$

We shall choose a particularly renormalized amplitude $\bar{A}_\ell(E)$ such that Eq. (7.21) has the form (i.e., incorporate 2π into the amplitude)

$$Im\bar{A}_\ell(E) = \sqrt{\frac{s - 4m^2}{s}} \, |\bar{A}_\ell(E)|^2. \tag{7.22}$$

Then

$$A_\ell(E) = 2\pi\bar{A}_\ell(E), \tag{7.23}$$

$$\bar{A}(E,\theta) = \sum (2\ell + 1)\bar{A}_\ell(E)P_\ell(z). \tag{7.24}$$

Hence we have from Eqs. (7.10) and (7.23), and omitting the bar on A from now on,

$$\frac{d\sigma}{d\Omega} = \frac{1}{E^2} |A(E,\theta)|^2. \tag{7.25}$$

c. Phase Shifts

The partial-wave amplitudes satisfying the unitarity Eq. (7.22) can always be written as

$$A_\ell(s) = \left(\frac{s}{s - 4m^2}\right)^{1/2} \exp(i\delta_\ell(s)) \sin \delta_\ell(s). \tag{7.26}$$

For physical values of ℓ and s, the *phase shifts* $\delta_\ell(s)$ are real. Equation (7.26) already incorporates the two-body unitarity condition.

d. Relation between Unitarity Equation and Partial Wave

The elastic unitarity condition can be considered as an integral equation for A^* (or the second-sheet amplitude A^{II}) for a given first-sheet amplitude A, or vice versa. The kernel of the integral equation [obtained from Eq. (7.12) or (7.14)], i.e.,

$$A^{II}(s,z) - A^{I}(s,z) = \frac{1}{i\pi} \sqrt{\frac{s - 4m^2}{4s}} \int dz'' \, dz' \, \frac{A^I(E,z')}{\sqrt{K(zz'z'')}} \, \theta(K)A^{II}(E,z''),$$

is

$$\frac{1}{i\pi} \int_{-1}^{+1} dz' \, \frac{A^I(E,z')}{\sqrt{K(zz'z'')}}. \tag{7.27}$$

In particular, if the amplitude A^I is approximated by a pole term in crossed channel, $A^I = g^2/(t - \mu^2) = \gamma/(z - \sigma)$; $\gamma = g^2/2q^2$, $\sigma = 1 + \mu^2/2q^2$, the kernel becomes [see also Eq. (7.61)] simply

$$\frac{g^2}{2q^2} \frac{1}{\sqrt{K(z,\sigma,z'')}}. \tag{7.27'}$$

Because the kernel is symmetric we can apply both the Hilbert-Schmidt and the Fredholm theories. In the case of Eq. (7.27′) the eigenfunctions and the eigenvalues of the symmetric kernel can be read off from the expansion

$$\frac{1}{\sqrt{z^2 + z'^2 + z''^2 - 2zz'z'' - 1}} = \sum_\ell (2\ell + 1)P_\ell(z')Q_\ell(z')P_\ell(z''). \qquad (7.28)$$

This expansion is valid for Im α > Im β + Im γ, where

$$\cos \alpha = z, \quad \cos \beta = z', \quad \cos \gamma = z''.$$

In the more general case of Eq. (7.27) we can write for the kernel

$$\frac{1}{i\pi} \int_{-1}^{+1} \sum_\ell (2\ell + 1)A^{\mathrm{I}}(E,z')P_\ell(z')Q_\ell(z)P_\ell(z'') \, dz'$$

$$= 2\sum_\ell (2\ell + 1)A_\ell(E)Q_\ell(z)P_\ell(z''). \qquad (7.29)$$

The general solution of the integral equation can be written in terms of the eigenfunctions u_n and eigenvalues λ_n of the symmetric kernel. This is because these eigenfunctions form a complete system and both sides of the integral equations can be expanded in terms of these eigenfunctions. The general formula is, with $\mathscr{K}u_n = (1/\lambda_n)u_n$,

$$A^{\mathrm{II}} = \sum_n \frac{A_n^{\mathrm{I}}(z)}{1 - \lambda_n} u_n(z); \quad A^{\mathrm{I}} = \sum_n A_n^{\mathrm{I}}u_n. \qquad (7.30)$$

Hence we obtain from Eq. (7.29) the solution

$$A^{\mathrm{II}}(s,z) = \sum_\ell (2\ell + 1) \frac{A_\ell^{\mathrm{I}}(s)}{1 + 2i\sqrt{\dfrac{s - 4m^2}{s}} A_\ell^{\mathrm{I}}(s)} P_\ell(z), \qquad (7.31)$$

which is exactly the same as we would first calculate the second-sheet partial-wave amplitudes from partial wave unitarity equation:

$$A_\ell^{\mathrm{II}} - A_\ell^{\mathrm{I}} = -2i\sqrt{\frac{s - 4m^2}{s}} A_\ell^{\mathrm{I}}A_\ell^{\mathrm{II}}; \qquad (7.32)$$

then sum up the series.

The general theory of the integral equation can be also used to find the singularities of the second-sheet amplitudes (see App. 7).

e. Passage to Nonrelativistic Potential Scattering

The ordinary quantum mechanical scattering problem by a potential corresponds to taking two-body intermediate state in the unitarity equation and nonrelativistic kinematics.[4]

[4] For a review of the analytic properties of nonrelativistic amplitude and for further references, see A. O. Barut, "Dispersion Relations and Resonance Scattering," in W. E. Brittin and B. W. Downs (eds.), *Lectures in Theoretical Physics, Vol. IV* (New York: Wiley, 1962); T. Regge, in *Theoretical Physics* (Vienna: International Atomic Energy Agency, 1963); M. L. Goldberger and K. M. Watson, *Collision Theory* (New York: Wiley, 1964); A. Martin, in *Progress in Elementary Particles and Cosmic Rays*, Vol. VIII (North Holland Pub. Co., 1965).

Indeed the unitarity equation of the type (7.20) or (7.26) can be obtained directly from the Schrödinger equation. For example, in the radial Schrödinger equation,

$$v_\ell'' + \left[k^2 - \frac{\ell(\ell+1)}{r^2} - V(r) \right] v_\ell = 0; \quad \frac{\hbar^2}{2m} = 1, \tag{7.33}$$

or, equivalently,

$$v_\ell(r) = \frac{j_\ell(kr)}{k^\ell+1} - \frac{1}{k} \int_0^r g_\ell(r,\xi,k)V(\xi)v_\ell(\xi)\, d\xi,$$

where

$$g_\ell(r,\xi,k) = j_\ell(kr)n_\ell(k\xi) - j_\ell(k\xi)n_\ell(kr).$$

the partial-wave amplitudes are defined by the asymptotic form of $v_\ell(r)$. We obtain

$$v_\ell(r) \xrightarrow[r\to\infty]{} \frac{1}{2(-ik)^{\ell+1}} [F_\ell e^{-ikr} + (-1)^{\ell+1}F_\ell^* e^{ikr}]$$

$$= \frac{F_\ell}{2(-ik)^{\ell+1}} [e^{-ikr} - S_\ell(k)e^{ikr}],$$

where

$$S_\ell(k) \equiv e^{2i\delta_\ell(k)} = (-1)^\ell \frac{F_\ell^*(k)}{F_\ell(k)} \tag{7.34}$$

and

$$F_\ell(k) = 1 + ik \int_0^\infty v_\ell(\xi)V(\xi)\{j_\ell(k\xi) + in_\ell(\xi)\}\, d\xi. \tag{7.35}$$

Because $\{F_\ell(k^*)\}^* = F_\ell(-k)$ we have the unitarity of the partial-wave S-matrix elements

$$S_\ell(k)\{S_\ell(k^*)\}^* = 1 \tag{7.36}$$

and the symmetry condition

$$S_\ell(-k) = \{S_\ell(k^*)\}^* = S_\ell^{-1}(k). \tag{7.37}$$

In terms of the partial-wave amplitudes defined by

$$f_\ell(k) = \frac{1}{2ik} [S_\ell(k) - 1] = \frac{e^{2i\delta_\ell} - 1}{2ik} = \frac{1}{k} \sin \delta_\ell e^{i\delta_\ell}, \tag{7.38}$$

the unitarity relation becomes

$$\operatorname{Im} f_\ell(k) = k|f_\ell|^2. \tag{7.39}$$

The total scattering amplitude is

$$f(k,\theta) = \sum (2\ell+1)f_\ell(k)P_\ell(\cos\theta), \tag{7.40}$$

which is defined by the asymptotic form of the wave function

$$\psi \to e^{ikz} + f(k,\theta)\frac{e^{ikr}}{r}$$

and the differential cross-section

$$\sigma(\theta) = \left| \sum_{\ell} (2\ell + 1) f_\ell(k) P_\ell(\cos\theta) \right|^2$$

$$= \frac{1}{k^2} \left| \sum_{\ell} (2\ell + 1) e^{i\delta_\ell} \sin\delta_\ell P_\ell(\cos\theta) \right|^2. \tag{7.41}$$

From here we obtain the total cross section

$$\sigma_{\text{tot}} = \frac{4\pi}{k^2} \sum_{\ell} (2\ell + 1) \sin^2\delta_\ell \tag{7.42}$$

and the *optical theorem*

$$Imf(k,\theta) = \frac{1}{k} \sum_{\ell} (2\ell + 1) \sin^2\delta_\ell = \frac{k}{4\pi} \sigma_{\text{tot}}. \tag{7.43}$$

f. Poles in the Second Sheet

We shall now show that another type of simple singularity required by the analytic continuation of the unitarity relation is that of the poles in the second sheet of energy of the partial-wave amplitudes.

Consider again the elastic two-body scattering of spinless particles and s to be below the inelastic threshold. The unitarity relation (7.22) can be written, if we use second-sheet amplitudes, in the form

$$A^{\text{II}}(s,\ell) - A^{\text{I}}(s,\ell) = -2i \sqrt{\frac{s - 4m^2}{s}} A^{\text{I}}(s,\ell) A^{\text{II}}(s,\ell). \tag{7.22'}$$

If we solve this equation for A^{II} we get [see also Eq. (7.32)]

$$A^{\text{II}}(s,\ell) = \frac{A^{\text{I}}(s,\ell)}{1 + 2i \sqrt{\dfrac{s - 4m^2}{s}} A^{\text{I}}(s,\ell)} = \frac{A^{\text{I}}(s,\ell)}{S^{\text{I}}(s,\ell)}. \tag{7.32'}$$

Consequently the zeros of the quantity $S^{(\text{I})}$ (not the amplitude) in the first sheet correspond to poles of the amplitude in the second sheet.

A pole of the partial-wave scattering amplitude, in the second sheet but close to the physical region (i.e., small imaginary part), implies a resonance in the crossed section, as was first pointed out in the case of potential scattering.[5] But the origin of these poles is a dynamical question. We shall come back to this point later in detail (Chap. 11). Here we note that an amplitude with a second-sheet pole of the form

$$A(s,\ell) = g^2/(s - s_r^{\text{II}})$$

or

$$A(s,\ell) = g'^2/(\sqrt{s_r} + \sqrt{s}) = g'^2(\sqrt{s} - \sqrt{s_r})/(s - s_r) = g^2/(s - s_r)$$

---

[5] R. E. Peierls, in *Proceedings of the Glasgow Conference on Nuclear and Meson Physics* (New York: Pergamon, 1954), p. 296.

gives a contribution to the cross section of the form

$$|A(s,\ell)|^2 = \frac{\bar{g}^4}{(s-a)^2 + b^2}, \qquad s_r = a + ib,$$

which is the Breit-Wigner resonance form.

7.4   The Definition of the Physical Sheet

We have seen that the unitarity condition implies normal threshold branch points in the amplitude. For the one particle state we get simply a pole at a value of the energy equal to the mass of the particle, because the phase-space factor is proportional to a δ-function. (The one-particle intermediate state will be discussed in detail in the next chapter.) We must of course write the unitarity in all crossed channels and each of these relations will imply pole and threshold branch points. In simple cases all these unitarity singularities can be taken to be on the real axis of energy variables in all channels. Are there any other singularities? The analysis in the preceding section has shown that the second-sheet amplitudes can have also complex singularities. Are there also complex singularities in the first sheet?

The unitarity equation is symmetric with respect to the exchange $A \leftrightarrow A^*$. As a matter of fact it is symmetric under the exchange $S \leftrightarrow S^\dagger$. Thus together with S, $S^\dagger$ also satisfies invariance principle and unitarity. Yet there is an asymmetry in their analytic behavior, because a zero of S corresponds to a pole of $S^\dagger$, and vice versa. Whether S has actually zeros is a dynamical question and does not follow immediately from the unitarity condition. From the physical points $E_+ = E + i\varepsilon$ just above the cut, we can continue in both directions to the first sheet or through the cut, into the second sheet. The physical points have neighbors in both sheets.

We shall take the sheet where the points $E + i\varepsilon$ lie as the *physical sheet* and shall assume for the present that there are no other singularities on this sheet except those which have a physical meaning as one and more particle thresholds in all channels. The justification of this assumption comes from the Schrödinger theory where one can show that a complex pole in the first sheet corresponds to waves which asymptotically grow or which disappear in a sink; this of course violates the conservation of probability (see Exercise 8). Similarly, the amplitudes calculated in perturbation theory do not have any complex singularities in the first sheet.

Thus it seems reasonable to say that there are no singularities except those required by unitarity which have definite physical meaning. At least this would be accepted as a working hypothesis. What singularities are required by the unitarity condition in all channels and in all orders is however a difficult problem not yet solved.

7.5   Anomalous Threshold

We will show now starting from unitarity that under certain conditions the cut in the s-plane starts from a point lower than the normal threshold points $s = (m_1 + m_2)^2$.

Consider the two-body unitarity condition (Fig. 7.5). For $4M^2 < t < 9m^2$

$$Im A(t,z_t) = \frac{-1}{2\pi} \sqrt{\frac{t - 4m^2}{t}} \int dz_1 \, dz_2 \, B(t,z_1) C^*(t,z_2) \theta(K) / \sqrt{K(z,z_1,z_2)}.$$

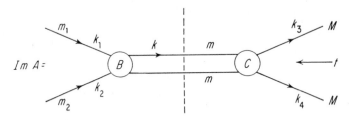

Figure 7.5   Labeling of masses and momenta.

Let us approximate the B-amplitude by a pole term in the t-channel:

$$B = \frac{g_1^2}{\mu_1^2 - t^2}$$

and the C-amplitude by a pole term in the s-channel:

$$C = \frac{g_2^2}{\mu_2^2 - s_2} \qquad \text{with} \qquad s_2 = (k_3 - k)^2.$$

The resultant unitarity diagram may be written as follows [6] (Fig. 7.6).

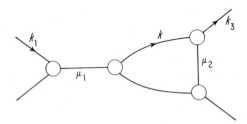

Figure 7.6   Pole approximation of the B- and C-amplitudes of Fig. 7.5.

---

[6] The corresponding Feynman-amplitude in perturbation theory is the triangular diagram shown in Fig. 7.7. [R. Karplus, C. M. Sommerfield, and E. H. Wichman, *Phys. Rev.*, **111**, 1187 (1958).]

We have now in the center-of-mass frame $k: (E,\mathbf{p})$, $k_3: (E,\mathbf{q})$, $t = 4E^2$, hence

$$s_2 = M^2 + m^2 - \frac{t}{2} + 2pqz_2,$$

where

$$p = \tfrac{1}{2}\sqrt{t - 4m^2}, \qquad q = \tfrac{1}{2}\sqrt{t - 4M^2}.$$

We can do the z_1-integration and obtain

$$\text{Im}A(t,z_t) = -\frac{1}{2\pi}\sqrt{\frac{t - 4m^2}{t}}\,\frac{g_1^2}{\mu_1^2 - t}\,\frac{g_2^2}{2pq}\,g(t,M^2), \tag{7.44}$$

where

$$g(t,M^2) = \int_{-1}^{+1}\frac{dz_2}{z_2 - h(t,M^2)} \tag{7.45}$$

with

$$h(t,M^2) = \frac{t - 4m^2 + 2(m^2 + \mu_2^2 - M^2)}{\sqrt{(t - 4M^2)(t - 4m^2)}}.$$

The normal threshold is at $t = 4m^2$. If $M^2 < m^2$, the unitarity is valid from normal threshold on and in the dispersion relation

$$A(t,z_t) = \frac{1}{\pi}\int_{4m^2}^{\infty} dt'\,\frac{\text{Im}A(t',z_t)}{t' - t}, \tag{7.46}$$

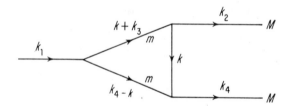

Figure 7.7 Feynman amplitude corresponding to part of the unitarity diagram of Fig. 7.6.

The Feynman amplitude is given by (for scalar particles)

$$A^{(3)} = \frac{g^3}{(2\pi)^3}\int d^4k[(k^2 - \mu^2)\{(k + k_3)^2 - m^2\}\{(k - k_4)^2 - m^2\}]^{-1}.$$

If we inspect this amplitude as a function of k_1^2, we see that the denominator can never vanish for complex k_1^2, and, for real $k_1^2 < m_{\text{threshold}}^2$. Thus $A^{(3)}$ is holomorphic in the $t = k_1^2$ plane cut from $t_1 = m_{\text{th}}^2$ to ∞. The branch point t_1 depends on the masses involved and one finds

$$t_1 = 4m^2, \quad \text{if} \quad M^2 < (m^2 + \mu^2)$$

$$= 4m^2 - \frac{(m^2 + \mu^2 - M^2)^2}{\mu^2}, \quad \text{if} \quad M^2 > (m^2 + \mu^2).$$

The physical value of such a triangle diagram is $A(t = m_1^2)$ and is a number. In the unitarity relation such diagrams will always occur multiplied by the one particle phase space $\rho_1 \propto \delta(t - m_1^2)$ and we can consider the amplitude as a function of t.

we do not need to continue $ImA(t',z)$ analytically. In this region of integration $ImA(t,z)$ is regular, for in order $g(t,M^2)$ to be singular, $|h|$ should be $\leqslant 1$ (see App. 7). Indeed $h^2 = 1$ when

$$t = t_1 = 4m^2 - \frac{(m^2 + \mu^2 - M^2)^2}{\mu^2} \tag{7.47}$$

so that $t_1 < 4m^2$ for $M^2 < m^2 + \mu^2$. One can actually do the integral and obtain

$$g(t,M^2) = \ln \frac{\sqrt{(t - 4m^2)(t - 4M^2)} + t + 2\mu^2 - 2(M^2 + m^2)}{\sqrt{(t - 4m^2)(t - 4M^2)} - t - 2\mu^2 + 2(M^2 + m^2)}; \tag{7.48}$$

the branch point of the logarithmus is at $t = t_1$.

At $M^2 = m^2 + \mu^2$, t_1 becomes equal to $4m^2$, the lower limit of integration in Eq. (7.46). For $M^2 > m^2 + \mu^2$, t_1 is again less than $4m^2$, but now Eq. (7.46) is no longer the proper analytic continuation.

To obtain the correct continuation[7] we give, in the neighborhood of $M^2 = m^2 + \mu^2$, a small complex part to M^2:

$$M^2 = m^2 + \mu^2 + x + iy, \qquad y > 0, \quad \text{fixed}.$$

Then

$$t_1 = 4m^2 - \frac{1}{\mu^2}(x^2 + 2ixy - y^2)$$

and the position of the branch point as a function of x is shown in Fig. 7.8.

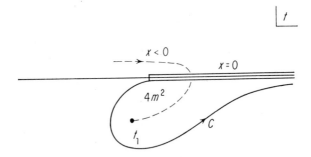

Figure 7.8.

The dotted line being the branch cut of $ImA(t,z)$, the integration Eq. (7.46) must avoid this branch line, and the analytic continuation of Eq. (7.46) is then

$$A(t,z_t) = \frac{1}{\pi} \int_c dt' \frac{ImA(t',z_t)}{t' - t}. \tag{7.49}$$

[7] S. Mandelstam, *Phys. Rev. Letters*, **4**, 84 (1960).

If we now let $y \to 0$, we get, for $M^2 > m^2 + \mu^2$,

$$A(t,z_t) = \frac{1}{\pi} \int_{t_1}^{4m^2} dt' \, \frac{\text{disc. } A(t',z_t)}{t' - t} + \frac{1}{\pi} \int_{4m^2}^{\infty} dt' \, \frac{ImA(t',z_t)}{t' - t}. \qquad (7.50)$$

As an example, we consider $e^- - d$ scattering (s-channel, Fig. 7.9). We

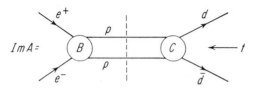

Figure 7.9 Two particle unitarity in e-d scattering.

approximate the first amplitude by the photon pole (t-channel) and the second by the neutron pole in s-channel (Fig. 7.10). Thus, in the previous notation, we have to put

$$m_1 = m_e, \quad m = m_p; \quad \mu_1 = 0, \quad \mu_2 = m_p; \quad M = 2m_p - B.$$

Hence the condition for anomalous threshold is satisfied and

$$t_1 = 4m_p^2 - \frac{(2m_p^2 - 4m_p^2 + 4m_pB - B^2)^2}{m_p^2}$$

$$\cong 16m_pB, \qquad (7.51)$$

where B is the binding energy of the deuteron.

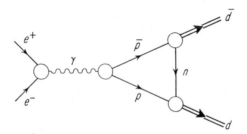

Figure 7.10 Pole approximation of Fig. 7.9.

The scattering amplitude in this approximation will be obtained by Eq. (7.50). It is not clear whether the anomalous threshold is a property of the full amplitude or that of approximative diagrams used above.

7.6 Single- and Double-Dispersion Relations

Let us consider the amplitude of two-body spinless particles $A(s,t,u)$ and assume that no anomalous threshold exists. We want to discuss first the analyticity in a single variable when the other is fixed.

Let $t = $ fixed. In the variable s we have the normal threshold singularities beginning at $s = M_s^2 = $ lowest mass square of the particles allowed in the s-channel (i.e., the channel in which s is the square of the total energy in the center-of-mass frame). We also have the u-channel. Let M_u be the lowest mass of the particles in the u-channel. Because $s + t + u = \sum m_i^2 = h$, the branch cut in u from M_u^2 to ∞ corresponds to a branch cut in s from $-\infty$ to $h - M_u^2 - t$. These two branch cuts are in general distinct. The second branch cut is obtained from the unitarity in the u-channel, the first from the unitarity in the s-channel as discussed in Sec. 7.2 above.

If the amplitude has a suitable asymptotic behavior in $|s|$ for large $|s|$ we can write the following Cauchy relation:

$t = $ fixed:

$$A(s,t,u) = \frac{1}{\pi} \int_{M_s^2}^{\infty} ds' \, \frac{A_1(s',t,u')}{s' - s} + \frac{1}{\pi} \int_{-\infty}^{h - M_u^2 - t} ds' \, \frac{A_3(s',t,u')}{s' - s}, \qquad (7.52)$$

with possible subtraction terms if the integrals do not converge. Here A_1 and A_3 are the so-called *absorptive parts* of the amplitude in the s- and u-channels, respectively; in the respective physical regions they are real and equal to the imaginary part of the amplitude as determined from unitarity. Equation (7.52) can be written in a more symmetric way:

$t = $ fixed:

$$A(s,t,u) = \frac{1}{\pi} \int_{M_s^2}^{\infty} ds' \, \frac{A_1(s', t, h - s' - t)}{s' - s}$$

$$+ \frac{1}{\pi} \int_{M_u^2}^{\infty} du' \, \frac{A_3(h - u' - t, t, u')}{u' - u}. \qquad (7.53)$$

Outside the physical region of the s- and u-channels A_1 and A_2, respectively, become in general complex. They are equal to the imaginary part of the amplitude only in their respective physical regions.

In the case of potential scattering we have only the first term of Eq. (7.53), the second term corresponds to an *exchange potential*. In addition, because we have three coupled channels, we can also consider the variables u and s to be fixed and obtain two more single-dispersion relations:

$u = $ fixed:

$$A(s,t,u) = \frac{1}{\pi} \int_{M_s^2}^{\infty} ds' \, \frac{A_1(s', h - s' - u, u)}{s' - s}$$

$$+ \frac{1}{\pi} \int_{M_t^2}^{\infty} dt' \, \frac{A_2(h - t' - u, t', u)}{t' - t}. \qquad (7.54)$$

$s =$ fixed:

$$A(s,t,u) = \frac{1}{\pi} \int_{M_t^2}^{\infty} dt' \frac{A_2(s, t', h - s - t')}{t' - t}$$

$$+ \frac{1}{\pi} \int_{M_u^2}^{\infty} du' \frac{A_3(s, h - s - u', u')}{u' - u}. \qquad (7.55)$$

In the last equation, for example, if we put, for equal mass case,

$$s = 4(q_s^2 + m^2), \quad t = -2q_s^2(1 - \cos\theta), \quad u = -2q_s^2(1 + \cos\theta)$$

we obtain

$q^2 =$ fixed:

$$A(q^2, \cos\theta) = \frac{1}{\pi} \int_{M_t^2}^{\infty} dt' \frac{A_2(s, t', h - t' - s)}{t' + 2q_s^2(1 - \cos\theta)}$$

$$+ \frac{1}{\pi} \int_{M_u^2}^{\infty} du' \frac{A_3(s, h - u' - s, u')}{u' + 2q_s^2(1 + \cos\theta)}. \qquad (7.56)$$

The $\cos\theta$-dependence of the amplitude comes entirely from the denominators and the two terms have opposite $\cos\theta$-dependence, as it should be for an exchange potential. For comparison the amplitude in a Born approximation from a Yukawa potential gives

$$A(q^2, \cos\theta) = \frac{C}{1/r_0^2 + 2q^2(1 - \cos\theta)},$$

where $r_0 = 1/\mu$ is the range of the potential; the exchange Yukawa potential gives the same terms with $\cos\theta$ replaced by $-\cos\theta$. We can thus interpret Eq. (7.56) as an infinite superposition of *Born terms of Yukawa potentials* and exchange potentials with range from $1/\sqrt{t'} = 1/M_t$ to zero, and $1/\sqrt{u'} = 1/M_u$ to zero. The lowest mass intermediate states correspond to longest-range potentials.

The three equations (7.53–7.55) express the analyticity in each variable s, t, or u, when one variable is fixed: The amplitude is holomorphic in each variable except the pole and branch-point singularities on the real axis.

a. Analyticity in Two Variables

We want now to study if we can express the analyticity of the amplitude in both independent variables, s and t, e.g., simultaneously. How can we continue Eq. (7.53), e.g., written for a fixed t, to all values of t? This involves an analytic continuation of the absorptive parts A_1 and A_3 in t. We can obtain the desired analytic continuation explicitly from unitarity in simple approximations of the unitarity condition.

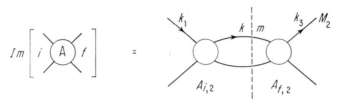

Figure 7.11   Two-body unitarity.

Consider the two-body unitarity shown schematically in Fig. (7.11).

$$Im A(t,z) = -\frac{1}{\pi} \sqrt{\frac{t - 4m^2}{4t}} \int_{-1}^{+1} dz_2 \int_{z_1^-}^{z_1^+} dz_2 \frac{\theta(K)}{\sqrt{K}} A_{f,2}(t,z_2) A_{i,2}^*(t,z_1), \quad (7.57)$$

where

$$z_1^\pm = zz_2 \pm \sqrt{(1 - z^2)(1 - z_2^2)}$$

are the roots of

$$K = 1 - z^2 - z_1^2 - z_2^2 + 2zz_1z_2.$$

We now approximate the amplitudes $A_{f,2}$ and $A_{i,2}$ by pole terms in the s-channels,

$$\begin{aligned} A_{f,2} &= g_2^2/(s_2 - \mu_2^2), \\ A_{i,2} &= g_1^2/(s_1 - \mu_1^2), \end{aligned} \quad (7.58)$$

so that the resultant unitarity diagram (Fig. 7.12) corresponds to the box diagram in perturbation theory.[8] We then have

$$s_1 = (k_1 - k)^2 = M_1^2 + m^2 - \frac{t}{2} + 2p_1qz_1,$$

$$\quad (7.59)$$

$$s_2 = (k - k_3)^2 = M_2^2 + m^2 - \frac{t}{2} + 2p_2qz_2,$$

where p_1, p_2, and q are the magnitudes of the momenta in the center-of-mass frame of the initial, final, and intermediate particles:

$$p_1 = (t - 4M_1^2)^{1/2}, \quad p_2 = (t - M_2^2)^{1/2}; \quad q = (t - 4m^2)^{1/2}.$$

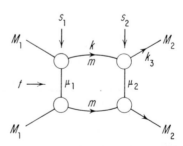

Figure 7.12   Pole approximation to Fig. 7.11.

[8] In perturbation theory the analyticity of fourth-order diagrams in both variables was first studied by S. Mandelstam [*Phys. Rev.*, **115**, 1741 and 1752 (1959)]. Consider the particular "box" diagram of spinless equal mass particle shown in Fig. (7.13).

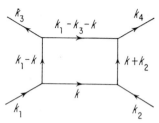

Figure 7.13 Feynman diagram corresponding to the approximate unitarity diagram of Fig. 7.12.

The Feynman amplitude of this particular fourth-order diagram (there are of course other fourth-order diagrams) is given by

$$A^{(4)} = i \frac{g^4}{(2\pi)^4} \int d^4k [(k^2 - m^2)\{(k_1 - k)^2 - m^2\}$$
$$\times \{(k + k_1)^2 - m^2\}\{(k_1 - k_3 - k)^2 - m^2\}]^{-1}.$$

For t real and negative the denominator never vanishes for all complex s and for all real $s < 4m^2$. Hence we can write

$$A^{(4)}(s,t,u) = \frac{1}{\pi} \int_{4m^2}^{\infty} ds' \frac{Im A^{(4)}(s', t, h - s' - t)}{s' - s}, \quad t \text{ real and} < 0.$$

We can calculate $Im A^{(4)}$ explicitly from the first formula. One obtains

$$Im A^{(4)} = \frac{1}{16\pi \sqrt{y(s,t)}} \ln \frac{\alpha(s,t) + q\sqrt{y/s}}{\alpha(s,t) - q\sqrt{y/s}}, \quad s > 4m^2$$
$$= 0, \quad s < 4m^2$$

where

$$y(s,t) = 4st [st - 4m^2(s + t) + 12m^4],$$
$$\alpha(s,t) = st - 2m^2 s - 4m^2 t + 6m^4.$$

We see from its explicit form that $Im A^{(4)}$ is analytic in t except a branch point and we can write

$$Im A^{(4)} = \frac{1}{\pi} \int dt' \frac{\rho^{(4)}(s,t')}{t' - t}$$

where

$$\rho(s,t) = -\frac{1}{8\sqrt{y(s,t)}} \quad \text{for} \quad y > 0, \ t > 0, \ s > 4m^2$$
$$= 0, \text{ otherwise.}$$

Thus we have the double-dispersion relation

$$A^{(4)} = \frac{1}{\pi^2} \int ds' \, dt' \frac{\rho^{(4)}(s',t')}{(s' - s)(t' - t)}.$$

Other and higher-order Feynman diagrams have been extensively studied. It seems that for equal mass case the double-dispersion relation of the above type is probably valid in all orders of perturbation theory.

See, e.g., R. J. Eden, *Phys. Rev.*, **121**, 1567 (1961); P. Landshoff, J. Polkinghorne, J. G. Taylor, *Nuovo Cimento*, **19**, 939 (1961). But the perturbation theory does not tell us how many subtractions are needed in the dispersion relation (see Chap. 9). For some higher-order diagrams of unequal masses there seems to be however, a priori, some complex singularities: R. J. Eden, P. Landshoff, J. Polkinghorne, and J. G. Taylor, *Phys. Rev.*, **122**, 307 (1961).

Inserting Eqs. (7.58) and (7.59) into Eq. (7.57), we obtain

$$ImA(t,z) = -\frac{1}{\pi}\sqrt{\frac{t - 4m^2}{t}}\,\frac{g_1^2}{2p_1q}\,\frac{g_2^2}{2p_2q}\,g(t,z) \tag{7.60}$$

where

$$g(t,z) = \int_{-1}^{+1}\frac{dz_2}{z_2 - h_2(t,M_2^2)}\int_{z_1^-}^{z_1^+}\frac{dz_1}{(z_1 - h_1(t,M_1^2))\sqrt{K(z,z_1,z_2)}} \tag{7.61}$$

with

$$h_i(t,M_i^2) = \frac{t + 2\mu_i^2 - 2(M_i^2 + m^2)}{\sqrt{(t - 4M_i^2)(t - 4m^2)}}; \qquad i = 1, 2.$$

If all masses are equal, $\mu_i = M_i = m$, we have

$$h_1 = h_2 = \frac{t - 2m^2}{t - 4m^2}.$$

Our objective is to study the analytic continuation of $ImA(t,z)$, therefore of $g(t,z)$, in the other variable z. The integrals in Eq. (7.61) can be evaluated explicitly and the singularities in z may be studied (see Exercise 5). Let us, however, determine these singularities without carrying on the integrations but using the lemma of App. 7.

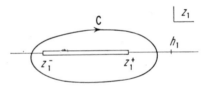

Figure 7.14   Region of integration.

In the physical region, $z^2 < 1$, $t > 4m^2$ (assuming no anomalous threshold) in which Eq. (7.60) first holds, we have $z_1^\pm < 1$ but h_1, $h_2 \geqslant 1$. In the z-plane we can transform the z_1-integration into a contour integral shown in Fig. 7.14, and then it is equal to the residue of the integrand at the pole $z_1 = h_1$:

$$\int_{z_1^-}^{z_1^+}\frac{dz_1}{(z_1 - h_1)\sqrt{K}} = \frac{1}{2}\oint\frac{dz_1}{(z_1 - h_1)\sqrt{K}} = i\pi\,\frac{1}{\sqrt{K(z,h_1,z_2)}}.$$

Hence

$$g(t,z) = i\pi\int_{-1}^{+1}\frac{dz_2}{(z_2 - h_2)\sqrt{K(z,h_1,z_2)}}.$$

We want to continue this integral to unphysical region $z^2 > 1$. In the z_2-plane the integrand has a pole at h_2 and branch points at

$$z_2^\pm = zh_1 \pm \sqrt{(z^2 - 1)(h_1^2 - 1)}.$$

At first, because $h_{1,2} \geqslant 1$, the pole is outside the region of integration, and for $z^2 < 1$ the branch points are complex. When $z \to 1$ the branch points approach $z_2^\pm \to h_1 > 1$, but still outside the region of integration. When $z > 1$, the branch point z_2^+ moves to the right and z_2^- to the left.

A dangerous point is reached when $z_2^- = 1$. This happens for $z = h_1$. To continue beyond we must deform the contour of integration. If we make z slightly complex (in a similar way as we made M^2 complex in Sec. 5), the path of z_2^- is shown in Fig. 7.15. We can deform the contour along C; hence

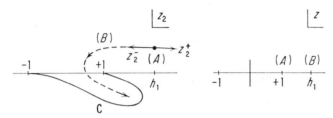

Figure 7.15.

the point $z = h_1$ is not a singular point. When we make z again real, the integration is along the following contour shown in Fig. 7.16. This process can be continued until z_2^- reaches h_2, which happens when $z = z_p$,

$$z_p = h_1 h_2 + \sqrt{(h_2^2 - 1)(h_1^2 - 1)}.$$

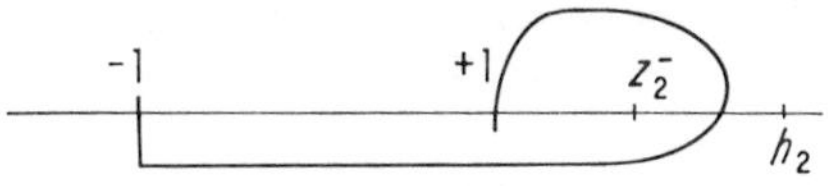

Figure 7.16.

Thus along the curve $z_p(t)$, $Im A(t,z)$ has a branch point, everywhere else it can be continued analytically, and we can write

$$Im A(t,z) = \frac{1}{\pi} \int_{z_p(t)}^{\infty} dz' \, \frac{\rho(t,z')}{z' - z}$$

or, in s, $\hspace{6cm}$ (7.62)

$$Im A(t,s) = \frac{1}{\pi} \int_{s_p(t)}^{\infty} ds' \, \frac{\rho(t,s')}{s' - s}.$$

For equal-mass case,

$$z_p = 2h^2 - 1 = 1 + \frac{2s_p}{t - 4m^2}$$

or

$$s_p = (t - 4m^2)(h^2 - 1) = \frac{4m^2}{t - 4m^2}(t - 3m^2).$$

If we combine Eq. (7.62) with the relation

$$A(t,s) = \frac{1}{\pi} \int_{4m^2}^{\infty} dt' \frac{\mathrm{Im} A(t',s)}{t'-t},$$

we obtain the double-dispersion relation

$$A(t,s) = \frac{1}{\pi^2} \int_{4m^2}^{\infty} dt' \int_{s_p(t')}^{\infty} ds' \frac{\rho(t',s')}{(t'-t)(s'-s)}. \tag{7.63}$$

There are two other "box" diagrams similar to Fig. 7.12 corresponding to the s- and u-channels. We have therefore two other double-dispersion relations of the type (7.63) in which the integrals are over $dt' \, du'$ and $ds' \, du'$, respectively.

Thus, at least as far as nearby singularities are concerned, we can write

$$
\begin{aligned}
A(s,t,u) = {} & \frac{1}{\pi^2} \int_{M_s^2}^{\infty} ds' \int_{M_u^2}^{\infty} dt' \frac{\rho_{st}(s',t')}{(s'-s)(t'-t)} \\
& + \frac{1}{\pi^2} \int_{M_s^2}^{\infty} ds' \int_{M_u^2}^{\infty} du' \frac{\rho_{su}(s', h-s'-u', u')}{(s'-s)(u'-u)} \\
& + \frac{1}{\pi^2} \int_{M_t^2}^{\infty} ds' \int_{M_u^2}^{\infty} du' \frac{\rho_{tu}(h-t'-u', t', u')}{(t'-t)(u'-u)} \tag{7.64}
\end{aligned}
$$

plus possible pole terms and subtraction terms. This form of the double dispersion relations with three terms is dictated by the crossing symmetry and unitarity.[9] (See also Sec. 7.6c) The real functions ρ_{st}, ρ_{su}, ρ_{tu} are called the spectral functions.

It has been conjectured by Mandelstam[10] that the representation Eq. (7.54), with possible subtraction terms, is valid quite generally. If the remaining singularities of the amplitude are all on the real axis of the type of inelastic normal threshold singularities, then all inelastic effects may be lumped phenomenologically into the spectral functions, and the representation is true if the amplitude has suitable bounded asymptotic behavior. Otherwise the representation will break down. We do not need to take Eq. (7.64) as a postulate. We take the point of view of approximating the unitarity condition by taking more and more terms in the intermediate states. In the context of these approximations—neglecting possible distant complex singularities—it is certainly true.

To show the effect of the pole terms we also write Eq. (7.64) for the example of πN-scattering. In the s- and u-channels ($\pi N \to \pi N$) we have the N-pole

[9] Given the branch points in each variable for all values of the others the form of Eq. (7.64) may be also proved by the so-called S. Bergmann-Weil formula of the theory of many complex variables (see App. 9).

[10] S. Mandelstam, *Phys. Rev.*, **112**, 1344 (1958).

term, but not in the t-channel ($\pi\pi \to N\bar{N}$). The scalar amplitudes A and B then satisfy

$$A(s,t,u) = \frac{g^2}{s - M^2} + \frac{g^2}{u - M^2}$$

$$+ \frac{1}{\pi^2} \int_{(M+\mu)^2}^{\infty} \frac{ds'}{s' - s} \int_{4\mu^2}^{\infty} dt' \frac{\rho_{st}}{t' - t}$$

$$+ \frac{1}{\pi^2} \int_{(M+\mu)^2}^{\infty} \frac{ds'}{(s' - s)} \int_{(M+\mu)^2}^{\infty} ds' \frac{\rho_{su}}{u' - u}$$

$$+ \frac{1}{\pi^2} \int_{(M+\mu)^2}^{\infty} \frac{du'}{u' - u} \int_{4\mu^2}^{\infty} dt' \frac{\rho_{ut}}{t' - t}. \qquad (7.65)$$

The actual boundary of the spectral functions will be determined from unitarity; it is shown schematically in Fig. 7.17. Only inside the shaded regions the ρ's are real and different from zero.

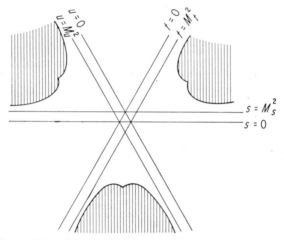

$$s = M_s^2$$
$$s = 0$$

Figure 7.17   Schematical region of the spectral functions.

b. Derivation of Single-Dispersion Relation from the Double-Dispersion Relation

Consider the physical region of the s-channels $s > M_s^2$, $t < 0$. In this region, using the relation

$$\frac{1}{x' - x - i\epsilon} = P\frac{1}{x' - x} + i\pi\,\delta(x' - x)$$

we may evaluate the imaginary part of the amplitude:

$$\mathrm{Im}\,A(s,t,u)\Big|_{\substack{s > M_s^2 \\ t < 0}} \equiv A_1(s,t,u) = \frac{1}{\pi}\int_{M_t^2}^{\infty} dt' \frac{\rho_{st}}{t' - t} + \frac{1}{\pi}\int_{M_u^2}^{\infty} du' \frac{\rho_{su}}{u' - u}. \qquad (7.66)$$

The function A_1 is real in this physical region; it can now be continued analytically by Eq. (7.66) outside this region where it will be in general complex. Similarly, we obtain A_2 and A_3 by

$$\text{Im}A(s,t,u)\Big|_{t>M_t^2} \equiv A_2(s,t,u)$$

$$= \frac{1}{\pi}\int_{M_s^2}^{\infty} ds'\, \frac{\rho_{st}}{s'-s} + \frac{1}{\pi}\int_{M_u^2}^{\infty} du'\, \frac{\rho_{ut}}{u'-u}, \qquad (7.67)$$

$$\text{Im}A(s,t,u)\Big|_{u>M_u^2} \equiv A_3(s,t,u)$$

$$= \frac{1}{\pi}\int_{M_s^2}^{\infty} ds'\, \frac{\rho_{su}}{s'-s} + \frac{1}{\pi}\int_{M_t^2}^{\infty} dt'\, \frac{\rho_{ut}}{t'-t}. \qquad (7.68)$$

It will be convenient to verify the double-dispersion relation. Consider the equation:

$u = $ fixed:

$$A(s,t,u) = \frac{1}{\pi}\int_{M_s^2}^{\infty} ds'\, \frac{A_1}{s'-s} + \frac{1}{\pi}\int_{M_t^2}^{\infty} dt'\, \frac{A_2}{t'-t}$$

and insert Eqs. (7.66) and (7.67) into this equation; we get the following four terms:

$$A(s,t,u) = \frac{1}{\pi^2}\int \frac{ds'}{s'-s}\int dt'\, \frac{\rho_{st}}{t'-(h-s'-u)} + \frac{1}{\pi^2}\int \frac{ds'}{s'-s}\int du'\, \frac{\rho_{su}}{u'-u}$$

$$+ \frac{1}{\pi^2}\int \frac{dt'}{t'-t}\int ds'\, \frac{\rho_{st}}{s'-(h-t'-u)} + \frac{1}{\pi^2}\int \frac{dt'}{t'-t}\int du'\, \frac{\rho_{ut}}{u'-u}.$$

The second and the fourth terms are those of Eq. (7.64). We combine first and third terms, because $s' - (h - t' - u) = t' - (h - s' - u) = (s' - s) + (t' - t)$ and

$$\frac{1}{s'-s+t'-t}\left(\frac{1}{s'-s} + \frac{1}{t'-t}\right) = \frac{1}{(s'-s)(t'-t)}.$$

The sum of the first and third terms is the remaining third term of Eq. (7.64). The other two single-dispersion relations may be treated in a similar way.

c. Consistency with Elastic Unitarity; Spectral Functions

We shall now determine the restrictions imposed by unitarity on the form of Eq. (7.64).

For $s < (3m)^2$ the unitarity in s-channel is (all masses equal, no spin)

$$A_1(s,t,u) = -\frac{1}{\pi}\sqrt{\frac{s-4m^2}{4s}}\int d^3\hat{n}\, A(s,t',u')A^*(s,t'',u'')$$

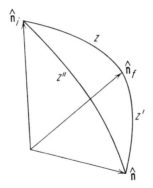

Figure 7.18   Unit vectors in the direction of momenta.

where (Fig. 7.18)

$$z' = \hat{n} \cdot \hat{n}_f, \qquad t' = -2q_s^2(1 - z'),$$
$$z'' = \hat{n} \cdot \hat{n}_i, \qquad t'' = -2q_s^2(1 - z''),$$
$$z = \hat{n}_i \cdot \hat{n}_f, \qquad t = -2q_s^2(1 - z).$$

In the left-hand side of the unitarity we express A_1 by Eq. (7.66) and in the right-hand side, under integral, we express the amplitudes by the fixed s, one-dimensional dispersion relation (7.55), and obtain

$$\frac{1}{\pi} \int dt' \frac{\rho_{st}}{t' - t} + \frac{1}{\pi} \int du' \frac{\rho_{su}}{u' - u}$$

$$= -\frac{1}{\pi} \sqrt{\frac{s - 4m^2}{4s}} \int d^3\hat{n}$$

$$\times \left[\frac{1}{\pi} \int dt_1 \frac{A_2(s, t_1, h - s - t_1)}{t_1 + 2q^2(1 - z_1)} + \frac{1}{\pi} \int du_1 \frac{A_3(s, h - s - u_1, u_1)}{u_1 + 2q^2(1 + z_1)} \right]$$

$$\times \left[\frac{1}{\pi} \int dt_2 \frac{A_2^*(s, t_2, h - s - t_2)}{t_2 + 2q^2(1 - z_2)} + \frac{1}{\pi} \int du_2 \frac{A_3^*(s, h - s - u_2, u_2)}{u_2 + 2q^2(1 + z_2)} \right]$$

$$(7.69)$$

Our method will be as follows. If we continue this equation to the region $t > 4m^2$ (or $u > 4m^2$, respectively), the imaginary part of the left-hand side gives us ρ_{st} (or ρ_{su}, respectively) so that the spectral functions are given by the imaginary part of the right-hand side. To calculate the imaginary part of the right-hand side for $t > 4m^2$ we have first to manipulate the integrals in such a way as to have denominators of the form $1/(t' - t)$ or $1/(u' - u)$.

The product of the terms on the right of Eq. (7.69) and the change of the order of integrations give integrals of the form

$$I = \int d^3\hat{n} \frac{1}{[t_1 + 2q^2(1 - z_1)][t_2 + 2q^2(1 - z_2)]}$$

$$= \frac{1}{(2q^2)^2} \int d^3\hat{n} \frac{1}{(\alpha_1 - z_1)(\alpha_2 - z_2)} \quad \text{with} \quad \alpha_i = 1 + \frac{t_i}{2q^2}, \qquad i = 1, 2.$$

Using the definite integral $(ab)^{-1} = \int_0^1 dx[ax + b(1 - x)]^{-2}$ we have

$$I = \frac{1}{(2q^2)^2} \int d^3\hat{n} \int_0^1 dx[\alpha_1 x + \alpha_2(1 - x) - (\hat{n}_i x + \hat{n}_f(1 - x)) \cdot \hat{n}]^{-2}.$$

We interchange the order of integrations, take the fixed vector $\hat{n}_i x + \hat{n}_f(1 - x)$ in the z-direction, and use the identity:

$$\int d^3\hat{n}[A + B \cos \theta]^{-2} = \frac{4\pi}{A^2 - B^2}$$

to obtain

$$I = \frac{4\pi}{(2q^2)^2} \int_0^1 dx[\{\alpha_1 x + \alpha_2(1 - x)\}^2 - \{2x(1 - x)(x - 1) + 1\}]^{-1}.$$

The quantity inside the square brackets can be written as $c(x + a)(x + b)$ and we get

$$c = \alpha_1^2 + \alpha_2^2 - 2\alpha_1\alpha_2 - 2(1 - z),$$
$$ca + cb = 2\alpha_2(\alpha_1 - \alpha_2) + 2(1 - z),$$
$$cab = \alpha_2^2 - 1,$$

and hence

$$\left.\begin{array}{c} ca \\ cb \end{array}\right\} = \alpha_2(\alpha_1 - \alpha_2) + (1 - z) \pm \sqrt{-K(z,\alpha_1,\alpha_2)}$$

where, as before,

$$K(z,\alpha_1,\alpha_2) = 1 - z^2 - \alpha_1^2 - \alpha_2^2 + 2\alpha_1\alpha_2 z.$$

Thus

$$I = \frac{4\pi}{(2q^2)^2} \int_0^1 dx[c(x + a)(x + b)]^{-1} = \frac{4\pi}{(2q^2)^2} \frac{1}{c(b - a)} \ln \frac{b + ab}{a + ab}$$

or

$$I = \frac{2\pi}{(2q^2)^2} \frac{1}{\sqrt{-K}} \ln \frac{\alpha_1\alpha_2 - z + \sqrt{-K}}{\alpha_1\alpha_2 - z - \sqrt{-K}}, \tag{7.70}$$

which can be written in a more symmetric form:

$$I = \frac{2\pi}{(2q^2)^2} \frac{1}{\sqrt{(z - z_+)(z - z_-)}} \ln \frac{z_+ + z_- - 2z + 2\sqrt{(z - z_+)(z - z_-)}}{z_+ + z_- - 2z - 2\sqrt{(z - z_+)(z - z_-)}}$$

with

$$z_\pm = \alpha_1\alpha_2 \pm \sqrt{(\alpha_1^2 - 1)(\alpha_2^2 - 1)}. \tag{7.71}$$

The integral I and therefore the right-hand side of Eq. (7.69) is analytic in z (or t) except the square root and logarithmic branch points. Because we want to write a dispersion relation for it in z (or t), we shall locate these singularities.

The factor $\sqrt{-K}$ has two branch points at z_- and z_+. If we choose the branch cut to run from z_- to z_+, then the square root is real and positive for real $z > z_+$ and $z < z_-$. For $z_- < z < z_+$, it is purely imaginary.

The logarithmic factor has the same branch points, $z_\pm$, due to the $\sqrt{-K}$ in the argument, plus a third branch point at infinity (the argument goes as

$1/z^2$ as $z \to \infty$). Between z_+ and ∞ the discontinuity of the logarithmus is $4\pi i$. (The real part of ln above and below the cut are equal, but the imaginary parts are $2\pi i$ and $-2\pi i$, respectively.)

Between z_- and z_+ the discontinuous of $\sqrt{(-K)}$ and ln actually cancel; the integral I is finite at z_-, as can be seen by expanding it around z_-, whereas it is infinite at z_+. Thus I is analytic in the z-plane cut from z_+ to ∞ with

$$\frac{1}{2i}[I(z + i\varepsilon) - I(z - i\varepsilon)] = \frac{1}{(2q^2)^2} \frac{4\pi}{\sqrt{-K}}, \quad z > z_+;$$

hence,

$$I = \frac{4\pi}{(2q^2)^2} \int_{z_+}^{\infty} \frac{dw}{w - z} \frac{1}{\sqrt{-K(w,\alpha_1,\alpha_2)}}. \tag{7.72}$$

We now transform Eq. (7.72) to the variable t and insert the values of $\alpha_i = 1 + t_i/2q^2$. We have

$$t_+ = -2q^2(1 - z_+)$$

$$= t_1 + t_2 + \frac{t_1 t_2}{2q^2} + 2\sqrt{t_1 t_2}\sqrt{\left(1 + \frac{t_1}{4q^2}\right)\left(1 + \frac{t_2}{4q^2}\right)}$$

$$\sqrt{-K(z,\alpha_1,\alpha_2)} = \frac{1}{2q^2}\left[t^2 + t_1^2 + t_2^2 - 2(tt_1 + tt_2 + t_1 t_2) - \frac{tt_1 t_2}{q^2}\right]^{\frac{1}{2}}$$

$$\equiv \frac{1}{2q^2}\sqrt{K'(q';t,t_1,t_2)}$$

and

$$I = \frac{4\pi}{(2q^2)} \int_{t_+}^{\infty} \frac{dt'}{t' - t} \frac{1}{\sqrt{K'(q';t',t_1,t_2)}}$$

$$= \frac{4\pi}{(2q^2)} \int_{4\mu^2}^{\infty} \frac{dt'}{t' - t} \frac{\theta(t' - t_+)}{\sqrt{K'(q';t',t_1,t_2)}}, \tag{7.73}$$

The other integrals in Eq. (7.69) are similar and we get

$$\frac{1}{\pi}\int_{4\mu^2}^{\infty} dt' \frac{\rho_{st}(s,t')}{t' - t} + \frac{1}{\pi}\int_{4\mu^2}^{\infty} du' \frac{\rho_{su}(s,u')}{u' - u}$$

$$= \lambda\theta(s - 4\mu^2) \frac{4\pi^2}{\sqrt{s(s - 4\mu^2)}}$$

$$\times \left\{\frac{1}{\pi}\int_{4\mu^2}^{\infty} \frac{dt'}{t' - t} \iint_{4\mu^2}^{\infty} dt_1\, dt_2 \frac{\theta[t' - t + (s,t_1,t_2)]}{\sqrt{K'(s;t',t_1,t_2)}}\right.$$

$$\times [A_2(s,t_1)A_2^*(s,t_2) + A_3(s,t_1)A_3^*(s,t_2)]$$

$$+ \frac{1}{\pi}\int_{4\mu^2}^{\infty} \frac{du'}{u' - u} \iint du_1\, du_2 \frac{\theta(u' - u + (s,t_1,t_2)]}{\sqrt{K'(s;u',u_1,u_2)}}$$

$$\times [A_2(s, K - u_1 - s, u_1)A_3^*(s, K - u_2 - s, u_2)$$

$$\left. + A_3(s, K - u_1 - s_1, u_1)A_3^*(s, K - u_2 - s, u_2)]\right\}.$$

Note that t_+ is just the root of K' and the θ-function means that we are integrating in the region of positive K'.

Now we can easily continue this equation to $t > 4\mu^2$ and take the imaginary part of both sides. We obtain

$$\rho_{st}(s,t) = \frac{-2\pi}{s(s - 4\mu^2)} \int\!\!\int_{4\mu^2}^{\infty} dt_1\, dt_2\, \frac{\theta(t - t_+)}{\sqrt{K(s;t,t_1,t_2)}}$$

$$\times\, [A_2(s,t_1)A_2^*(s,t_2) + A_3(s,t_1)A_3^*(s,t_2)]. \quad (7.74)$$

Similarly, for $u > 4\mu^2$,

$$\rho_{su}(s,t,u) = \frac{-2\pi}{s(s - 4\mu^2)} \int\!\!\int_{4\mu^2}^{\infty} du_1\, du_2\, \frac{\theta(u - u_+)}{\sqrt{K'(s;u,u_1,u_2)}}$$

$$\times\, [A_2(s,t_1,u_1)A_3^*(s,t_2,u_2) + A_3(s,t_1,u_1)A_3^*(s,t_2,u_2)]. \quad (7.75)$$

These equations are exact below the inelastic threshold. From Eq. (7.67) we see that the spectral function ρ_{st} gets also contribution from unitarity in t-channel. Therefore, if we start from the unitarity in t-channel and go through the steps (7.69)–(7.74) we will get an equation for ρ_{st} like Eq. (7.74) in which s and t are interchanged.

The θ-function in Eq. (7.74) gives us the boundary of ρ_{st}. Now t_+ is monotonically increasing in t_1 and t_2; therefore, the argument of θ-function, $t - t_+$, is maximum for the minimum value of t_1, t_2, which is $4\mu^2$. Hence we obtain

$$(t - t_+)_{\max} = t - \frac{16s\mu^2}{s - 4\mu^2}.$$

Similarly, from the unitarity in t-channel, we obtain the boundary

$$(s - s_+)_{\max} = s - \frac{16t\mu^2}{t - 4\mu^2}.$$

The boundaries of the spectral functions are given by the hyperbola $(t - t_+)_{\max} = 0$ and $(s - s_+)_{\max} = 0$, with asymptotes at $4\mu^2$ and $16\mu^2$ as shown in Fig. 7.19. The maximum of the hyperbola occurs at

$$\frac{dt}{ds} = \frac{16\mu^2}{s - 4\mu^2} - \frac{16s\mu^2}{(s - 4\mu^2)^2} = -1 \quad \text{or} \quad s_0 = 12\mu^2,$$

or $t_0 = 24\mu^2$ (and vice versa), which correspond to a tangent at $u = -32\mu^2$ (Fig. 7.19).

For $s > 9\mu^2$ (in the case of $\pi\pi$ problem for $s > 16\mu^2$ because the next intermediate state is 4π; see Chap. 10) we shall get contributions to ρ_{st} from the inelastic unitarity condition which is more difficult to evaluate. But below the inelastic threshold, (7.74) is exact as we have noted.

The discussion of the other two spectral functions is exactly the same.

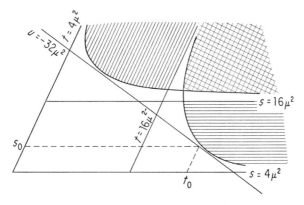

Figure 7.19   Spectral regions derived from elastic unitarity condition.

d. Special Case; Potential Scattering

We may at this point again comment about the special case of potential scattering, which is characterized by the fact that the two-body unitarity relation holds for all $s > 0$. Furthermore, we have a single channel s and no crossing relations. Consequently the single- and double-dispersion relations contain only one term and we have a single spectral function ρ_{st}:

$$A(s,t) = \frac{1}{\pi} \int ds' \, \frac{A_1(s',t)}{s' - s},$$

$$A(s,t) = \frac{1}{\pi^2} \int ds' \, dt' \, \frac{\rho(s',t')}{(s' - s)(t' - t)},$$

plus the bound state and subtraction terms.

The equation corresponding to Eq. (7.74) is now

$$\rho(s,t) = \text{const.} \int \int dt_1 \, dt_2 \, \frac{\theta(t - t_+)}{\sqrt{K'(s;t,t_1,t_2)}} \, A_1(s,t_1) A_1^*(s,t_2),$$

which is an integral equation for ρ:

$$\rho(s,t) = \text{const.} \int \int dt_1 \, dt_2 \, \frac{\theta(t - t_+)}{\sqrt{K'}} \left[\int dt' \, \frac{\rho(s,t')}{t' - t_1} \int dt'' \, \frac{\rho(s,t'')}{t'' - t_2} \right].$$

These equations have been indeed proved for a superposition of Yukawa potentials directly from the Schrödinger equation.[11]

If we have in addition an exchange potential we get the spectral function ρ_{su}, but the third spectral function is still absent.

---

[11] R. Blanckenbecler, M. L. Goldberger, N. N. Khuri, and S. B. Treiman, *Ann. Phys.*, **10**, 62 (1960); A. Bottino, A. M. Longoni, and T. Regge, *Nuovo Cimento*, **33**, 954 (1962).

Problems and Further Developments

1. Make principal axes transformations and write the unitarity Eq. (7.12) in terms of (a) principal axis of the ellipse $K = 0$, (b) an integral over a circle (transform the ellipse into a circle).

2. Comparing two forms of unitarity Eqs. (7.12) and (7.19), prove the identity

    $$\frac{1}{2\pi} \frac{\theta(1 - z^2 - z'^2 - z''^2 + 2zz'z'')}{\sqrt{1 - z^2 - z'^2 - z''^2 + 2zz'z''}} = \sum_{\ell} (2\ell + 1)P_{\ell}(z)P_{\ell}(z')P_{\ell}(z'').$$

    Prove also Eq. (7.29).

3. Consider the "triangle" approximation of Sec. 7.5 with $M^2 < m^2 + \mu^2$ (no anomalous threshold). Calculate the amplitude from Eqs. (7.48) and (7.46).

4. Discuss the *e-d* scattering in the approximation of Fig. 7.10 with the anomalous threshold given by Eq. (7.51). Evaluate the amplitude and the deuteron form factor.

5. Evaluate $g(t,z)$ given by Eq. (7.61), study its analytic continuation in z and write a dispersion integral for $Im A(t,z)$ in z, find the spectral function.

6. Discuss in the approximation of Sec. 7.6, the anomalous threshold when the mass M is increased in analogy to the discussion of Sec. 7.5. For the corresponding Feynman diagram, see R. Karplus, C. M. Sommerfield, and E. M. Wichman, *Phys. Rev.*, **114**, 376 (1959). As an example, obtain the following anomalous thresholds shown in Fig. 7.20. Here we have

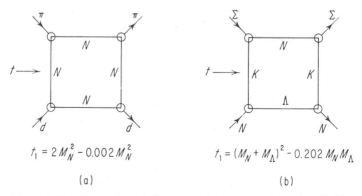

$$t_1 = 2 M_N^2 - 0.002 M_N^2$$

(a)

$$t_1 = (M_N + M_\Lambda)^2 - 0.202 M_N M_\Lambda$$

(b)

Figure 7.20   Examples of diagrams giving anomalous thresholds.

approximated the $\pi D \to NN$ amplitude by an N-pole in the πN-channel, the $\Sigma N \to N\Lambda$ by a K-pole in the ΣN-channel. The results are the same as those of corresponding Feynman diagrams.

7. Show from the unitarity relation written in the form

    $$A = \sqrt{\frac{s}{s - 4}} \, \eta e^{i\delta} \sin \delta,$$

where η is an inelasticity factor, $\eta = 1$ corresponds to elastic unitarity, that the real and imaginary parts of the amplitude can be described as shown in Fig. 7.21. Show the position of a resonance point.

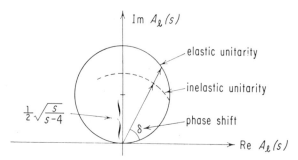

Figure 7.21 Unitarity limit of partial-wave amplitudes.

Do the same problem if η is introduced by the equation

$$A = \sqrt{\frac{s}{s-4}} \frac{\eta e^{2i\delta} - 1}{2i}.$$

8. Given the partial-wave S-matrix $s_\ell(k)$ for a scattering particle the wave function is of the form

$$\psi = \sum_\ell (2\ell + 1) P_\ell(\cos \theta) \left\{ s_\ell(k) \frac{e^{ikr}}{r} - \frac{e^{-ikr}}{r} (-1)^\ell \right\} e^{-i\omega t}.$$

Show that poles of the S-matrix at $k = ix, x > 0$ [or, because $s(k)s^*(k) = 1$, a zero at $k = -ix, x > 0$] correspond to a bound-state wave function behaving like e^{-xr}/r, $x > 0$, complex poles in the lower-half k-plane (zeros in the upper-half plane) to an exponentially decaying wave function, but complex poles in the upper-half plane (zeros in the lower-half k-plane) to a wave function which does not satisfy the continuity equation at $r = 0$; the wave is swallowed up (sink) or is created (source) at the center of force ($r = 0$).

CHAPTER 8

Approximate Determination of the Amplitude from Unitarity and Cauchy Relations

> The purpose of science is to achieve a more and more precise agreement of our knowledge with the reality....
>
> *Paul Langevin*

We discussed the contribution to unitarity of one and two-particle intermediate states, the normal (and anomalous) threshold singularities, and an analytic continuation of the amplitudes. We will now show that if the amplitude has no other singularities (or if other singularities can be neglected), and has suitable asymptotic behavior, it can be determined.

8.1 Pole Approximation

Consider a single-particle intermediate state in the unitarity relation, for definiteness the "pion pole" in the $N\bar{N}$-scattering (Fig. 8.1). The quantum

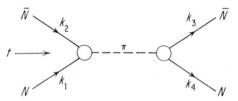

Figure 8.1 Contribution of the π-state to unitarity in NN-scattering.

numbers allow a single particle in the $N\bar{N}$-channel, but not in the NN-channel. Neglecting the spin and isospin for the moment, the unitarity is

$$M(t) + M^*(t) = -M_{N\bar{N}\pi}\rho_1 M^*_{N\bar{N}\pi} \qquad (8.1)$$

where $M_{N\bar{N}\pi}$ is the triangular amplitude (Fig. 8.2). For stable particles this is

126

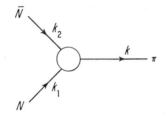

Figure 8.2 $N\bar{N}\pi$-vertex amplitude.

not a physical process ($\mu < 2M$). This amplitude can be considered to be a function of $k^2 = \mu^2$ alone and can be continued analytically; it is a number if all particles are on their mass shell. We are using the unitarity as an analytic equation below the physical threshold (extended unitarity).

The phase factor ρ_1 is singular at $t = \mu^2$:

$$\rho_1 = 4\pi\delta(t - \mu^2).$$

Hence with $M = 2\pi i A$,

$$Im A(t) = g^2\,\delta(t - \mu^2) \tag{8.2}$$

where

$$g^2 = \frac{1}{\pi}\, M_{N\bar{N}\pi} M_{N\bar{N}\pi}^*.$$

We want now to determine the amplitude to a first approximation so that it has the imaginary part given by Eq. (8.2). If the amplitude has no other singularities and goes to zero at infinity in the t-plane, we can write in this approximation, a Cauchy relation:

$$A(t) = \frac{1}{\pi}\int_{-\infty}^{\infty} \frac{Im A(t')}{t' - t}\, dt'. \tag{8.3}$$

Indeed the integral here converges and we do not need any subtractions so that our assumption about the asymptotic behavior of the amplitude to this order of approximation is a posteriori justified. Now we can solve Eqs. (8.2) and (8.3) and obtain[1]

$$A(t) = g^2/(\mu^2 - t). \tag{8.4}$$

Thus, in this approximation the amplitude consists of a simple pole term, a pole occurring in the unphysical region $t = \mu^2$. By crossing symmetry we can also use the approximate solution $A(t)$ in other channels. The s-channel, the

[1] Note that

$$Im \frac{1}{x' - x - i\varepsilon} = \pi\delta(x' - x)\frac{\varepsilon}{|\varepsilon|}.$$

For another derivation of the pole term, see M. L. Goldberger, Y. Nambu, and R. Oehme, *Ann. Phys.*, **2**, 226 (1957).

NN-scattering, amplitude is then obtained by an analytic continuation of Eq. (8.4):

$$A(s,t) = \frac{g^2}{\mu^2 - t} = \frac{g^2}{\mu^2 + 2q_s^2(1 - \cos\theta_s)}, \qquad t < 0, \qquad (8.5)$$

where q_s and θ_s are now center of mass momentum and scattering angle for NN-scattering.

We note at this point that in perturbation theory the NN-scattering amplitude due to the exchange of a single pion also leads to the pole term, Eq. (8.5). But there are renormalization effects so that g^2 in Eq. (8.5) corresponds to the renormalized coupling constant of the field theory. It is also interesting that with a Yukawa potential between the nucleons the nonrelativistic scattering amplitude in Born approximation (*not* the full scattering amplitude of the Yukawa potential) has also the form of a pole in the crossed channel:

$$f_{\text{Born}} = \frac{1}{4\pi}\int e^{i\mathbf{\Delta}\cdot\mathbf{r}}V(r)\,d\mathbf{r} = \frac{V_0}{4\pi}\int e^{i\mathbf{\Delta}\cdot\mathbf{r}}\frac{e^{-\mu r}}{r}\,d\mathbf{r} = \frac{V_0}{\mu^2 - t}. \qquad (8.6)$$

Thus the existence (or the exchange) of a single particle in the $N\bar{N}$-channel provides "forces" in the NN-channel.

Under what conditions is a single-pole term, Eq. (8.5), a reasonable approximation to the scattering amplitude? The pole of the amplitude in $\cos\theta$ occurs at the unphysical value

$$\cos\theta = 1 + \frac{\mu^2}{2q_s^2} \equiv X. \qquad (8.7)$$

We can then write

$$A(s,t) = \frac{g^2/2q^2}{X - \cos\theta} + R, \qquad (8.8)$$

where R is the remainder of the amplitude. Hence the corresponding differential cross section becomes

$$\frac{d\sigma}{d\Omega} = K(s)\left[\frac{(g^2/2q^2)^2}{(X - \cos\theta)^2} + \frac{2Rg^2/2q^2}{(X - \cos\theta)} + R^2\right], \qquad (8.9)$$

where $K(s)$ is the kinematical phase-space factor. If we plot

$$\frac{1}{K}[X - \cos\theta]^2\frac{d\sigma}{d\Omega}$$

as a function of $\cos\theta$ and extrapolate the experimental data to the point $\cos\theta = X$, the value at this point is proportional to the "coupling constant" g^2. The forward direction is the closest to the pole at X (Fig. 8.3).

An experimental fit of the NN-scattering by this method gives a value of g^2 very close to its value known from other instances.[2] In the actual analysis spin must be taken into effect.

[2] G. F. Chew, *Phys. Rev.*, **112**, 134 (1958); P. Cziffra and M. J. Moravcik, *Phys. Rev.*, **116**, 226 (1959).

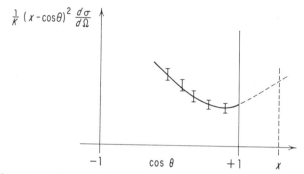

Figure 8.3 Extrapolation to the pole in the crossed channel.

We give below a few more examples of processes in which a pole term appears.

(1) Photon Pole in e^+e^--channel in electrodynamic processes and form factors (Fig. 8.4):

$$A = \frac{g_1 g_2}{t} F(s;t) \tag{8.10}$$

where $F(s;t)$ denote spin factors due to the spin of e and γ.

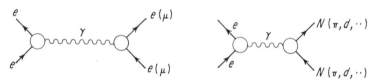

Figure 8.4 The photon pole.

(2) Neutron Pole in $\pi^+ p$-scattering. The pole is now in the u-channel of the process (Fig. 8.5) and because

$$u = -2q^2(1 + \cos \theta)$$

Figure 8.5 The nucleon pole.

we obtain

$$A = \frac{g^2}{u - M^2} = -\frac{g^2}{(2q^2 + M^2 + 2q^2 \cos \theta)}; \tag{8.11}$$

the pole in $\cos \theta$ occurs at $-1 - M^2/2q^2$, which is close to the *backward* direction.

(3) Pion Pole in NN-scattering (Fig. 8.6).   We have now poles on both t- and u-channels:
$$A = g_1^2/(t - \mu^2) + g_2^2/(u - \mu^2).$$

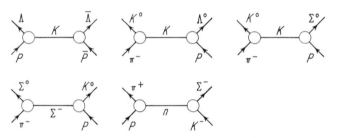

Figure 8.6   The pion-pole in t- and u-channels in np-scattering.

(4) Nucleon Pole in photoproduction:
$$\gamma + N \rightarrow N + \pi.$$

(5) Strange Particles (Fig. 8.7):

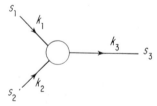

Figure 8.7   Examples of Born terms in strange-particle reactions.

8.2   Effect of Spin and Isospin

If spin is introduced we need the general form of the triode or vertex amplitude (Fig. 8.8).

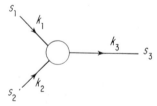

Figure 8.8   Vertex-amplitude with arbitrary spins.

Because this amplitude depends on the spin and parity of the three particles the pole approximation can be used to determine relative parities.[3]   (See

[3] This was first pointed out by J. G. Taylor, *Nucl. Phys.*, **9**, 357 (1959); *Phys. Rev.*, **116**, 768 (1959).

For a rough $\Sigma\Lambda$-parity determination by this method, see S. Iwao, *Nuovo Cimento*, **23**, 516 (1962). Relative parities are discussed in Sec. 10.1 (j).

Exercise 3.) For this purpose we must establish the general form of the amplitudes.

The scalar products which we can form out of k_1, k_2, k_3, are all numbers, functions of the masses, unless we make an analytic continuation in the masses. Therefore the scalar amplitudes A_i are all numbers. But we need the spin basis functions Y_i.

a. Exchange of a Spin ℓ Particle between Two Spinless Particles

Let us consider the very instructive case of an exchange of a particle with mass μ and integer spin ℓ in the t-channel (Fig. 8.9). We need for this purpose

Figure 8.9   Exchange of a spin ℓ particle.   **Figure 8.10** (00ℓ)-π vertex.

the amplitude for the vertex (00ℓ), Fig. 8.10. We have seen that for $\ell = 1$ the spin particle is described by the polarization vector ε_μ, so that the vertex amplitude is given by

$$M = g(k_1 + k_3) \cdot \varepsilon(k); \quad k = k_1 - k_2.$$
$$\varepsilon \cdot k = 0. \tag{8.12}$$

The $\ell = 2$ particle can be described by a tensor

$$\rho_{\mu\nu}^\alpha(k) = [112]_{mn}^\alpha \varepsilon_\mu^m(k)\varepsilon_\nu^n(k),$$

with

$$\rho_{\mu\nu}k^\nu = \rho_{\mu\nu}k^\mu = 0,$$

so that the vertex amplitude becomes

$$M = g(k_1 + k_3)^\mu (k_1 + k_3)^\nu \rho_{\mu\nu}(k). \tag{8.13}$$

This process can be continued to $\rho_{\mu\nu\sigma}(k) = [123]\rho_{\mu\nu}\varepsilon_\sigma$, and so on, so that in the general case we will get a tensor of rank ℓ and the vertex amplitude has the form

$$M = g(k_1 + k_3)^\mu (k_1 + k_3)^\nu \ldots \rho_{\mu\nu} \ldots (k). \tag{8.14}$$

For arbitrary ℓ there is always a single amplitude of parity $(-1)^\ell$ because the term $v^\mu \varepsilon_\mu$ has negative parity.

We now insert the vertex amplitude, Eq. (8.14), into the unitarity equation in the t-channel [shown schematically in Fig. 8.9]:

$$Im A(s,t) = 4\pi \, \delta(t - \mu^2) M_{f,1}(k_2, k_4) D^\ell\left(\frac{k \cdot \tilde{\sigma}}{m}\right) M_{i,1}(k_1, k_3). \tag{8.15}$$

In evaluating the right-hand side of this equation we notice that

$$\varepsilon_\mu(k)D^1\left(\frac{k\cdot\tilde{\sigma}}{m}\right)\varepsilon_\nu^\dagger(k) = g_{\mu\nu},\tag{8.16}$$

which follows from the definition of ε_μ and the decomposition of D^1 by Clebsch-Gordan coefficients.

If we take the products of Eq. (8.16) and use the orthogonality of the Clebsch-Gordan coefficients $[\ell_1\ell_2\ell]$, we can generalize it to

$$\rho_{\mu\nu}(k)D^2\left(\frac{k\cdot\tilde{\sigma}}{m}\right)\rho_{\mu'\nu'}^\dagger(k) = g_{\mu\mu'}g_{\nu\nu'}\tag{8.17}$$

and further to

$$\rho_{\mu\nu\ldots}(k)D^\ell\left(\frac{k\cdot\tilde{\sigma}}{m}\right)\rho_{\mu'\nu'\ldots}(k) = g_{\mu\mu'}g_{\nu\nu'\ldots}.\tag{8.17'}$$

Thus, using Eq. (8.17) and the unitarity, we have

$$\mathrm{Im}A(s,t) = 4\pi g^2\,\delta(t-\mu^2)[(k_1+k_3)\cdot(k_2+k_4)]^\ell.\tag{8.18}$$

Or, introducing the invariant variables s and t, we get, in the equal-mass case,

$$\mathrm{Im}A(s,t) = 4\pi g^2\,\delta(t-\mu^2)[2s+t-4m^2]^\ell$$

$$= 4\pi g^2\,\delta(t-\mu^2)(t-4m^2)^\ell\left[1+\frac{2s}{t-4m^2}\right]^\ell.\tag{8.19}$$

Again we use the Cauchy relation to obtain the amplitude $A(s,t)$ itself from its imaginary part, Eq. (8.19). Because now the imaginary part behaves like t^ℓ for large t, we must use *a dispersion relation with ℓ subtractions*:

$$A(s,t) = \frac{(t-t_0)^\ell}{\pi}\int\frac{\mathrm{Im}A(s,t')}{(t'-t_0)^\ell(t'-t)}\,dt' + \sum_{j=1}^{\ell-1}\frac{(t-t_0)^j}{j!}\,c_i(s)$$

$$= 4g^2(t-4m^2)^\ell\int\frac{\delta(t'-\mu^2)z_t^\ell}{(t'-t)}\,dt' + \sum_{j=1}^{\ell-1}\frac{(t-4m^2)^j}{j!}\,c_i(s)$$

$$z_t = 1+\frac{2s}{t-4m^2},\tag{8.20}$$

where we have chosen the subtractions point at $t_0 = 4m^2$. Now we can integrate this equation

$$A(s,t) = 4g^2(t-4m^2)^\ell\frac{z_t^\ell(t-\mu^2)}{\mu^2-t} + \sum_{j=1}^{\ell}\frac{(t-4m^2)^j}{j!}\,c_i(s).\tag{8.21}$$

The ℓ arbitrary subtraction constants must actually be all determined. Because the amplitude in the t-channel has the partial-wave expansion

$$A(s,t) = \sum_{\ell=0}^{\infty}(2\ell+1)A_\ell(t)P_\ell(z_t),$$

so that if a single partial-wave contributes with $A_\ell(t) = g^2/(t - \mu^2)$ the residue of the full amplitude at the pole is proportional to

$$P_\ell(z_t)|_{t=\mu^2}, \tag{8.22}$$

whose highest power is z_t^ℓ as in Eq. (8.21).

It is important to emphasize that in the use of the extended unitarity *the $\delta(t - \mu^2)$ factor in $\text{Im}A$, Eq. (8.19), has an operational significance.* We must use this δ-function only in the dispersion relation under the integral sign, as in Eq. (8.20). This is because $\delta(t - \mu^2)$ is nonanalytic; we use it symbolically.

b. Exchange of Spin $\frac{1}{2}$ Particle in Spin 0–Spin $\frac{1}{2}$ Scattering

Consider the case $S_1 = \frac{1}{2}$, $S_3 = \frac{1}{2}$, and $S_2 = 0$. The transformation equation of the M-function is the same as Eq. (4.16′). But because we have now only two linearly independent fourvectors (instead of four in the case of scattering of two particles into two), there are only two basis vectors of definite parity [see Eq. (5.9)]:

$$Y_1 = \left(\frac{k_3}{m_3} + \frac{k_1}{m_1}\right)\cdot\sigma, \quad\text{parity} +,$$

$$Y_2 = \left(\frac{k_3}{m_3} - \frac{k_1}{m_1}\right)\cdot\sigma, \quad\text{parity} -. \tag{8.23}$$

Y_3 and Y_4 give nothing new. Thus, for the N-pole in π-N problem, for example, we have (with parity conservation) from the unitarity condition (3.18)

$$M + M^* = -\rho_1 M_{f,1}\left(\frac{k_3}{m_3} - \frac{k}{m}\right)\cdot\sigma\,\frac{k\cdot\tilde\sigma}{m}\left(\frac{k}{m} - \frac{k_1}{m_1}\right)\cdot\sigma M_{i,2}^*.$$

For k we can take the symmetric form

$$k = \tfrac{1}{2}(k_1 + k_2 + k_3 + k_4).$$

The amplitude on the left consists of two terms so that

$$(A + A^*)\left(\frac{k_3}{m_3} + \frac{k_1}{m_1}\right)\cdot\sigma + (B + B^*)\frac{1}{2}\left(n\cdot\sigma + \frac{k_3}{m_3}\cdot\sigma n\cdot\tilde\sigma\,\frac{k_1}{m_1}\cdot\sigma\right)$$

$$= 4\pi\,\delta(u - m^2)g^2\left(\frac{k_3}{m_3} - \frac{k}{m}\right)\cdot\sigma\,\frac{k}{m}\cdot\tilde\sigma\left(\frac{k}{m}\cdot\sigma - \frac{k_1}{m_1}\cdot\sigma\right)$$

$$= 4\pi g^2\,\delta(u - m^2)\left(\frac{k_3}{m_3}\cdot\sigma\,\frac{k}{m}\cdot\tilde\sigma - 1\right)\left(\frac{k}{m}\cdot\sigma - \frac{k_1}{m_1}\cdot\sigma\right)$$

$$= 4\pi g^2\,\delta(u - m^2)\left[\frac{k_3}{m_3}\cdot\sigma + \frac{k_1}{m_1}\cdot\sigma - \frac{1}{2m}(k_1 + k_2 + k_3 + k_4)\cdot\sigma\right.$$

$$\left. - \frac{1}{2m}\frac{k_3}{m_3}\cdot\sigma(k_1 + k_2 + k_3 + k_4)\cdot\tilde\sigma\,\frac{k_1}{m_1}\cdot\sigma\right].$$

Or, if we introduce mass difference, we obtain

$$(A + A^*)\left(\frac{k_3}{m_3} + \frac{k_1}{m_1}\right)\cdot\sigma + (B + B^*)\frac{1}{2}\left(n\cdot\sigma + \frac{k_3}{m_3}\cdot\sigma n\cdot\tilde{\sigma}\frac{k_1}{m_1}\cdot\sigma\right)$$

$$= 4\pi g^2\,\delta(u - m^2)\left\{\frac{2m - m_1 - m_3}{2m}\left(\frac{k_3}{m_3} + \frac{k_1}{m_1}\right)\cdot\sigma\right.$$

$$\left. - \frac{1}{2m}\left[(k_2 + k_4)\cdot\sigma + \frac{k_3}{m_3}\cdot\sigma(k_2 + k_4)\cdot\tilde{\sigma}\frac{k_1}{m_1}\cdot\sigma\right]\right\}. \quad (8.24)$$

The above equation shows that if the masses of the fermions are the same only the B amplitude has the pole terms in the s- and u-channels; consequently, the pole approximation gives

$$B = \frac{g^2}{s - m^2} + \frac{g^2}{u - m^2}. \quad (8.25)$$

The odd parity of pions is responsible for this fact; if parity of pion were $+1$, we would get pole terms in both A and B. If the mass differences are taken into account (e.g., in the study of the electromagnetic corrections to strong interactions) the A amplitude has also a pole term proportional to Δm. It should be remarked that this term occurs with both signs depending on the process: positive for n exchange and negative for p exchange.

The isospin is easily taken into account. Only the amplitudes belonging to $I = I^j = $ isospin of the intermediate particle have the pole term. For example, in πN case, the $B^{(\frac{1}{2})}$ amplitude has the N-pole terms, $B^{(\frac{3}{2})}$ does not have.

8.3   Two-Body and Higher Intermediate State Approximations

We have seen that we can determine the amplitude approximately by taking in the unitarity the pole term alone and by assuming suitable asymptotic behavior and analyticity.

The next step would be to take the two-body intermediate state in the unitarity:

$$Im A_{if}(t,s) = \pi g^2\,\delta(t - \mu^2) + \int \rho_2 A_{f,2} A_{i,2}^*\,d\Omega. \quad (8.26)$$

Thus we take the first two nearby singularities, a pole, and a normal threshold branch point into account. Again, this equation is not sufficient to determine A_{if} itself. We need to know the analytic and the asymptotic behavior of A_{if}. If we can write, in addition to unitarity, a Cauchy or dispersion relations for A_{if}, then we have a possibility to determine it.

But, looking at Eq. (8.26), we see that there are other complications. The amplitudes $A_{f,2}$ and $A_{i,2}$ on the right are, in general, new amplitudes different from A_{if}. We must know these in order to use this equation for the determination of A_{if}. Quite generally, the unitarity condition relates one amplitude to many others:

$$Im A = f \quad \text{(other amplitudes)}. \quad (8.27)$$

We can write equations of this type for all other amplitudes and obtain a set of coupled equations. But because the left-hand sides are *ImA* and not *A* itself, the set of coupled equations is not complete unless the amplitudes are analytic functions. However, to establish analyticity and asymptotic behavior from unitarity we must consider the full unitarity condition. Very much short of this goal we try to make reasonable assumptions on analyticity and asymptotic behavior of each amplitude to solve the set of coupled Eq. (8.27). This is the basic idea behind the dispersion theoretical calculations.[4]

In the next chapter we shall discuss some connections between the asymptotic behavior of the amplitudes and the existence of bound states and resonances in crossed channels.

The approximations based on the one- and two-particle intermediate states can be qualitatively justified by the fact that the value of an analytic function at some point is in general determined by the *nearby singularities*. Thus at low energies the important singularities come from poles, threshold branch points, and possible resonance poles in the second sheet. The situation may be quite different at high energies.

Let us illustrate this approach by some examples to show the intimate coupling of all processes and the nature of approximations:

(1) $\gamma + N \rightarrow N + \pi$. The intermediate states of lowest masses are the one N-state and the π-N state. The pole term may be evaluated. Unitarity shows that the photoproduction amplitude is related to the πN elastic scattering amplitude. Thus, if we know, for example, by experiment the πN phase shifts at relevant energies, we get an integral equation for $\gamma N \rightarrow \pi N$ amplitude in terms of these phase shifts in this approximation. Indeed, a resonance in the π-N system, say the $I = \frac{3}{2}$, $J = \frac{3}{2}$ N^*-resonance at 1236 Bev (see Chap. 10), shows itself also in the photoproduction process.

(2) $K \rightarrow 2\pi$. The lowest intermediate state is the 2π-state. Hence, $K \rightarrow 2\pi$ amplitude is related to $\pi\pi$ elastic scattering amplitude:

$$Im[K \rightarrow 2\pi] = \lambda[K \rightarrow 2\pi][\pi\pi \rightarrow \pi\pi]^* + \cdots.$$

If the latter is known and under the assumed analyticity of the $K \rightarrow 2\pi$ amplitude in, say, m_K^2 we obtain an integral equation for the K-decay amplitude. The $K \rightarrow 2\pi$ coupling constant is the value of this amplitude on the mass shell.

(3) $\pi \rightarrow \mu + \nu$. An extremely good agreement with experiment has been obtained for this case,[5] even neglecting the lowest mass intermediate state of 3π. If we keep only the $N\overline{N}$ intermediate state, $Im(\pi \rightarrow \mu\nu)$ is related to $\pi \rightarrow N\overline{N}$ and $N\overline{N} \rightarrow \mu\nu$ amplitudes. Again neglecting 3π intermediate state,

[4] For a further general discussion of this philosophy, see G. F. Chew, *Strong Interactions of Elementary Particles* (New York: Benjamin, 1961); S. Mandelstam, *Reports on Progress of Physics* (London: Physical Society, 1962).

[5] M. L. Goldberger and S. Treiman, *Phys. Rev.*, **111**, 354 (1958).

$Im(\pi \to N\bar{N})$ is related to $\pi \to N\bar{N}$ and $N\bar{N} \to N\bar{N}$ amplitudes, and $Im(N\bar{N} \to \mu\nu)$ to $N\bar{N} \to \pi$ and $\pi \to \mu\nu$ amplitudes via one-pion intermediate state. These unitarity relations plus the analyticity assumptions allows one then to calculate the pion lifetime (Exercise 3).

Finally we discuss briefly three techniques of approximations for the determination of amplitudes from unitarity and analyticity.

(1) Successive Pole Approximation.   We approximate the amplitudes on the right-hand side of the unitarity equation successively by their pole terms. For example, in Eq. (8.26) the amplitudes $A_{f,2}$ and $A_{i,2}$ are themselves approximated by pole terms in s-, t-, or u-channels. In Secs. 7.5 and 7.6 we have discussed two important examples of approximations of this type. At that point we were interested in analyticity properties. The formula there can be carried a little further to obtain the amplitude itself. One can determine using unitarity and analyticity (in every order of unitarity) an expression for the amplitude as a series in the coupling constant which corresponds to the *renormalized* perturbation theory of quantum field theory with all the renormalization infinities being eliminated. It is expected that this approach will work well in the case of small coupling constants. We shall see in Chap. 13 how the theory of electromagnetic interactions can be developed entirely within the S-matrix theory, based on this successive pole approximation.

(2) Iteration of Unitarity and Analyticity.   Let us consider the two-body unitarity equation

$$Im A(t,s) = -\frac{1}{2\pi} \sqrt{\frac{t - 4m^2}{t}} \int dz_1 \, dz_2 \, A(t,z_1)A^*(t,z_2) \frac{\theta(K)}{\sqrt{K(z,z_1,z_2)}}.$$

We can start by taking a zeroth-order approximation to the amplitude, say a constant, to the right-hand side of this equation and then calculate the imaginary part of A, $Im A$. This imaginary part can now be introduced into the Cauchy relation:

$$A(t,s) = \frac{1}{\pi} \int \frac{Im A(t,s)}{t' - t}$$

to obtain A to this order. This is then the first-order approximation, which we can insert into the right-hand side of the unitarity equation, calculate $Im A$, then calculate A to second order from the Cauchy relation, and so on. Thus, by alternate use of the two equations above one can obtain an iterative solution for the amplitude.

(3) N/D Method.   This approximation technique uses partial-wave amplitudes and is discussed in detail in Chap. 11.

Problems and Further Developments

1. Consider the πN-scattering. Evaluate the contribution to the extended unitarity of a spin 1 particle (ρ-meson) in the t-channel, and of a spin $\frac{3}{2}$ particle (N^*) in the s- or u-channels. How many subtractions does one need to evaluate the amplitudes by Cauchy relations?

2. Discuss in more detail the lowest order unitarity approximations to the processes $\gamma N \rightarrow N\pi$, $K \rightarrow 2\pi$, $\pi \rightarrow \mu\nu$ discussed in Sec. 8.3.

3. Consider the Σ^+-pole in $\pi^- p \rightarrow \Sigma^0 K^0$ and N-pole in $K^- p \rightarrow \Sigma^- \pi$ and derive expressions for the contribution of these pole terms for (a) ΣN-parity even, (b) ΣN-parity odd. Obtain similar results for the pole terms shown in Fig. 8.7. Extrapolate the experimental results to the pole in an attempt to determine relative parities.

4. Show that the differential cross section is independent of the parity of the basis in Eq. (8.23) for the decay of a spin $\frac{1}{2}$ particle into a spin $\frac{1}{2}$ and spin 0 particle. (Minami ambiguity.)

5. Consider the reaction $\pi N \rightarrow \pi\pi N$. Evaluate the contribution of the π-pole in the channel $N\bar{N} \rightarrow \pi\pi\pi$ in terms of the $\pi\pi$-scattering amplitude, and that of the N-pole in the channel $\pi N \rightarrow \pi N\pi$ in terms of the πN elastic scattering amplitude.

CHAPTER 9

Asymptotic Properties and Bounds of the Amplitudes and Cross Sections

It is the *unknown* and the mysterious which attracts our attention.

R. Brauer

In the previous chapters we discussed approximate methods to solve the unitarity equation for two-body amplitudes by combining it with the Cauchy relations. In order to write the Cauchy relations, however, we must know (1) the distant singularities of the amplitudes (other than the poles and the threshold singularities), if there are any, (2) the asymptotic behavior of the amplitude for large complex values of the arguments. These are the two *unknown* features of the theory.

If there are complex singularities, then the usual simple forms of the dispersion relations must be modified. However, if such singularities are distant, we may neglect them at low-energy regions. But above all we need the nature of all threshold singularities, i.e., the discontinuities across the cuts corresponding to many-particle intermediate states.

With respect to the second point, one has to remark that if the amplitudes behave as polynomials at infinity, the Cauchy relations need subtraction terms; therefore arbitrary constants are introduced into the theory. In other words, we would not have unique solutions. Fortunately, it seems that the asymptotic behavior of the amplitude, hence the subtraction constants, are related to the parameters of bound states and resonances that the given quantum numbers allow. This is reasonable because, due to many-particle intermediate states, the dynamics, which determines the asymptotic behavior, is also responsible for the formation of bound states and resonances. And this fits very well into the spirit of self-consistency of the S-matrix approach.

In this chapter we shall then discuss the general features of the asymptotic behavior. which follow from unitarity and crossing relations (or self-consistency), as well as general upper and lower bounds for the amplitudes and cross sections.

9.1   Asymptotic Form of the Amplitude

a. Potential Scattering

We begin with the asymptotic form of the amplitude $A(s,t)$ in potential scattering where the complete solution is known. For a superposition of Yukawa potentials we have at high energies the following limit:

$$A(s,t) - A(s,t)_{\text{Born}} \xrightarrow[|s| \to \infty]{} 0, \qquad (9.1)$$

so that an unsubtracted dispersion relation holds; it is of the form [1]

$$A(s,t) - A_{\text{Born}}(s,t) = \sum_B \frac{\Gamma_B(t)}{s - s_B} + \frac{1}{\pi} \int_0^\infty ds' \frac{\text{Im}A(s',t)}{s' - s}, \qquad (9.2)$$

for fixed $t > 4\mu^2$. Here $1/\mu$ is the largest range of the Yukawa potentials, s_B the positions of the bound, states and $\Gamma_B(t)$ their residues; $s = 4q^2$ and $t = 2q^2(1 - \cos \theta)$ (nonrelativistic values). Note that the integral in Eq. (9.2) extends in general over the unphysical region $0 \leqslant s \leqslant -t$; the amplitude can be continued analytically by means of the Born series to this unphysical region if $t > 4\mu^2$. The Born term in Eq. (9.2) converges, however, only if $t > -\mu^2$.

For fixed s, the amplitude is analytic in the $\cos \theta$-plane cut from $\cos \theta = 1 + 8\mu^2/s$ to ∞. The Born term gives a pole at $1 + 4\mu^2/s$. In the variable t this means a fixed branch point at $t = 4\mu^2$ (for all s) and a cut going from $4\mu^2$ to ∞. The asymptotic behavior of the amplitude in t cannot be easily determined from the Born series. We will see that this behavior is connected with the existence of bound states and resonances, and one can see that if there are bound states and resonances, a behavior of the form $A(s,t) \xrightarrow[|t| \to \infty]{} 0$ is inconsistent so that, in general, one cannot write an unsubtracted dispersion relation in t. We see here a certain asymmetry of the variables s and t (there is, of course, no crossing symmetry in potential scattering) in such a way that pole terms in the variable s express themselves as symptotic polynomial terms in the variable t. We have discussed in Chaps. 7 and 8 the reason why Yukawa potentials show a behavior similar to the relativistic theory. In one and two particle approximations of the unitarity the amplitudes obtained can be interpreted as due to Born terms of an infinite superposition of Yukawa potentials.[2]

---

[1] This asymptotic form can ᵇe proved, e.g., from the integral form of the Schrödinger equation (7.33) or (7.35) by using the analyticity properties of the Fredholm equation in the parameter (see App. 7). N. N. Khuri, *Phys. Rev.*, **107**, 1148 (1957); A. Klein and C. Zemach, *Ann. Phys.*, **7**, 400 (1959); M. L. Goldberger in C. de Witt and R. Omnès (eds.), *Dispersion Relations and Elementary Particles* (New York: Wiley, 1961). See also Ref. 4, Chap. 7.

[2] Other type of potentials, such as square well, have quite different analytical properties in all variables than the Yukawa potential. This is connected with the nonanalyticity of the potential itself.

b. Watson-Sommerfeld Transformation

It is interesting that the most elegant and physically meaningful way to obtain the asymptotic behavior in t is by way of partial-wave amplitudes using a trick due to Sommerfeld.[3]

We consider scattering of two spinless equal-mass particles and transform, at first formally, the partial-wave expansion

$$A(s,t) = \sum_{\ell=0}^{\infty} (2\ell + 1)A(s,\ell)P_\ell\left(1 + \frac{2t}{s - 4}\right) \tag{9.3}$$

into a contour integral over C, which avoids all the possible poles of $A(s,\ell)$ as shown in Fig. 9.1. We then obtain

$$A(s,t) = \frac{1}{2i}\oint d\ell'\, \frac{(2\ell' + 1)A(s,\ell')P_{\ell'}\left(-1 - \dfrac{2t}{s - 4}\right)}{\sin \pi\ell'}, \tag{9.4}$$

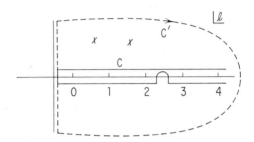

Figure 9.1   Sommerfeld-Watson contours C and C'.

assuming that we have continued analytically the function $A(s,\ell)$ from the positive integer values of ℓ to all complex values of ℓ.

If $A(s,\ell)$ is *meromorphic* in the half-plane $\mathrm{Re}\,\ell > -\frac{1}{2} + \varepsilon$ we can transform Eq. (9.4) into the new contour C' so that

$$A(s,t) = \frac{1}{2i}\oint_{C'} d\ell'(2\ell' + 1)\, \frac{A(s,\ell')P_{\ell'}\left(-1 - \dfrac{2t}{s - 4}\right)}{\sin \pi\ell'}$$

$$+ \sum_n \frac{\bar\beta_n(s)P_{\alpha_n(s)}\left(-1 - \dfrac{2t}{s - 4}\right)}{\sin \pi\alpha_n(s)}, \tag{9.5}$$

where the second term in Eq. (9.5) is due to the poles of $A(s,\ell)$ at $\alpha_n(s)$ inside C' for a fixed value of s with

$$\bar\beta_n(s) = 2[\alpha_n(s) + 1]\beta_n(s),$$

$$\beta_n(s) = \text{Residue } A(s,\ell). \tag{9.6}$$

[3] A. Sommerfeld, *Partial Differential Equations in Physics, Lectures in Theoretical Physics*, Vol. 6 (New York: Academic, 1949), p. 279; T. Regge, *Nuovo Cimento*, **14**, 951 (1959).

If, furthermore, the integral over the large semicircle of C' vanishes, Eq. (9.5) reduces to

$$A(s,t) = \frac{1}{2i} \int_{-\frac{1}{2}+\varepsilon-i\infty}^{-\frac{1}{2}+\varepsilon+i\infty} d\ell' \, \frac{(2\ell' + 1)A(s,\ell')P_{\ell'}\left(-1 - \dfrac{2t}{s-4}\right)}{\sin \pi\ell'}$$

$$+ \sum_n \frac{\bar{\beta}_n(s)P_{\alpha_n(s)}\left(-1 - \dfrac{2t}{s-4}\right)}{\sin \pi\alpha_n(s)}. \tag{9.7}$$

It is now easy to derive the asymptotic behavior of $A(s,t)$ for large t. Because $P_\nu(z) \xrightarrow[|z|\to\infty]{} z^\nu$; $|\arg z| < \pi$ (see App. 8), the t-dependence of the first integral in Eq. (9.7) is $t^{-\frac{1}{2}+\varepsilon}$, whereas if $a(s)$ is the pole with the largest real part, that pole term is going to give the dominant factor, and we obtain the desired result, under the conditions stated:

$$A(s,t) \xrightarrow[|t|\to\infty]{} t^{\alpha(s)}. \tag{9.8}$$

We remark that we perform in general first the Sommerfeld-Watson transformation in a limited region of t for which the large integral vanishes, and then continue the final result (9.7) analytically. The branch point in t-plane of the second term of Eq. (9.7) at $t = 0$ is only apparent; indeed if we take the discontinuity of Eq. (9.7) for $t < 0$ we get, using Eq. (9) of App. 8,

$$\text{disc. } A(s,t) = \frac{1}{2i} \int_{\text{Re}\,\ell = -\frac{1}{2}+\varepsilon} d\ell'(2\ell' + 1)A(s,\ell')P_{\ell'}\left(1 + \frac{2t}{s-4}\right)$$

$$+ \frac{1}{\pi} \sum_n \bar{\beta}_n P_{\alpha_n}\left(1 + \frac{2t}{s-4}\right)$$

$$= \frac{1}{2i\pi} \int_{\supset} d\ell'(2\ell' + 1)A(s,\ell')P_{\ell'}\left(-1 + \frac{2t}{s-4}\right); \quad t < 0, \tag{9.9}$$

where the integral is taken over the semicircle alone in the ℓ-plane. Because (App. 8, Eq. (19))

$$P_\ell(z) \xrightarrow[|\ell|\to\infty]{} \frac{1}{\sqrt{\ell}} \exp(\ell\xi'); \quad \xi' = \text{arc cosh } z$$

we see that, if

$$A(s,\ell) \xrightarrow[|\ell|\to\infty]{} \exp(-\ell\xi); \quad \xi = \text{arc cosh}\left(1 + \frac{8m^2}{s-4}\right), \tag{9.10}$$

the discontinuity Eq. (9.9) vanishes for $t < 4m^2$. Turning back to Eq. (9.5), we see furthermore that if Eq. (9.10) holds, the passage from Eq. (9.5) to Eq. (9.7) is also possible in a larger domain in t because the factor $1/\sin \pi\ell$ gives a further convergence factor $e^{-\pi|\ell|}$. The *asymptotic form (9.10) is thus very crucial for the exact position of the cut.*

At this point we may mention a modification of the representation (9.7) which separates pole terms in such a way that they have the correct cuts, if Eq. (9.10) is assumed.[4] This is achieved by inserting the representation

$$-\frac{\pi}{2}\frac{(2\ell + 1)P_\ell(z)}{\sin \pi\ell} = (2)^{-3/2}\int_{-\infty}^{\infty}\frac{e^{(\ell + \frac{1}{2})x}\sinh x}{(\cosh x + z)^{3/2}}\,dx \qquad (9.11)$$

$$-1 < Re\ell < 0$$

in Eq. (9.7). We obtain then, after changing the order of integration,

$$A(s,t) = -\frac{1}{\sqrt{2}}\int_{-\infty}^{\infty}\frac{\sinh x\,dx}{\left(\cosh x + 1 + \dfrac{2t}{s - 4}\right)}\frac{1}{2\pi i}\int_{Re\ell = -\frac{1}{2}}d\ell\,e^{(\ell + \frac{1}{2})x}A(s,\ell)$$

$$+ \sum_n \tilde{\beta}_n(s)P_{\alpha_n(s)}\left(-1 - \frac{2t}{s - 4}\right)\bigg/\sin \pi\alpha_n(s).$$

We split now the $\int_{-\infty}^{\infty}$ integration into $\int_{-\infty}^{\xi}$ and $\int_{\xi}^{\infty}$:

$$A(s,t) = -(2)^{-\frac{1}{2}}\int_{\xi}^{\infty}\frac{\sinh x\,dx}{\left(\cosh x + 1 + \dfrac{2t}{s - 4}\right)}\frac{1}{2\pi i}\int_{Re\ell = -\frac{1}{2}}d\ell\,e^{(\ell + \frac{1}{2})x}A(s,\ell)$$

$$- (2)^{-\frac{1}{2}}\int_{-\infty}^{\xi}\frac{\sinh x\,dx}{\left(\cosh x + 1 + \dfrac{2t}{s - 4}\right)}\frac{1}{2\pi i}\int_{Re\ell = -\frac{1}{2}}d\ell\,e^{(\ell + \frac{1}{2})x}A(s,\ell)$$

$$+ \sum_n \tilde{\beta}_n(s)P_{\alpha_n(s)}\left(-1 - \frac{2t}{s - 4}\right)\bigg/\sin \pi\alpha_n(s).$$

In the second term, $x < \xi$; hence by Eq. (9.10) the integral over ℓ converges and we can close the contour in the right-hand plane, thereby obtaining the poles of $A(s,\ell)$ in the right-hand ℓ-plane again:

$$A(s,t) = -(2)^{-\frac{1}{2}}\int_{\xi}^{\infty}\frac{\sinh x\,dx}{\left(\cosh x + 1 + \dfrac{2t}{s - 4}\right)}\frac{1}{2\pi i}\int_{Re\ell = -\frac{1}{2}}d\ell\,e^{(\ell + \frac{1}{2})x}A(s,\ell)$$

$$+ \sum_n \tilde{\beta}_n(s)\left[\frac{P_{\alpha_n(s)}\left(-1 - \dfrac{2t}{s - 4}\right)}{\sin \pi\alpha_n} - \frac{(2)^{-\frac{1}{2}}}{2\pi(\alpha_n + \frac{1}{2})}\right.$$

$$\left. \times \int_{-\infty}^{\xi}\frac{e^{(\alpha_n + \frac{1}{2})x}\sinh x\,dx}{\left(\cosh x + 1 + \dfrac{2t}{s - 4}\right)}\right]. \qquad (9.12)$$

In this representation both terms have now the correct branch points.

[4] N. N. Khuri, *Phys. Rev.*, **130**, 429 (1963).

c. Relation to Mandelstam Representation

It is clear from the previous discussion that the Watson-Sommerfeld transformation and the resultant Eq. (9.7) constitute at the same time an analytic continuation in z or t. For the original partial-wave expansion Eq. (9.3) converges within an ellipse in the z-plane with foci ± 1 and semimajor axes.[5] Thus

$$\tfrac{1}{2}(h \pm h^{-1})$$

where

$$h = \lim_{\ell \to \infty} \left| \frac{1}{A(\ell)} \right|^{1/\ell} = e^{\xi}$$

by Eq. (9.10), whereas the form (9.7) has the same domain of analyticity in z (or t) for fixed s as $P_\alpha(-z)$, i.e., the whole cut z-plane. The cut runs from $z = +1$ to $z = \infty$ (from $t = 0$ to $t = \infty$ for $(s - 4) > 0$). We have seen that under the asymptotic condition (9.10) the cut actually starts at $t = 4m^2$ for $(s - 4) > 0$. Due to the exchange potential there will be, as we shall see, a second term like Eq. (9.7) coming from the u-channel; this term will depend on $P_\ell(z)$ and give the left-hand cut of the amplitude in t.

Clearly if we can prove Eq. (9.7) for all s and the corresponding one in the t-channel (i.e., Watson-Sommerfeld transformation in the angular momentum plane of the crossed channel) for all s, we have proved the Mandelstam representation. But the converse is not true so that the Mandelstam representation holds under much weaker conditions than the Watson-Sommerfeld transformation. Thus to prove the Mandelstam representation by this method we must establish the limit (9.10) for all complex s and also the same in the crossed channel, $A(t,\ell)$ for all t.

The conclusions of this section rest, we repeat, on the following assumptions:

(i)   Analytic continuation of $A(s,\ell)$ from positive integers values of ℓ to complex ℓ.

(ii) Meromorphy of $A(s,\ell)$ in ℓ for $Re\,\ell > -\tfrac{1}{2}$.

(iii) Suitable asymptotic properties of $A(s,\ell)$ for large $|\ell|$, $Re\,\ell > N$ to ensure Watson-Sommerfeld transformation in some region of z; at least the validity of Eq. (9.10).

There is another basic motivation of introducing complex angular momenta. Although the partial-wave amplitudes $A_\ell(s)$ for all integers ℓ carry the same information in the region of convergence of the Legendre series as the full amplitude $A(s,t)$ for real s and t, it does not clearly contain as much information if both s and t are complex; we must go to complex ℓ to see the two-dimensional singular surfaces in the complex variables s and t.

We now discuss whether the above assumptions are realized.

---

[5] This is the so-called Lehmann ellipse (H. Lehmann, *Nuovo Cimento*, **10**, 579 (1958)) and is due to the Faber's theorem; E. T. Whittaker and G. N. Watson, *Modern Analysis* (New York: Cambridge U. P., 1952), p. 95.

d. Uniqueness of the Analytic Continuation in ℓ

A function given for positive integers cannot be uniquely continued into the complex plane, because the accumulation point of the integers, the infinity, does not, in general, belong to the domain of holomorphy of the function. In fact with $A(s,\ell)$, all functions of the form

$$A(s,\ell) + f(s,\ell) \sin \pi\ell, \tag{9.13}$$

for example, are also possible analytic continuations. One therefore needs to put further restrictions. We will now show that among all analytic continuations, there is *at most one* for which Watson-Sommerfeld transformation can be made[6]; there may be none.

Asymptotic properties along and to the right of a line which is parallel to the imaginary axis is rather restrictive for an analytic function. A holomorphic function $f(z)$ with the property that

$$|f(z)| < e^{-\lambda|z|}, \quad \lambda > 0$$

for $Rez \geqslant a \geqslant 0$ must be identically zero. The crucial point is along the line $Rez = a$, the imaginary axis. The scattering amplitude could not decrease that fast.

A function $f(z)$ holomorphic in $Rez > a$, satisfying $f(z) \rightarrow 0(e^{\lambda|z|})$ as $z \rightarrow \infty$ in $Rez \geqslant a$, with $\lambda < \pi$ and vanishing for positive integral z, vanishes identically according to Carlson's theorem (App. 6). Now the difference of two analytic continuations vanishes at positive integral ℓ. Consequently the requirement on the amplitude for a *unique* analytic continuation is

$$A(s,\ell) \xrightarrow[|\ell| \rightarrow \infty]{} 0(e^{\lambda|\ell|}); \quad \lambda < \pi, \quad Re\ell < N. \tag{9.14}$$

The limit $\lambda < \pi$ is also crucial; note that the term with $\sin \pi\ell$ in Eq. (9.13) behaves as $\exp(\pi|\ell|)$.

On the other hand, if we had started from two functions $A(s,\ell)$ and $A'(s,\ell)$ both satisfying the conditions of the Watson-Sommerfeld transformation, we can form the function

$$\frac{A(s,\ell) - A'(s,\ell)}{\ell - \ell_0} + A(s,\ell)$$

which also satisfies the same conditions. If $Re\ell_0 > Re\alpha$, we have for large z, an asymptotic behavior of the form

$$[A(s,\ell_0) - A'(s,\ell_0)](2\ell_0 + 1)z^{\ell_0}/(\sin \pi\ell_0).$$

Thus $A(s,\ell) = A'(s,\ell)$ for $Re\ell > ReN$; hence in the domain of meromorphy $A(s,\ell)$ is unique, if the amplitude $A(s,z)$ behaves as z^N uniformly in s.

---

[6] See also E. J. Squires, *Nuovo Cimento*, **25**, 242 (1962); G. Prosperi, *Nuovo Cimento*, **24**, 957 (1962).

e. Unitarity Relation for Complex ℓ

In Chap. 7 we have extended the unitarity to complex s. However, the unitarity condition for partial-wave amplitudes was written for physical ℓ values.

Now if $A(s,\ell)$ is holomorphic in some domain in the ℓ-plane, $A^*(s,\ell)$ is not. However $A^*(s,\ell^*)$ for fixed s is again holomorphic in ℓ. We can write, therefore, the elastic unitarity condition in the form

$$A(s,\ell) - A^*(s,\ell^*) = \text{const. } A(s,\ell)A^*(s,\ell^*); \quad 4 < s < s_{in}, \quad (9.15)$$

which for physical ℓ is the same as before. The function

$$f(s,\ell) \equiv A(s,\ell) - A^*(s,\ell^*) - \text{const. } A(s,\ell)A^*(s,\ell^*)$$

vanishes for positive integral ℓ values and behaves as $0(e^{\lambda|\ell|})$ for large ℓ as $A(s,\ell)$ does. Therefore it must vanish everywhere in the domain of holomorphy and the unitarity in the form of Eq. (9.15) holds for complex ℓ.

Combining Eq. (9.15) with the unitarity for complex s we have in general in terms of the second-sheet amplitudes

$$A^{(I)}(s,\ell) - A^{(II)}(s,\ell^*) = \text{const. } A^{(I)}(s,\ell)A^{II}(s,\ell^*). \quad (9.16)$$

It is important to realize that if ℓ is complex the unitarity takes us in the second sheet to the value ℓ^*.

f. Relation to Bound States and Resonances

Starting from representation Eq. (9.7) of the amplitude $A(s,t)$ we can now evaluate the physical partial-wave amplitudes by

$$A(s,\ell) = \frac{1}{2} \int_{-1}^{+1} dz\, A(s,t)P_\ell(z).$$

Inserting Eq. (9.7) into this equation and using the definite integral

$$\frac{1}{2} \int_{-1}^{+1} dz\, P_m(z)P_n(-z) = \frac{1}{\pi} \frac{\sin \pi\alpha}{(\alpha - m)(\alpha + m + 1)} \quad (9.17)$$

we obtain

$$A(s,\ell) = A_0(s,\ell) + \sum_n \frac{1}{\pi} \frac{(2\alpha_n + 1)\beta_n(s)}{(\alpha_n - \ell)(\alpha_n + \ell + 1)} \quad (9.18)$$

where the background term

$$A_0(s,\ell) = \frac{1}{2i\pi} \int_{Re\ell = -\frac{1}{2}} d\ell'(2\ell' + 1) \frac{A(s,\ell')}{(\ell' - \ell)(\ell' + \ell + 1)} \quad (9.19)$$

is holomorphic in ℓ. Equation (9.18) shows indeed the poles of $A(s,\ell)$ at $\ell = \alpha_n$ and could be obtained directly in ℓ-plane by means of Mittag-Leffler theorem (see App. 6). Indeed the Cauchy formula in the ℓ-plane in the form

$$A(s,\ell) = \frac{1}{2\pi i} \oint_c \frac{(2\ell' + 1)A(s,\ell')\, d\ell'}{(\ell + \ell' + 1)(\ell' - \ell)}$$

over a contour in which $A(s,\ell)$ is meromorphic gives Eq. (9.18). A similar formula holds in the s-plane (second sheet). As a matter of fact the resonance poles in the second sheet of energy and the poles in angular-momentum plane belong to the same two-dimensional singularity surfaces in the space of two complex variables s and ℓ. Their relationship is discussed toward the end of this chapter.

Turning back to Eq. (9.18), we expect $\alpha(s)$ to be real below threshold, then we obtain bound states if $\alpha(s)$ becomes equal to an integral value of ℓ; and that above threshold we expect $\alpha(s)$ to be complex. In the latter case, if $Re\alpha(s_0) = \ell$, using a linear expansion near s_0 of a single-pole term, we obtain, with $\alpha = \alpha_R + i\alpha_I$,

$$A(s,\ell)|_{\text{Pole}} = \frac{1}{\pi} \frac{\beta(s_0)[2\alpha(s_0) + 1]/(\alpha + \ell + 1)}{(s - s_0)\dfrac{d\alpha_R}{ds} + i\alpha_I(s)}, \qquad (9.20)$$

which has a resonance form of the Breit-Wigner type with width proportional to

$$\Gamma \propto \alpha_I \bigg/ \frac{d\alpha_R}{ds}. \qquad (9.21)$$

The resonance is sharp if α_I is small. When we consider the motion of a single pole as a function of energy, $\alpha(s)$, we will in general obtain a *family of bound states and resonances* all belonging to the same two-dimensional singularity surface.

The partial-wave projection of the representation (9.12) gives

$$A(s,\ell) = A'_0(s,\ell) - \sum_n \frac{(2\alpha + 1)\beta(s)e^{-(\alpha - \ell)\xi}}{(\alpha - \ell)}. \qquad (9.22)$$

Near a pole both Eqs. (9.18) and (9.22) give the same result qualitatively.

We shall derive some properties of the functions $\alpha(s)$ and $\beta(s)$ later on. It is clear that their form is closely related to the properties of possible bound states and resonances. Therefore, the asymptotic behavior of the amplitude in t,

$$A(s,t) \xrightarrow[|t| \to \infty]{} t^{\alpha(s)},$$

is determined essentially by these bound states and resonances. Similarly we have in the t-channel,

$$A(s,t) \xrightarrow[|s| \to \infty]{} s^{\alpha(t)},$$

so that the high-energy behavior in one channel is determined by certain low-energy parameters in crossed channels. This is an important result in the sense that there are no arbitrary subtraction parameters in dispersion relations, but these constants are intimately related to the existence of actual particles. If the amplitude in the relativistic case will turn out to be meromorphic in ℓ we can actually separate the divergent part and need only to consider unsubtracted dispersion relations.

g. Watson-Sommerfeld Transformation for Potential Scattering[7]

It has been shown first by Regge[8] that for a superposition of Yukawa potentials there is an analytic continuation of the amplitude in ℓ which is meromorphic for $Re\ell > -\frac{1}{2}$ and for which one can make the Watson-Sommerfeld transformation. Luckily this continuation is the same one as for integer ℓ (i.e., without the additional $f(s,\ell) \sin \pi\ell$ term (9.13)). For the asymptotic form in ℓ, Regge has used the Born approximation. It turns out that *all analytic potentials* $V(r)$ with r^2V bounded at $r = 0$ and $r = \infty$ have suitable asymptotic properties.[9] The analyticity of the potential plays an essential role; for example, for cutoff potentials, such as square well, no continuation will satisfy the Watson-Sommerfeld transformation,[10] for the amplitude has an essential singularity at infinity and is meromorphic (as seen by its explicit form).

The scattering amplitude for a large class of potentials is actually meromorphic in the whole ℓ-plane,[11] but we do not need at this point the properties of the amplitude in the left-hand plane.

The properties of the poles in the ℓ-plane, namely the positions $\alpha(s)$ and residue $\beta(s)$, have also been extensively studied for potential scattering.[10,12] We shall refer later in the discussion of the relativistic case to the corresponding situation in potential scattering. Here we may summarize that for analytic potentials [with $r^2V(r)$ bounded at $r = 0$ and $r = \infty$] all trajectories are bounded, they do not extend to infinity.[9] For $Re\ell > -\frac{1}{2}$, all trajectories for real s lie on the upper half-plane. The behavior of the poles in the left-hand ℓ-plane is much more complicated.[12] (See Fig. 9.2.)

h. Relativistic Case

The first problem is the definition of the proper analytic continuation in angular momentum. This problem is not trivial. For if we take the "natural" definition of the partial-wave amplitudes,

$$A'(s,\ell) = \frac{1}{2} \int_{-1}^{+1} dz \, A(s,z)P_\ell(z), \qquad (9.23)$$

---

[7] Much work has been done on complex angular momentum in potential scattering. Because we are using this case as an analogy or as a guide, we give here only a summary of relevant results. See the following monographs: M. Froissart and R. Omnés, *Mandelstam Theory and Regge Poles* (New York: Benjamin, 1963); S. Frautschi, *Regge Poles and S-Matrix Theory* (New York: Benjamin, 1963); E. J. Squires, *Complex Angular Momentum and Particle Physics* (New York: Benjamin, 1963); R. Newton, *Complex Angular Momentum Plane* (New York: Benjamin, 1964).

[8] T. Regge, *Nuovo Cimento*, **14**, 951 (1959); **18**, 947 (1960); A. Bottino, A. M. Longoni, and T. Regge, *Nuovo Cimento*, **23**, 954 (1962). For the crucial asymptotic behavior along the imaginary axis in the ℓ-plane, see F. Calogero, *Nuovo Cimento*, **28**, 761 (1963).

[9] A. O. Barut and J. Dilley, *J. Math. Phys.*, **4**, 1401 (1963).

[10] For a detailed study of these potentials, see A. O. Barut and F. Calogero, *Phys. Rev.*, **128**, 1383 (1962).

[11] M. Froissart, *J. Math. Phys.*, **3**, 922 (1962); H. Cheng, *Phys. Rev.*, **127**, 647 (1962); S. Mandelstam, *Ann. Phys.*, **21**, 302 (1963).

[12] A. Ahmadzadeh, P. Burke, and C. Tate, *Phys. Rev.*, **131**, 1315 (1963); C. Lovelace and D. Mason, *Nuovo Cimento*, **26**, 472 (1962).

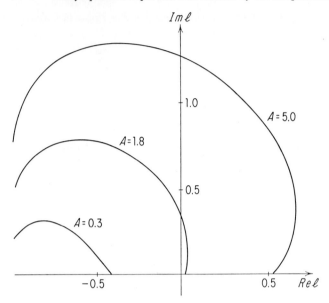

Figure 9.2   The leading trajectories for a single Yukawa potential, $V(r) = -Ae^{-r}/r$. (A. Ahmadzadeh, P. C. Burke, and C. Tate, *Phys. Rev.* **131**, 1315, (1963).)

the integral is over a finite region where both A and P_ℓ are regular, and we obtain a holomorphic function $A(s,\ell)$ in the whole ℓ-plane. This function has, however, an essential singularity at $|\ell| = \infty$ just as P_ℓ so that the Watson-Sommerfeld transformation and the resultant conclusions are not applicable. The proper analytic continuation for which this transformation is possible must differ from Eq. (9.23) by a term of the type $f(s,\ell) \sin \pi\ell$ or $f(s,\ell)/\Gamma(-\ell)$ to cancel the essential singularity of Eq. (9.23).

If the Mandelstam representation holds there is another representation of the partial-wave amplitudes which is equivalent to Eq. (9.23) for integer ℓ:

$$A(s,\ell) = \frac{1}{\pi} \int_{z_0}^{\infty} dz\, [A_2(s,z) + (-1)^\ell A_3(s,z)] Q_\ell(z). \tag{9.24}$$

To prove Eq. (9.24) we first rewrite Eq. (9.23) in terms of s and t:

$$A(s,\ell) = \frac{1}{s - 4\mu^2} \int_{-(s-4\mu^2)}^{0} dt\, A(s,t,u) P_\ell\left(1 + \frac{2t}{s-4}\right)$$

$$= \frac{1}{s - 4\mu^2} \int_{-(s-4\mu^2)}^{0} du\, A(s,t,u) P_\ell\left(-1 - \frac{2u}{s-4}\right)$$

$$= \frac{1}{4v} \int_{-4v}^{0} dt\, A(s,t) P_\ell(1 + t/2v). \tag{9.23'}$$

If we use now a fixed s (energy) dispersion relation for $A(s,t,u)$ as discussed in Chap. 7, i.e.,

$$A(s,t,u) = \frac{1}{\pi}\int dt' \frac{A_2(s,t',u')}{(t'-t)} + \frac{1}{\pi}\int du' \frac{A_3(s,t',u')}{(u'-u)},$$

and insert this in Eq. (9.23'), we obtain

$$A(s,\ell) = \frac{1}{(s-4\mu^2)}\int_{-(s-4\mu^2)}^{0} dt\, P_\ell\!\left(1 + \frac{2t}{s-4\mu^2}\right)$$

$$\times \left\{\frac{1}{\pi}\int_{4\mu^2}^{\infty} dt' \frac{A_2(s,t',u')}{(t'-t)} + \frac{1}{\pi}\int_{4\mu^2}^{\infty} du' \frac{A_3(s,t',u')}{(u'-u)}\right\}.$$

We then use the identity[13]

$$\frac{1}{t'-t} = \sum_{\ell=0}^{\infty} (2\ell+1)P_\ell(t)Q_\ell(t')$$

$$= \frac{2}{s-4\mu^2}\sum_\ell (2\ell+1)P_\ell\!\left(1+\frac{2t}{s-4\mu^2}\right)Q_\ell\!\left(1+\frac{2t'}{s-4\mu^2}\right) \quad (9.23'')$$

where $Q_\ell(t)$ is the Legendre function of the second kind with the properties[14] (see App. 8):

$$Q_\ell(-z) = -e^{\pm i\pi\ell}Q_\ell(z) \quad \text{according to } Imz \lessgtr 0$$

and

$$\frac{1}{2}\int_{-1}^{+1} \frac{P_\ell(t)\,dt}{t'-t} = Q_\ell(t'),$$

or

$$\frac{1}{s-4\mu^2}\int_{-(s-4\mu^2)}^{0} dt\, \frac{P_\ell\!\left(1+\dfrac{2t}{s-4\mu^2}\right)}{t'-t} = Q_\ell\!\left(1+\frac{2t'}{s-4\mu^2}\right),$$

and the similar result in the u-variable

$$\frac{1}{s-4\mu^2}\int_{-(s-\mu^2)}^{0} dt\, \frac{P_\ell\!\left(1+\dfrac{2t}{s-4\mu^2}\right)}{u'-u} = -Q_\ell\!\left(-1-\frac{2u'}{s-4\mu^2}\right),$$

we obtain finally the desired result:[15]

[13] E.T. Whittaker and G. N. Watson, *Modern Analysis*, 4th ed. (New York: Cambridge U. P., 1958), pp. 302ff.
   This formula is valid for t inside an ellipse passing through t' with foci ±1 and the expansion converges in t' for fixed t.
[14] *Ibid*. This so-called Neumann's formula is valid for ℓ a positive integer and for all t' except when t' is real and between $(-1,+1)$.
[15] Note that

$$\frac{1}{u'-u} = \frac{1}{u'-(4\mu^2-s-t)} = \frac{2}{s-4\mu^2}\frac{1}{1+\dfrac{2t}{s-4\mu^2}-\left(-1-\dfrac{2u'}{s-4}\right)}.$$

$$A(s,\ell) = \frac{2}{\pi}\left\{\int_{4\mu^2}^{\infty}\frac{dt}{s-4\mu^2}\,A_2(s,t,4-s-t)Q_\ell\left(1+\frac{2t}{s-4}\right)\right.$$

$$\left. + (-1)^\ell\int_{4\mu^2}^{\infty}\frac{du}{s-4}\,A_3(s,u)Q_\ell\left(1+\frac{2u}{s-4}\right)\right\}$$

$$= \frac{1}{\pi}\int_{z_0}^{\infty}dz\{A_2(s,z)+(-1)^\ell A_3(s,z)\}Q_\ell(z). \tag{9.24}$$

In Eq. (9.24) $z_0 = 1 + (8m^2/s - 4)$ and A_2 and A_3 are the absorptive parts of the amplitudes in the t- and u-channels respectively. This equation is also valid even if we start from a fixed energy-dispersion relation with N subtractions. In that case A_2 and A_3 behave as t^N and u^N, respectively, for large t and u. Consequently, because

$$Q_\ell\left(1+\frac{2t}{s-4}\right)\xrightarrow[|t|\to\infty]{}t^{-(\ell+1)},$$

Eq. (9.24) defines a holomorphic function in ℓ for $\mathrm{Re}\,\ell > N$. The function Q_ℓ decreases exponentially for large $|\ell|$ in the right-hand plane [App. 8, Eq. (20)]:

$$Q_\ell(z)\xrightarrow[|\ell|\to\infty]{}\frac{1}{\sqrt{\ell}}\,e^{-(\ell+\frac{1}{2})\xi};\quad \xi = \cosh^{-1}z. \tag{9.25}$$

The factor $(-1)^\ell$ in Eq. (8.24) is seemingly disastrous for large complex ℓ. One can however introduce two amplitudes $A^\pm$ for values of $(-1)^\ell = \pm 1$ and continue analytically these two amplitudes.[16] We shall proceed differently.

We start again from the partial-wave expansion with Eq. (9.24) written for positive integers ℓ:

$$A(s,z) = \sum_\ell (2\ell+1)P_\ell(z)\left[\frac{1}{\pi}\int_{z_0}^{\infty}dz'\,A_2(s,z')Q_\ell(z')\right.$$

$$\left. + (-1)^\ell\frac{1}{\pi}\int dz'\,A_3(s,z')Q_\ell(z')\right]$$

or

$$A(s,t) = \sum_\ell (2\ell+1)\frac{1}{\pi}\int_{z_0}^{\infty}dz'\,Q_\ell(z')[A_2(s,z')P_\ell(z)+A_3(s,z')P_\ell(-z)]. \tag{9.26}$$

We now perform the Watson-Sommerfeld transformation on both terms separately. There is a region of the z-plane such that if the Watson-Sommerfeld transformation is possible with $P_\ell(z)$ it is also possible with $P_\ell(-z)$. We then have

$$A(s,t) = \frac{1}{2i}\int_{\mathrm{Re}\,\ell = -\frac{1}{2}}d\ell\,\frac{(2\ell+1)}{\sin\pi\ell}\,[A_t(s,\ell)P_\ell(-z)+A_u(s,\ell)P_\ell(z)]$$

$$+ \sum_n\left\{\frac{\beta_t(s)}{\sin\pi\alpha_n^t}\,P_{\alpha^t}(-z)+\frac{\beta_u(s)}{\sin\pi\alpha_n^u}\,P_{\alpha^u}(z)\right\} \tag{9.27}$$

---

[16] It has been implied that this is the reason of the *J*-parity (or *signature*). See, e.g., E. J. Squires, *Nuovo Cimento*, **25**, 242 (1963); V. Singh, *Phys. Rev.*, **129**, 1889 (1963).

where we have introduced the amplitudes

$$A_t(s,\ell) \equiv \frac{1}{\pi} \int_{z_0}^{\infty} dz \; Q_\ell(z) A_2(s,z)$$
_u

and

$$A(s,\ell) = A_t(s,\ell) + (-1)^\ell A_u(s,\ell).$$

We will now show that $A_t(s,\ell)$ and $A_u(s,\ell)$ have the same poles and residues with either equal and opposite sign of the residues as a result of unitarity. If we define the amplitudes

$$A^\pm(s,\ell) = A_t(s,\ell) \pm A_u(s,\ell), \tag{9.28}$$

then the unitarity separates for A^+ and A^- and not for $A_t(s,\ell)$ and $A_u(s,\ell)$. In the elastic region one has

$$\begin{aligned}
ImA^+ &= \lambda|A^+|^2, \\
ImA^- &= \lambda|A^-|^2.
\end{aligned} \tag{9.29}$$

It is thus natural that A^+ and A^- will have in general distinct poles as they are two disjoint amplitudes. Consequently the amplitudes

$$\begin{aligned}
A_t(s,\ell) &= \tfrac{1}{2}(A^+ + A^-), \\
A_u(s,\ell) &= \tfrac{1}{2}(A^+ - A^-),
\end{aligned}$$

have the same poles with the same residue if it is a pole of A^+ and with the opposite sign of residues if it is a pole of A^-. The point we want to make here is that not the analytic continuation in ℓ, but the unitarity condition necessitates consideration of the two amplitudes A^+ and A^-.

Equation (9.18) becomes then

$$A(s,t) = \frac{1}{2i} \int d\ell \frac{2\ell + 1}{\sin \pi\ell} \{A_t(s,\ell)P_\ell(-z) + A_u(s,\ell)P_\ell(z)\}$$

$$+ \sum_n \frac{\beta_n(s)}{\sin \pi\alpha_n(s)} \{P_{\alpha_n}(-z) \pm P_{\alpha_n}(z)\}. \tag{9.30}$$

Here, $+$ sign has to be taken if the pole is in A^+ and $-$ sign if the pole is in A^-. We have also

$$\begin{aligned}
A(s,\ell) &= A^+(s,\ell) \quad \text{for} \quad \ell = \text{even}, \\
A(s,\ell) &= A^-(s,\ell) \quad \text{for} \quad \ell = \text{odd}.
\end{aligned} \tag{9.31}$$

Note that A^+ is not zero at odd integers, nor is A^- at even integers; they are simply not physical. Also we could not take the amplitude, say, at even integers alone and obtain an analytic continuation; one gets a factor $\sin \pi\ell/2$ in the Sommerfeld transformation which is not sufficient for convergence.

The existence of independent poles in A^+ and A^- and Eq. (9.20) implies two trajectories $\alpha^+(s)$ and $\alpha^-(s)$ for the same quantum numbers. These two trajectories may be distinguished by the so-called signature (or J-parity), $+$ for poles of A^+, and $-$ for poles of A^-. Along the $+$ signature trajectory only $\ell = 0, 2, 4, \ldots$, points are physical particles or resonances, and along $(-)$ signature trajectory only $\ell = 1, 3, 5, \ldots$.

9.2 Asymptotic Behavior of the Cross Sections

We shall discuss now the relations between the asymptotic form of the cross section and the assumed asymptotic behavior of the amplitudes determined by the exchange of a pole in the crossed channels.

a. *Constant Total Cross Section and Pure Imaginary Forward-Scattering Amplitude*

On the basis of a single-pole term of the type (9.19) the asymptotic behavior of the amplitude in momentum transfer is

$$A(s,t) \xrightarrow[|t| \to \infty]{} \frac{\beta(s)}{\sin \pi\alpha(s)} \left[u^{\alpha(s)} \pm t^{\alpha(s)}\right]\left(\frac{2}{s-4}\right)^{\alpha(s)}$$

$$= \frac{\beta(s)}{\sin \pi\alpha(s)} \, t^{\alpha(s)}\left[-e^{i\pi\alpha(s)} \pm 1\right]\left(\frac{2}{s-4}\right)^{\alpha(s)}. \quad (9.32)$$

By crossing symmetry the asymptotic behavior in energy is determined by the poles in angular momentum in the t-channel:

$$A(s,t) \xrightarrow[|s| \to \infty]{} \frac{\beta(t)}{\sin \pi\alpha(t)} \, s^{\alpha(t)}\left[-e^{i\pi\alpha(t)} \pm 1\right]\left(\frac{2}{t-4}\right)^{\alpha(t)}$$

$$\equiv f(t)s^{\alpha(t)}. \quad (9.33)$$

First let us, phenomenologically, see what this form implies for the cross section. Near the forward direction, $t \cong 0$, and writing

$$\alpha(t) = 1 + \varepsilon t \quad (9.34)$$

to ensure a constant total cross section,[17] we have

$$A(s,t) \xrightarrow[|s| \to \infty]{} \frac{\beta(t)}{-\pi\varepsilon t} \frac{s^{1+\varepsilon t}}{(-2)^{1+\varepsilon t}} \left[-(1 + \pi i\varepsilon t) \pm 1\right].$$

The $+$ signature gives

$$A(s,t) \xrightarrow[|s| \to \infty]{} \frac{i\beta(t)s^{1+\varepsilon t}}{(-2)^{1+\varepsilon t}}, \quad (9.35)$$

---

[17] Experimentally the total cross sections up to 20 Gev are either constants (such as K^+n, K^+p), or are approaching a constant value logarithmically or with a very small exponent ($K^-n, K^-p, \pi^+p, pp, pn, \bar{p}p, \bar{p}n$). The ratio $\mathrm{Re}\,A(s,0)/\mathrm{Im}\,A(s,0)$ has been estimated from Coulomb interference effects $[d\sigma/d\Omega = |A_{\mathrm{coul}} + A|^2]$ to be about -0.2 to -0.3 for πp-scattering in the momentum range between 8 to 20 Bev/c: see S. Foley et al., *Phys. Rev. Letters*, **14**, 863 (1965).

so that in the forward direction the amplitude in this approximation is *purely imaginary*:

$$A(s,0) = \frac{i\beta(0)}{-2} s. \tag{9.36}$$

And, if $\beta(0)$ is real, we find from the optical theorem

$$Im A(s,0) = \beta\sigma_{\text{tot}}, \quad \beta = 4\pi/q\sqrt{s}, \quad \sigma_{\text{tot}} = -\tfrac{1}{2}\beta(0)$$

and [17]

$$Re A(s,0) \xrightarrow[|s|\to\infty]{} 0. \tag{9.37}$$

The $-$ signature pole term blows up at $t = 0$. We conclude, therefore, that the constant cross sections at infinity may be consistently and *phenomenologically* described by a leading trajectory of $+$ signature with $\beta(0) = 1$, the so-called Pomeranchuk-Regge trajectory. Because, however, the high energy behavior is the result of a large number of inelastic processes we can view this trajectory as an elegant "summary" of all these inelastic effects; it may not correspond to a trajectory of particles.

b. Pomeranchuk Theorem

The above form is also consistent with the Pomeranchuk theorems about the equality of particle and antiparticle cross sections.[18] We shall now show that if we carry the above analysis with isospin for $\pi\pi$, for example, we find easily the equality of $\pi^{\pm,0}$ total cross sections.

If the elastic forward-diffraction peak is due to the exchange of some "signal" in the t-channel with quantum numbers of the vacuum, i.e., in particular with $I = 0$, the amplitudes belonging to total isotopic spin I are given by (these formulas will be derived in Chap. 11):

$$
\begin{aligned}
s\text{-channel:} \quad & A^0 = 3A + B + C \\
& A^1 = B - C \\
& A^2 = B + C \\
t\text{-channel:} \quad & A^0 = 3B + A + C \\
& A^1 = A - C \\
& A^2 = A + C \\
u\text{-channel:} \quad & A^0 = 3C + B + A \\
& A^1 = B - A \\
& A^2 = B + A.
\end{aligned}
$$

A pole term which would contribute in the t-channel to A^0 only must be in the B-amplitude and not in A and C. Thus in the s-channel at high energies we get

$$A^0(s,0) = A^1(s,0) = A^2(s,0) \to -i\beta(0)\frac{s}{2},$$

$$\sigma_{\text{tot}}^0 = \sigma_{\text{tot}}^1 = \sigma_{\text{tot}}^2 \to -\tfrac{1}{2}\beta(0).$$

[18] I. Ya. Pomeranchuk, *JETP*, **7**, 499 (1958). More generally [without the assumption (9.32)] the Pomeranchuk theorem has been proved by additional assumptions on the difference of particle and antiparticle amplitudes at high energies. For a recent discussion and other references see R. J. Eden, *Phys. Rev. Lett.*, **16**, 39 (1966).

Similarly, for backward-diffraction peak, only C-amplitude contributes to $I = 0$ part of the u-channel and we get[19]

$$A^0(s, u = 0) = -A^1(s, u = 0) = A^2(s, u = 0).$$

c. Diffraction Peak

Let us now consider the elastic cross section near the diffraction peak. From Eq. (9.33) we obtain

$$\sigma_{\text{elastic}}(s,t) = \frac{1}{s^2}|A(s,t)|^2 \xrightarrow[s \to \infty]{} |f^2(t)|^2 s^{2\alpha(t)-2}$$
$$= |f(t)|^2 s^{2\varepsilon t} = |f(t)|^2 e^{2\varepsilon t \log s}. \tag{9.38}$$

We have here the exponential decrease in t (in the physical region $t < 0$) and at the same time a dependence of the width of the diffraction peak on s. The larger the energy the smaller is the width: the peak shrinks. This last conclusion is peculiar to our hypothesis that the asymptotic cross section is given by a pole in angular momentum. We recall that the quantum mechanical scattering from a rigid sphere of radius a gives

$$\sigma_{\text{tot}} \xrightarrow[s \to \infty]{} 2\pi a^2,$$

$$\sigma_{\text{elast}} \to \tfrac{1}{4}a^2\left[1 + \cot^2\frac{\theta}{2} J_1(ka\sin\theta)\right] \simeq \frac{a^2}{4}\left[1 + \frac{4k^2}{t}J_1\left(\frac{a}{t}\right)\right] = \frac{a^2}{4}\left[1 - \frac{2k^2 a}{\sqrt{t}}\right].$$

Hence

$$\frac{d\sigma_{\text{el}}}{dt} = k^2 a t^{-3/2}; \quad \log\left(\frac{d\sigma_{\text{el}}}{dt}\right) = -\tfrac{3}{2}k^2 a \log t.$$

Experimentally, the shrinkage of the diffraction peak with energy has been observed in pp-scattering,[20,21] but apparently not for πp-scattering[21]; $\bar{K}p$ and $\bar{p}p$ diffraction peaks seem even to expand.[22] One has to keep in mind, however, that there are other poles contributing to the asymptotic behavior as well as possibly other singularities (see Sec. 9.7). Also the slope of the trajectories is, of course, unknown and is introduced here only phenomenologically. At any rate the behavior of the diffraction peak is not as simple as one has first expected.

9.3   Upper and Lower Bounds for the Amplitudes and Cross Sections from Analyticity and Unitarity

In the previous section we have phenomenologically assumed constant total cross sections at infinity in our considerations. In this section we shall

---

[19] For other results of this type see S. C. Frautchi, M. Gell-Mann, and F. Zachariasen, *Phys. Rev.*, **126**, 2204 (1962).

[20] A. N. Diddens, E. Lillethun, G. Manning, A. E. Taylor, T. G. Walker and A. M. Wetherel, *Phys. Rev. Letters*, **9**, 108, 111 (1962).

[21] K. J. Foley, S. J. Lindenbaum, W. A. Love, S. Ozaki, J. J. Russell, and L. C. L. Yuan, *Phys. Rev. Letters*, **10**, 376 (1963).

[22] For a recent review see S. J. Lindenbaum, *Proceedings of the Oxford International Conference on Elementary Particles* (London: Oxford U. P., 1965).

see what limits are imposed on the amplitude and cross sections by the more general properties of analyticity and unitarity without making any dynamical assumptions.

a. Upper Bound from Analyticity in z-Plane and Unitarity

Let us assume that the amplitude $A(s,z)$ is analytic in the z-plane inside the region G shown in Fig. 9.3, where $z_0 = [1 + (2t/s - 4)]$, and that there are no poles in G.

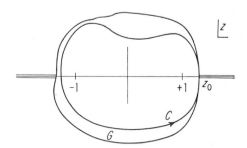

Figure 9.3   Domain of holomorphy in z-plane.

Consider any finite contour C in the domain of holomorphy. By the Cauchy theorem we have

$$A(s,z) = \frac{1}{2\pi i} \oint dz' \, \frac{A(s,z')}{z' - z}.$$
(9.39)

If we project both sides of this equation into partial waves we get

$$A(s,\ell) = \frac{1}{2\pi i} \oint dz' \, A(s,z')Q_\ell(z').$$
(9.40)

Note that if the contour C is deformed to infinity everywhere in the domain of holomorphy Eq. (9.40) goes over into Eq. (9.24):

$$A(s,\ell) = \frac{1}{\pi} \left\{ \int_{-\infty}^{z_0} + \int_{z_0}^{\infty} \right\} dz' \, \text{disc.} \, A(s,z')Q_\ell(z'),$$

as it should.

From Eq. (9.40) we obtain an upper limit to the amplitude

$$|A(s,\ell)| \leqslant \frac{1}{2\pi} |A(s,z')|_{\max} |Q_\ell(z)|_{\max} \, y,$$
(9.41)

where y is the length of the contour C and subscript "max" means the maximum value of the function along the contour C. We assume, as in the whole theory of dispersion relations, that the amplitude $A(s,t)$ is uniformly bounded by a polynominial in s (the so-called *temperedness assumption*); hence

$$|A(s,z)|_{\max} \leqslant R_1(s) = \text{polynomial in } s \text{ of degree } n \geqslant 1.$$
(9.42)

The maximum of $Q_\ell(z)$ is known if C is an ellipse with foci ± 1 and passing through z_0 :[23]

$$|Q_\ell(z)|_{\max} = \sqrt{\frac{\pi}{\ell}} \frac{y^{-\ell}}{\sqrt{y^2 - 1}},$$

$$y = z_0 + \sqrt{z_0^2 - 1}. \tag{9.43}$$

Hence

$$|A(s,\ell)| \leqslant R_1(s)\sqrt{\ell} \frac{z_0 y^{-\ell}}{\sqrt{y^2 - 1}} \approx \frac{1}{\sqrt{\ell}} y^{-\ell} R_2(s), \tag{9.44}$$

where $R_2(s)$ is another polynomial in s at high energies. The degree of the polynomial is not essential for our purpose. This bound on the partial-wave amplitudes alone does not give any new information on the full amplitude. We now use also the fact that the amplitude $A(s,\ell)$, quite generally, is also bounded by the unitarity condition in the s-channel by

$$\sqrt{\frac{s - 4m^2}{s}} |A(s,\ell)|^2 \leqslant A(s,\ell)$$

or

$$|A(s,\ell)| \leqslant \sqrt{\frac{s}{s - 4m^2}}. \tag{9.45}$$

Thus from unitarity alone the total amplitude is bounded by

$$A(s,t) \leqslant \sqrt{\frac{s}{s - 4m^2}} \sum_\ell (2\ell + 1) P_\ell(z),$$

which clearly diverges, and unitarity alone would not give any bound for the full amplitude either. (For example, at forward scattering $P_\ell(1) = 1$.) But we see from Eq. (9.44) that the higher partial waves are actually much smaller than the unitarity limit. Let L be the value of ℓ beyond which $A(s,\ell)$ is less than the unitarity limit (Fig. 9.4); L is determined by

$$(\sqrt{L})^{-1} y^{-L} R_2(s) = \sqrt{\frac{s}{s - 4m^2}},$$

or $L^{1/2} u^L = R(s)$; $R(s)$ a new polynomial of degree N. We then have

$$\tfrac{1}{2} \log L + L \log y = \log R(s).$$

Hence

$$L \leqslant \frac{\log R(s)}{\log y} = \frac{N \log s}{\log y}.$$

For large s, we have, on the other hand,

$$z_0 \xrightarrow[s \to \infty]{} 1 + \frac{2t}{s}; \quad y \xrightarrow[s \to \infty]{} 1 + 2\sqrt{\frac{t}{s}};$$

[23] E. W. Hobson, *The Theory of Spherical and Ellipsoidal Harmonics* (New York: Cambridge, U. P., 1931), pp. 61, 309.

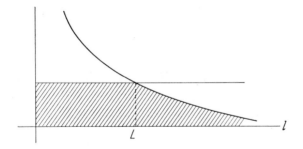

Figure 9.4   Bounds of amplitude in ℓ.

then
$$L \leqslant (\text{constant})\sqrt{s} \log s. \tag{9.46}$$

Now we use the unitarity limit Eq. (9.45) from $\ell = 0$ to $\ell = L$ and the analyticity limit Eq. (9.44) for $\ell > L$ (Fig. 9.4):

$$|A(s,t)| \leqslant \sqrt{\frac{s}{s - 4m^2}} \sum_{\ell=0}^{L-1} (2\ell + 1)P_\ell(z) + \sum_{\ell=L}^{\infty} (2\ell + 1)\frac{y^{-\ell}}{\sqrt{\ell}} R_2(s)P_\ell(z). \tag{9.47}$$

In the forward direction, $z = 1$, $P_\ell(1) = 1$, the sum in the first term becomes

$$\sum_{\ell=0}^{L-1} (2\ell + 1) = L^2 \leqslant s \log^2 s.$$

The second term in Eq. (9.47) is bounded by

$$R_2(s)y^{-L} \sum_{\ell=L}^{\infty} (2\ell + 1)y^{-(\ell - L)} = R_2(s)y^{-L}\left\{(2L + 1) \sum_{n=0}^{\infty} y^{-n} + 2 \sum_{n=0}^{\infty} ny^{-n}\right\}$$

$$= R_2(s)y^{-L}\left[(2L + 1)\frac{y}{y - 1} - 2\frac{y}{(y - 1)^2}\right]$$

$$\cong 2R_2(s)y^{-L+1}L$$

$$\approx s^{N'} \log s/y^L \xrightarrow[s \to \infty]{} 0, \quad \text{for} \quad u > 1.$$

We have then the upper limit, as $s \to \infty$,

$$A(s,t) \leqslant (\text{const.}) s(\log s)^2. \tag{9.48}$$

Consequently

$$\sigma_{\text{tot}} = \frac{1}{s} \text{Im}A(s,t) \xrightarrow[s \to \infty]{} \leqslant C(\log s)^2. \tag{9.49}$$

Away from the forward direction we need a limit on $P_\ell[1 + (2t/s - 4)]$ for fixed t and large s [Eq. (19) of App. 8]

$$|P_\ell(\cos \theta)| \xrightarrow[\ell \to \infty]{} (2\pi\ell)^{-\frac{1}{2}}(\sin \theta)^{-\frac{1}{2}}; \quad \theta \neq 0 \text{ or } \pi.$$

Then the first term of Eq. (9.47) gives for large s

$$A(s,t) \leqslant (2\pi \sin \theta)^{-\frac{1}{2}} \sum_{\ell=0}^{L-1} (2\ell + 1)\ell^{-\frac{1}{2}} \approx \text{const. } L^{\frac{3}{2}}$$

$$\leqslant (\text{const.}) \, s^{\frac{3}{4}}(\log s)^{\frac{3}{2}}. \tag{9.50}$$

The discontinuous change between the limits Eq. (9.48) and (9.50) for $\theta = 0$, and $\theta \neq 0$ indicates that we have not the best possible upper limits obtainable from analyticity for nonforward directions.

The above method is essentially due to Greenberg and Low,[24] who applied it to the so-called Lehmann ellipse in the z-plane. In that case,

$$z = 1 + \frac{\text{const.}}{s^2}$$

and one obtains the weaker upper limit $|A(s,t)| \leqslant s^2 \log^2 s$. The results, Eqs. (9.48) and (9.50), have been obtained first by Froissart[25] by a quite different method.

The second bound, Eq. (9.50), can be improved to

$$|A(s,t)| < (\text{const.}) \frac{(\log s)^{\frac{3}{2}}}{\sin^2 \theta}, \quad \theta \neq 0 \text{ or } \pi, \tag{9.51}$$

if use is made of more analyticity on the z-plane.[26]

We should emphasize that in the derivation of the above results the analyticity in s as well as unitarity in crossed channels have not been used. The only three assumptions were (i) analyticity in a certain domain in z; (ii) uniform power bound in s in this domain of z, and (iii) unitarity in s.

b. Lower Bounds

We discuss first a lower bound to elastic cross section: If the first L partial waves contribute to the process one has[27]

$$\sigma_{\text{el}} = \frac{\pi}{q^2} \sum_{\ell} (x_\ell^2 + y_\ell^2)/(2\ell + 1) \quad \text{and} \quad \sigma_{\text{tot}} = \frac{2\pi}{q^2} \sum_{\ell} x_\ell,$$

where x_ℓ and y_ℓ are the real and imaginary parts of the amplitude. Minimizing σ_{el} for a given value of σ_{tot} we obtain

$$\frac{\sigma_{\text{el}}}{\sigma_{\text{tot}}} \geqslant \frac{s}{4\pi(L + 1)^2}. \tag{9.52}$$

[24] O. W. Greenberg and F. E. Low, *Phys. Rev.*, **124**, 2047 (1961).

[25] M. Froissart, *Phys. Rev.*, **123**, 1053 (1961).

[26] T. Kinoshita, J. J. Loeffel, and A. Martin, *Phys. Rev. Letters*, **10**, 460 (1963); *Phys. Rev.*, **135**, B1464 (1964).

[27] See also the review article by T. Kinoshita, *Proceedings of the Conference on Particles and High Energy Physics* (Boulder, Colo.: U. of Colorado Press, 1965), Vol. VIIb of *Lectures in Theoretical Physics*; W. Rarita and P. Schwed, *Phys. Rev.*, **112**, 271 (1958); M. Levy, *Phys. Rev. Letters*, **5**, 380 (1960). See also A. Martin, *Nuovo Cimento*, **29**, 993 (1963).

If we choose L to be the same as Eq. (9.46) we find

$$\frac{\sigma_{el}}{\sigma_{tot}} > (\text{const.})(\log s)^{-2}$$

or, with Eqs. (9.48) and (9.49),

$$C_2 \leqslant \sigma_{el}(t = 0) \leqslant C_1(\log s)^2.$$

Low-energy bounds for certain integrated elastic cross sections are also known.[28]

c. More General Assumptions on Asymptotic Behavior

Because the asymptotic behavior of the amplitude based on the dominance of a single pole, Eq. (9.32), does not agree well with the experiment, a more general Ansatz is necessary. For the proof of Pomeranchuck's theorems it is sufficient to assume that[29]

(i) $A(s,t)$ is analytic in $Ims > 0$ and continuous in $Ims = 0$, for fixed t,

(ii) $A(s,t)$ is polynomial bounded in s for large s and for fixed t,

(iii) $$\frac{A(s + i0, t)}{s^{\alpha(t)}(\ln s)^{\beta(t)}} \xrightarrow[|s| \to \infty]{} c(t),$$

i.e., an asymptotic behavior which would correspond to that of an angular momentum pole and an angular momentum branch point (see Exercise 12).

d. Limits on the Width of the Diffraction Peak

The width of the diffraction peak is related to the change of the differential cross section with the angle, or momentum transfer t:

$$\frac{d\sigma}{dt} = \frac{d}{dt}\left[\frac{1}{s}|A(s,t)|^2\right]$$

$$= \frac{1}{s}\left[\frac{dA^*}{dt}A + A^*\frac{dA}{dt}\right] \leqslant \frac{1}{s}|A|\left|\frac{dA}{dt}\right|.$$

From the partial-wave expansion we get

$$|A| \leqslant \sum_\ell (2\ell + 1)|A_\ell(s)|\,|P_\ell(z)|$$

and

$$\left|\frac{dA(s,t)}{dt}\right| \leqslant \sum_\ell (2\ell + 1)|A_\ell(s)|\frac{dz}{dt}\left|\frac{dP_\ell}{dz}\right|,$$

where, if we again use analyticity in an ellipse in the z-plane, the change of order of sum and differentiation is allowed. We now have the bounds

$$|P_\ell(z)| \leqslant 1 \quad \text{and} \quad \left|\frac{dP_\ell}{dz}\right| \leqslant \frac{\ell(\ell + 1)}{2}$$

[28] F. Cerulus and A. Martin, *Phys. Rev. Letters*, **8**, 80 (1964).
[29] L. van Hove, in *International Seminar on High Energy Physics, Trieste* (Vienna: International Atomic Energy Agency, 1965).

and for the partial-wave amplitudes we assume, as before, the bounds

$$|A_\ell| \leqslant R(s) \exp(-\alpha(s)\ell),$$

where $R(s)$ is a polynomial and

$$\cosh \alpha = 1 + \frac{2\lambda^2}{s - 4}.$$

We then get

$$|A(s,t)| \leqslant \sum_{\ell=0}^{L_1 - 1} (2\ell + 1) + R(s) \sum_{\ell=L_1}^{\infty} (2\ell + 1)e^{-\alpha\ell}$$

and

$$\left|\frac{dA}{dt}\right| \leqslant \sum_{\ell=0}^{L_1 - 1} \frac{\ell(\ell + 1)(2\ell + 1)}{2} + R(s) \sum_{\ell=L_1}^{\infty} \frac{\ell(\ell + 1)(2\ell + 1)}{2} e^{-\alpha\ell}$$

where L_1 is the smallest integer larger than L_0 with

$$L_0 = \log R(s)/\alpha.$$

Hence

$$|A(s,t)| \leqslant C_1 [\log R(s)]^2,$$

$$\left|\frac{dA}{dt}\right| \leqslant C_2 [\log R(s)]^4.$$

Inserting these into the expression for $d\sigma/dt$ we get

$$\frac{d\sigma}{dt} \leqslant C'(\log R(s))^6 = C''(\log s)^6.$$

The width of the diffraction peak may be defined as follows (Fig. 9.5):

$$w = \frac{1}{2} \frac{\sigma(s,0)}{d\sigma(s,0)/dt}.$$

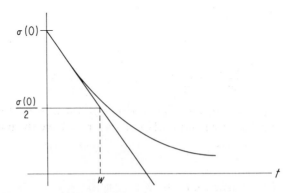

Figure 9.5   Definition of the width of the diffraction peak.

Hence[30]

$$w \geqslant C \frac{\sigma(s,0)}{(\log s)^6}.$$

If the amplitude is purely imaginary at high energies, the above limit can be improved:[31]

$$w \geqslant C \frac{1}{(\log s)^2}.$$

There is also a lower bound for the width of the diffraction peak.[32] If the amplitude is purely imaginary at high energies we have

$$\sigma_{tot} = \sum (2\ell + 1) Im A_\ell(s),$$

$$\sigma_{el} = \sum (2\ell + 1)[Im A_\ell(s)]^2.$$

Keeping these quantities fixed we evaluate the minimum of

$$\frac{dA(s,t)}{dt}\bigg|_{t=0} = \sum_\ell (2\ell + 1) \frac{\ell(\ell + 1)}{2} Im A_\ell(s),$$

which gives then an upper bound for the width

$$w < \frac{g}{4} \frac{1}{\left[\dfrac{\sigma_{tot}^2}{4\pi\sigma_{el}} - \dfrac{1}{k^2}\right]}.$$

9.4 Implication of the Asymptotic Behavior on Angular Momentum

We have found that for $t \leqslant 0$,

$$A(s,t) \underset{s \to \infty}{\longrightarrow} \leqslant s \log^2 s.$$

Comparing this with the amplitude due to the leading pole

$$A(s,t) \underset{s \to \infty}{\longrightarrow} f(t)s^{\alpha(t)}$$

we conclude that

$$\alpha(t) \leqslant 1 \quad \text{for} \quad t \leqslant 0.$$

This result together with the bound

$$A_2(s,t) \underset{|t| \to \infty}{\longrightarrow} t^N, \quad \text{uniformly in } s,$$

[30] A. C. Finn, *Phys. Rev.*, **132**, 836 (1963).
[31] T. Kinoshita, in *Lectures in Theoretical Physics*, Vol. VIIb (Boulder, Colo.: U. of Colorado Press, 1965).
[32] S. W. MacDowell and A. Martin, *Phys. Rev.*, **135**, B960 (1964).

gives us now a domain of holomorphy of $A(s,\ell)$ in angular momentum plane (Fig. 9.6):

$$
\begin{aligned}
Re\ell > N &\quad \text{for all } s, \\
Re\ell > 1 &\quad \text{for } s < 0 \text{ and real.}
\end{aligned}
\tag{9.53}
$$

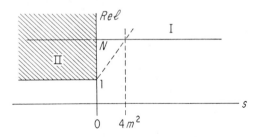

Figure 9.6 Domain of holomorphy of $A(s,\ell)$.

There cannot be a jump in the boundary of the domain of holomorphy. A domain such as above is not a domain of holomorphy. The argument in the previous section can be repeated in a neighborhood of the negative real s-axis, so that the second line of Eq. (9.53) can be written as

$$Re\ell > 1$$

for s in the neighborhood of the negative axis. To obtain a domain of holomorphy we use the mapping[33]

$$w = (2/\pi) \sin^{-1}[(s - 2m^2)/2m^2].$$

The cut s-plane is mapped into the strip between $-1 < Rew < +1$ (Fig. 9.7).

Figure 9.7 Conformal mapping from s- to w-planes.

Now we consider $A(s,\ell)$ in a diagram Rew versus $Re\ell$; the domains I and II map as shown in Fig. 9.8. The amplitude $A(s,\ell)$ is holomorphic in the shaded tube domain (arbitrary imaginary parts). A tube domain is a domain of holomorphy if and only if it is *convex* (see App. 9). Hence the *minimum* domain of holomorphy is given by the convex hull of I and II (dotted line), or

$$Rew = \left[\frac{2}{N-1} Re\ell - \frac{N+1}{N-1}\right] < 0, \quad -1 \leqslant Rew \leqslant +1,$$

[33] K. Bardakci, *Phys. Rev.*, **127**, 1832 (1962).

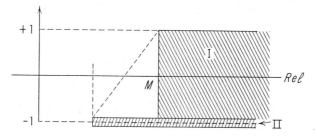

Figure 9.8 The domains I, II of Fig. 9.6 in the *w*-plane.

which can be written in the *s* variables as

$$2Re\ell - (N + 1) - (N - 1)\, Re\left[\frac{2}{\pi}\sin^{-1}\left(\frac{s - 2m^2}{2m^2}\right)\right] > 0$$

or

$$2Re(\ell - 1) - (N - 1)\, Re\left[1 + \frac{2}{\pi}\sin^{-1}\left(\frac{s - 2m^2}{2m^2}\right)\right] > 0 \qquad (9.54)$$

and is shown in the following figure in an *Reℓ* versus *Res* diagram (Fig. 9.9).

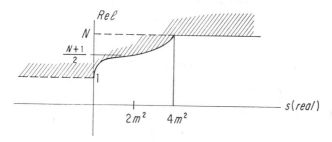

Figure 9.9 Completed domain of holomorphy.

There can be no singularity in the shaded region. The curve has infinite slope at $s = 0$ and $4m^2$ so that no useful upper limit is obtained for the slope of the Pomeranchuk trajectory at $\alpha = 1$.

9.5   Analytic Continuation in ℓ

Having obtained a minimum domain of holomorphy in the variables *s* and ℓ, we shall now use the unitarity condition to obtain more information on the amplitude, on the poles in ℓ, and possibly to extend domain of holomorphy or meromorphy.

We go back to Eq. (9.24), i.e.,

$$A(s,\ell) = \frac{2}{s - 4}\left[\frac{1}{\pi}\int_4^\infty dt\, A_2(s,t,u)Q_\ell\left(1 + \frac{2t}{s - 4}\right)\right.$$
$$\left. + (-1)^\ell \frac{1}{\pi}\int_4^\infty du\, A_3(s,t,u)Q_\ell\left(1 + \frac{2u}{s - 4}\right)\right]. \qquad (9.55)$$

Let us first see the singularities of $A(s,\ell)$ when ℓ is complex. Because the cut of $Q_\ell(z)$ runs now from $z = -\infty$ to $z = 1$, when ℓ is not a positive integer, we see that $A(s,\ell)$ is never real on the real s-axis; i.e., its cut in s runs from $s = -\infty$ to $s = +\infty$. This situation leads to difficulties: one cannot use the N/D-method and there is no way of analytic continuation from the upper-half s-plane to lower-half one. Because, however, part of the cut is due to Q_ℓ and is therefore kinematic, we can remedy the situation as follows.[34] We express Q_ℓ in terms of the hypergeometric function [Eq. (17) of App. 8]; i.e.,

$$Q_\ell\left(1 + \frac{2t}{s-4}\right) = \frac{1}{2}\frac{\Gamma^2(\ell+1)}{\Gamma(2\ell+1)}\left(\frac{s-4}{t}\right)^{\ell+1}$$

$$\times F\left(\ell + 1, \ell + 1; 2\ell + 2; -\frac{s-4}{t}\right). \qquad (9.56)$$

The cut of $F[\ell + 1, \ell + 1; 2\ell + 2; -(s - 4)/t]$ in s runs from $s = -\infty$ to $s = 4 - t$ and that of $(s - 4)^{\ell+1}$ from $s = -\infty$ to $s = 4$. If we insert this into the above equation for $A(s,\ell)$, the cut in $A(s,\ell)$ due to F is from $s = -\infty$ to $s = 0$, and the cut due to A_2 and A_3, as before, from $s = 4$ to $s = +\infty$. If we define a new amplitude $B(s,\ell)$ by

$$B(s,\ell) = \frac{A(s,\ell)}{(s-4)^\ell}$$

$$= \frac{\Gamma^2(\ell+1)}{\Gamma(2\ell+1)}\left[\frac{1}{\pi}\int_4^\infty dt\,\frac{A_2(s,t,u)}{t^{\ell+1}}F\left(\ell + 1, \ell + 1; 2\ell + 2; -\frac{s-4}{t}\right)\right.$$

$$\left. + (-1)^\ell\frac{1}{\pi}\int_4^\infty du\,\frac{A_3(s,t,u)}{u^{\ell+1}}F\left(\ell + 1, \ell + 1; 2\ell + 2; -\frac{s-4}{u}\right)\right],$$

$$\qquad (9.57)$$

then $B(s,\ell)$ has the same cuts for $\ell = $ complex, as has $A(s,\ell)$ for $\ell = $ positive integers.

The above equation also displays explicitly the asymptotic behavior of Q_ℓ, because $F[\ldots, -(s - 4)/t]$ behaves for large t as unity.

Furthermore, we can separate the singular parts of $B(s,\ell)$ in the ℓ-plane. For this purpose we write

$$F\left(\ell + 1, \ell + 1; 2\ell + 2; -\frac{s-4}{t}\right)$$

$$= F - \sum_{r=0}^R C_r(\ell)\left(\frac{s-4}{t}\right)^r + \sum_{r=0}^R C_r(\ell)\left(\frac{s-4}{t}\right)^r,$$

which gives rise respectively to two terms in B:

$$B(s,\ell) = B_0(s,\ell) + B_1(s,\ell). \qquad (9.58)$$

[34] A. O. Barut and D. E. Zwanziger, *Phys. Rev.*, **127**, 974 (1962).

The lowest power in $[(s - 4)/t]$ occurring in the B_0-integral is R, hence $B_0(s,\ell)$ is holomorphic in ℓ for $\mathrm{Re}\,\ell > N - R$, the singularities of $B(s,\ell)$ in $N - R < \mathrm{Re}\,\ell < N$ are therefore due to $B_1(s,\ell)$; in particular, the singularities between $\mathrm{Re}\,\ell = N - 1$ to N are in the integral

$$\int dt \, \frac{A_2(s, t, 4 - s - t)}{t^{\ell+1}},$$

and so on. Thus, the singularities of $B(s,\ell)$ are closely connected with those of the Mellin transforms of the absorptive parts

$$\int dt \, \frac{A_2}{t^{\ell+r+1}}, \qquad \int du \, \frac{A_3}{u^{\ell+r+1}}, \tag{9.59}$$

which have only the spectral cut.

a. Use of Elastic Unitarity

We can, as before, define $B_t(s,\ell)$ and $B_u(s,\ell)$, as well as $B^{\pm}(s,\ell)$-partial wave amplitudes. The elastic unitarity condition holds for B^+ and B^- amplitudes separately. From Eq. (7.22) we have in the s-variable

$$\mathrm{disc}_s \, A^{-1}(s,\ell) = -\sqrt{\frac{s - 4}{s}} = \mathrm{Im}[(s - 4)^{-\ell} B^{-1}(s,\ell)]$$

or

$$\mathrm{disc}_s \, B^{-1}(s,\ell) = -\frac{(s - 4)^{\ell+\frac{1}{2}}}{\sqrt{s}}; \quad 4 \leqslant s \leqslant s_{\text{inelastic}}. \tag{9.60}$$

The discontinuity of B^{-1} in $4 \leqslant s \leqslant s_{\text{inel}}$ is known; we can therefore write

$$B^{-1}(s,\ell) = \frac{1}{\sqrt{s}} \frac{Y(s,\ell) + [-(s - 4)]^{\ell+\frac{1}{2}}}{\cos \pi\ell},$$

where $Y(s,\ell)$ is a real meromorphic function with cuts $-\infty < s < 0$ and $s_{\text{in}} < s < \infty$. It is real between $s = 0$ and $s - s_{\text{inelastic}}$; $[-(s - 4)]^{\ell+\frac{1}{2}}$ has the cut from $s = 4$ to $s = +\infty$. We have indeed

$$\mathrm{disc}_s \, B^{-1}(s,\ell) = \frac{1}{\sqrt{s}} \frac{1}{\cos \pi\ell} \mathrm{Im}[e^{(\ell+\frac{1}{2})\log[-(s-4)-i\varepsilon]}]$$

$$= \frac{1}{\sqrt{s}} \frac{1}{\cos \pi\ell} \mathrm{Im}[e^{(\ell+\frac{1}{2})[\log(s-4)+i\pi]}]$$

$$= \frac{(s - 4)^{\ell+\frac{1}{2}}}{\sqrt{s}} \frac{\sin \pi(\ell + \frac{1}{2})}{\cos \pi\ell} = -\frac{(s - 4)^{\ell+\frac{1}{2}}}{\sqrt{s}}. \tag{9.61}$$

The above process can be continued if we know $\mathrm{Im} B^{-1}$ in the three-body inelastic region, and so on.

The representation of the B-amplitude in the form

$$B(s,\ell) = \sqrt{s} \, \frac{\cos \pi\ell}{Y(s,\ell) + [-(s - 4)]^{\ell+\frac{1}{2}}} \tag{9.62}$$

is rather interesting. Some authors have given soluble models in Regge representation.[35] We remark that any choice of the real analytic Y-function, real in the gap $0 < s < s_{in}$, gives us such a model. We further note that in the nonrelativistic case $Y(s,\ell)$ has no right-hand cut at all.

Let us now apply the analytic completion method in the variable ℓ to the function $Y(s,\ell)$,

$$Y(s,\ell) = \sqrt{s} \cos \pi\ell \, B^{-1}(s,\ell) - [-(s-4)]^{\ell+\frac{1}{2}}, \qquad (9.63)$$

which is holomorphic in $Re\,\ell > N$ for $s > 4$ and in $Re\,\ell > 1$ for $s < 0$. We now use the mapping

$$w = \frac{2}{\pi} \sin^{-1}\left[\frac{2s - s_{in}}{s_{in}}\right]$$

to obtain the same $Re\,w$ versus $Re\,\ell$ diagram as before. Outside the domain of holomorphy of B^{-1}, Y can have poles. The theorem about the convexity of the tube domain also applies to domains of meromorphy (meromorphy in s, holomorphy in ℓ). Consequently the domain of meromorphy is given by

$$2Re(\ell - 1) - (N - 1)Re\left[1 + \frac{2}{\pi} \sin^{-1}\left(\frac{2s - s_{in}}{s_{in}}\right)\right] > 0 \qquad (9.64)$$

and is shown in Fig. 9.10. In the shaded region poles can occur, but need not. (For example, the slope of the vacuum pole at $\alpha = 1$ is not infinite.) The

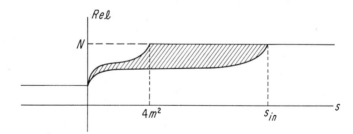

Figure 9.10 Domain of holomorphy enlarged by the elastic unitarity condition.

resultant new convex domain is probably still meromorphic in s and holomorphic in ℓ.

The process of the previous section can, in principle, be continued to include inelastic intermediate states. If we evaluate the discontinuity of B^{-1} across the three-particle cut we could separate this part in Y explicitly, then we would have a generalization of Eq. (9.62) in which the unknown function would have a cut starting at the four-particle threshold, and so on.

The extension of the previous theory to relativistic coupled channel problem is given elsewhere.[36]

[35] R. Acharya and A. Bhattacharjie, *Nuovo Cimento*, **26**, 369 (1962).
[36] A. O. Barut, *Phys. Rev.*, **128**, 1959 (1963); H. Cheng and D. Sharp, *Ann. Phys.*, **22**, 48 (1965); C. E. Jones, *Ann. Phys.*, **31**, 481 (1965).

9.6 Properties of Poles in the ℓ- and s-Planes

We have mentioned that the singularities in the ℓ- and s-planes belong to the same singularity surfaces in the four-dimensional space. In this section we study, parallelwise, the properties of the poles in both planes.

In a domain in the ℓ- and s-planes in which the amplitude $B(s,\ell)$ is meromorphic the poles are given by the solution of the equation

$$F(s,\ell) \equiv Y(s,\ell) + [-(s-4)]^{\ell+\frac{1}{2}} = 0 \tag{9.65}$$

with the following singularities in s- and ℓ-planes shown in Fig. 9.11; $F(s,\ell)$ is holomorphic in ℓ for $Re\,\ell \geqslant N$.

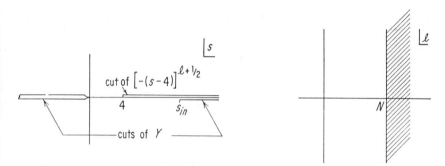

Figure 9.11 Singularities in s- and ℓ-planes.

We denote in particular the solutions of Eq. (9.65) for real s by $\ell = \alpha(s)$ and for real ℓ by $s = \sigma(\ell)$. If s and ℓ, respectively, are varied we obtain the pole trajectories $\alpha(s)$ and $\sigma(\ell)$ in the s- and ℓ-planes.

Relevant to the analyticity of these functions $\alpha(s)$ and $\sigma(\ell)$ is the so-called *implicit function theorem*:

Let $F(s,\ell)$ be holomorphic in some domain of the two complex variables s and ℓ and let $F(s_0,\ell_0) = 0$ but $\partial E/\partial \ell(s_0,\ell_0) \neq 0$. Then there exists a neighborhood of (s_0,ℓ_0) such that for each s in this neighborhood there is a unique solution $\ell = \alpha(s)$ of $F(s,\ell) = 0$ which is holomorphic in the same neighborhood. Similarly for $\sigma(\ell)$.

The theorem can be extended to domains of meromorphy, and it follows that $\alpha(s)$ is a meromorphic function in the s-plane cut from $-\infty$ to 0 and from 4 to ∞, except at the critical points where $\partial F/\partial \ell = 0$ (e.g., double poles). Similarly, $\sigma(\ell)$ is meromorphic in the domain of meromorphy of F in ℓ, if $\partial F/\partial s \neq 0$.

One can make stronger statements.[34] We have seen that the poles are actually due to the B_1-part of the amplitude [Eq. (9.58)]; they are given by $B_1^{-1}(s,\ell) = 0$. But $B_1(s,\ell)$ has only the spectral left-hand cut between $-\infty < s < s_L = -32$. The left-hand cut of $\alpha(s)$ is completely absent in the case of potential scattering because there is no spectral left-hand cut in this case. It may also be absent in the relativistic case.[37]

We can also obtain the analyticity of the residues $\beta(s)$. If a pole is distinct from all others we obtain from Cauchy theorem

$$b(s) = \frac{\beta(s)}{(s-4)^{\alpha(s)}} = \frac{1}{2\pi i} \oint_C B_1(s,\ell)\, d\ell, \tag{9.66}$$

where C is a small contour around $\ell = \alpha(s)$. Thus, $b(s)$ has the same analyticity as B_1 or as $\alpha(s)$.

To investigate the nature of the branch point at threshold we expand Eq. (9.65) around $s = 4$ and $\ell = \alpha_0$, the position of the pole at threshold, and obtain, with $Y(4,\alpha_0) = 0$,

$$Y_\ell(\alpha - \alpha_0) + Y_s(s-4) + 0[(s-4)^2] + [-(s-4)]^{\ell+\frac{1}{2}} = 0$$

or

$$\alpha(s) = \alpha_0 - \frac{Y_s}{Y_\ell}(s-4) + 0[(s-4)^2] - \frac{1}{Y_\ell}[-(s-4)]^{\alpha+\frac{1}{2}}, \tag{9.67}$$

where the derivatives Y_s and Y_ℓ at $(s = 4, \alpha_0)$ are real numbers because the function Y itself is real here.

The point $s = 4$ is indeed a branch point: below $s = 4$, $\alpha(s) =$ real, is a solution of Eq. (9.67), above $s = 4$ we have

$$Re\,\alpha(s) \simeq \alpha_0 - \frac{Y_s}{Y_\ell}(s-4) - \frac{1}{Y_\ell}|s-4|^{\alpha_0+\frac{1}{2}} \cos \pi(\alpha_0 + \tfrac{1}{2}),$$

$$Im\,\alpha(s) \simeq \frac{1}{Y_\ell}|s-4|^{\alpha_0+\frac{1}{2}} \sin \pi(\alpha_0 + \tfrac{1}{2}). \tag{9.68}$$

We also calculate the residue at the threshold. From the form of the B-amplitude, Eq. (9.62), we obtain

$$b(s) \simeq \frac{1}{2} \frac{\sqrt{s}}{Y_\ell} \sin \pi(\alpha_0 + \tfrac{1}{2}), \tag{9.69}$$

so that the residue, $b(s)$ and $Im\,\alpha(s)$, has the same sign just above threshold.

In the same way we look at the behavior of the trajectory in the s-plane around the pole $s = \sigma_0$ and $\ell = \ell_0 =$ real:

$$\sigma(\ell) = 4 - \frac{Y_\ell}{Y_s}(\ell - \alpha_0) - \frac{1}{Y_s}[-(\sigma - 4)]^{\ell+\frac{1}{2}}. \tag{9.70}$$

For ℓ real we can have a real solution of this trancendental equation if $\sigma(\ell) < 4$. If $\sigma(\ell) > 4$ it must become complex:

$$Re\,\sigma(\ell) = 4 - \frac{Y_\ell}{Y_s}(\ell - \alpha_0) - \frac{1}{Y_s} r^{\ell+\frac{1}{2}} \cos \varphi(\ell + \tfrac{1}{2}),$$

$$Im\,\sigma(\ell) = -\frac{1}{Y_s} r^{\ell+\frac{1}{2}} \sin \varphi(\ell + \tfrac{1}{2}), \tag{9.71}$$

[37] R. Oehme and G. Tiktopolous, *Phys. Rev. Letters*, **2**, 86 (1962).

where we have put

$$-(\sigma - 4) = r\ell^{i\varphi}.$$

Consider a pole with $\alpha_0 > \frac{1}{2}$. Then it follows from Eq. (9.67) that Y_s/Y_ℓ is negative. If we take Y_ℓ positive (see below) then Y_s is negative, which implies that $\sigma(\ell)$ and $\alpha(s)$ have opposite imaginary parts and we obtain the following

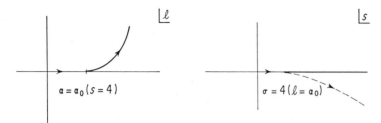

Figure 9.12   Threshold behavior of trajectories in ℓ- and s-planes.

behavior of the poles near threshold (Fig. 9.12). The residue $\sigma(\ell)$ of the pole in the s-plane is given by

$$r(\ell) \equiv (s - 4)^{-\ell}\rho(\ell) = \frac{\frac{1}{2}\sqrt{\sigma}\,\sin \pi(\ell + \frac{1}{2})}{Y_s - (\ell + \frac{1}{2})[-(\sigma - 4)]^{\ell - \frac{1}{2}}}$$

$$\approx \frac{1}{2Y_s}\,\sqrt{\sigma}\,\sin \pi(\ell + \frac{1}{2}). \tag{9.72}$$

Just above threshold φ in Eq. (9.71) is near $\pi/2$ so that again the residue and the imaginary part of the pole have the same sign. Thus, at threshold the poles and residues in both ℓ- and s-planes are determined by three parameters α_0, Y_s, and Y_ℓ. The sign of Y_s (positive) can be determined as follows.[38]

Consider the absorptive part $A_1(s,t,u)$ of the amplitude. This is obtained as an integral over the spectral regions along a line $s = $ const. (Fig. 7.17). Let us expand:

$$A_1(s,t) = \sum_{n=0}^{\infty} (2n + 1)a_1(s)P_n(z); \quad z = 1 + \frac{2t}{s - 4}.$$

For $s > 4$, $a_1(s) = ImA(s,\ell) > 0$ by unitarity. The series converges uniformly in z up to the first singularity of $A_1(s,t)$—the point $t_0(s)$ which is the beginning of the spectral region ρ_{st}. For $s > 4$ and $t > 0$, i.e., $z > 1$, and we have

$$P_n(z) > 0$$

---

[38] V. N. Gribov and I. Ya. Pomeranchuk, *Soviet Phys. JETP*, **16**, 220 (1963).

and

$$P'_n(z) = \sum_{n=1}^{N} (2n - 4m + 3)P_{n-2m+1}(z) > 0,$$

$$N = \frac{n}{2} \quad \text{for} \quad n \text{ even}; \quad N = \frac{(n+1)}{2} \quad \text{for} \quad n \text{ odd}.$$

Therefore $A_1(s,t)$ and its derivatives are positive in the small region $4 < t < t_0(s)$. Note that as $s \to \infty$, $t_0 \to 4$. Now if the amplitude is dominated by a pole term in the crossed channel we have

$$A_1(s,t) = Im \frac{\beta(t)[P_{\alpha(t)}(-z) + P_{(\alpha)t}(z)]}{\sin \pi \alpha(t)} \xrightarrow[s \to \infty]{} f(t)s^{\alpha(t)}.$$

Because A_1 is positive between $0 < t < 4$, we find then that the residue of the pole is positive in the range $0 < t < 4$.

Effective-Range Formula

As an application of the properties of pole trajectories we derive the effective-range formula based on a single dominant pole term in the direct channel. If a trajectory is very close to an integer at threshold, $1/(\alpha - \ell)$ becomes very large, and we may then take a single pole term at low energies. From Eq. (9.18) or Eq. (9.22) we have then

$$A(s,\ell) \cong \frac{1}{\pi} \frac{\beta(s)}{[\alpha(s) - \ell]} \tag{9.73}$$

or

$$A(s,\ell) = \frac{(2\alpha + 1)\beta(s)e^{-(\alpha-\ell)\xi}}{[\alpha(s) - \ell]}.$$

Inserting the form of $\alpha(s)$ into this equation we can relate the three parameters α_0, Y_s, and Y_ℓ to the scattering parameters, e.g., scattering length a, effective range r, and one other experimental point, or a bound-state point, such as deuteron in the n-p case and nucleon in the π-N, $I = \frac{1}{2}$ case.[39] We then obtain a convenient parametrization of the scattering data in terms of the trajectory. We shall come back to this point again in the next chapters. The determination of the parameters of the trajectory in the direct channel would complement and check its determination in the high-energy region of the channel if the diffraction scattering is dominated by a single-pole term in the crossed channel.

Problems and Further Developments

1. Evaluate the partial-wave projections of a pole term in Eq. (9.12) and prove Eq. (9.22).

[39] For the n-p scattering see A. O. Barut, *Phys. Rev.*, **126**, 1873 (1962); for π-N, $I = \frac{1}{2}$ scattering, see N. N. Khuri and B. W. Udgaonkar, *Phys. Rev. Letters*, **10**, 172 (1963), A. O. Barut and J. Dilley, *Phys. Rev.*, **134**, B873 (1964).

2. Prove rigorously the Mandelstam representation for a superposition of Yukawa potentials by means of the Watson-Sommerfeld transformation.

3. Show from the radial Schrödinger equation that the poles of the amplitude are given by

$$\lim_{R \to \infty} [Rek|\varphi(R)|^2] + Rek \, Im k \int_0^R |\varphi|^2 \, dr$$

$$- 2Re\lambda \, Im\lambda \int_0^R \{|\varphi|^2/r^2\} \, dr = 0, \quad \lambda = \ell + \tfrac{1}{2},$$

so that below threshold ($Rek = 0$) either $Re\lambda = 0$ and/or $Im\lambda = 0$; above threshold ($Imk = 0$) the poles in the half-plane $Re\lambda > 0$ have $Im\lambda > 0$ and those in the half-plane $Re\lambda < 0$ have $Im\lambda < 0$, provided that the last integral exists in the second case. In the k-plane, if λ is kept real, the poles occur either for $Rek = 0$ or for $Imk < 0$.

4. Write the radial Schrödinger equation for two-pole values k_1,k_2 and λ_1,λ_2 and obtain the relation

$$\frac{dk^2}{d\lambda^2} = \frac{\int_0^\infty \dfrac{\varphi^2}{r^2} \, dr}{\int_0^\infty \varphi^2 \, dr},$$

so that the slope of the trajectory may be roughly related to some average radius of the "state." Prove also that $d\alpha/ds < 0$ for s below threshold.

5. Discuss the complex angular momentum poles for the case of a hard sphere, a quantum mechanical top, and for a δ-function potential.

6. Same problem for the Coulomb potential. [Compare V. Singh, *Phys. Rev.*, **137**, 632 (1962).]

7. Show that the unitarity equation uncouples for the amplitudes A^+ and A^- in Eq. (9.28).

8. Show that if only partial waves up to an angular momentum $\ell = qr_0$ contribute to the elastic scattering, the total cross section is bounded by

$$\sigma_{tot} \leqslant 4\pi r_0^2.$$

(Use unitarity, $ImA_\ell \leqslant 1$, and optical theorem.)

9. Show that, however, if one keeps a finite number of partial waves in one channel, the crossing symmetry implies that the amplitude in another channel is a polynomial in energy which is, strictly speaking, impossible.

10. Show that if for $s > s_{in}$, the inelastic cross section vanishes for some energy, then the scattering amplitude is identically zero.

11. Show that if the amplitude behaves for large s as

$$A(s,t) = f(t)s^{\alpha(t)}[\log s]^{\beta(t)},$$

then $\alpha(0) \leqslant 1$. (Use optical theorem and the fact that

$$\sigma_{\text{tot}} \geqslant \frac{1}{s} \int_{-T}^{0} |A(s,t)|^2 \frac{dt}{2q^2},$$

where $T < 4q^2$.) If $\alpha(0) = 1$, obtain the bound $\sigma_{\text{tot}} \leqslant C \log s$. [E. Leader, *Phys. Rev. Letters*, **5**, 75 (1963), and A. Martin, *Phys. Rev.*, **129**, 1432 (1963).]

12. Show that branch point singularities in the angular momentum plane, e.g., a cut between $\alpha_1(t)$ and $\alpha_2(t)$ gives a contribution to the amplitude of the form $\int_{\alpha_1(t)}^{\alpha_2(t)} d\gamma \, [\beta(\gamma,t)/\ell - \gamma(t)]$ and in the s-channel for large s:

$$\int_{\alpha_1(t)}^{\alpha_2(t)} d\gamma \, b(\gamma,t) s^{\gamma(t)} \xrightarrow[s \to \infty]{} \frac{s^{\alpha_1(t)}}{\ln s}, \quad (\alpha_2 \text{ large}).$$

13. Show that the contribution of a double pole at $\alpha(t)$, in the angular momentum plane, to the scattering amplitude in the s-channel for large s is of the form

$$s^{\alpha(t) \log s}.$$

14. Obtain a different representation of the dispersion relation by using Mehler's identity,

$$\frac{1}{t' - t + i\varepsilon} = \frac{i}{2} \int_{-\frac{1}{2}-i\infty}^{-\frac{1}{2}+i\infty} d\phi \, \frac{2\phi + 1}{\sin \pi\phi} P_\phi(-z + i\varepsilon) Q_\phi(t')$$

$$= \frac{i}{2} \int_{-\frac{1}{2}-i\infty}^{-\frac{1}{2}+i\infty} d\phi (2\phi + 1) \cot \pi\phi P_\phi(t') Q_\phi(t),$$

instead of Neumann's identity (9.23″) used in the text. [Cf. D. Fivel, *Phys. Rev.*, **125**, 1085 (1962).]

Whereas the Neumann formula is a sum over irreducible representations of the rotation group, the Mehler formula is an integral over the continuous principal series of representations of the $(2 + 1)$-Lorentz group. As we have seen in Chap. 2, the rotation group is the little group of the Poincaré group for the class of (total) momenta being timelike, $p^2 > 0$; the $(2 + 1)$ Lorentz group is the little group in the case $p^2 < 0$, and applies for the cross-channel total momenta, i.e., t. [Cf. H. Joos, *Lectures in Theoretical Physics*, Vol. VIIa (Boulder, Colo.: U. of Colorado Press, 1965).]

PART TWO

Fundamental Particle Processes

CHAPTER 10

How to Assign Quantum Numbers to Particles

We have defined the so-called external or space-time quantum numbers, spin, mass, and intrinsic parity. There are a large number of other (so-called internal) quantum numbers, such as charge and isospin. We have to go to experimental situations to see how these quantum numbers are realized in nature. Also the mass values at present have to be taken from experiment. The method by which we assign the quantum numbers is to compare the selection rules derived from the invariance principle to observed experimental reactions to obtain a consistent set of properties. Usually the quantum numbers are introduced to describe the regularities of the observed reactions. One of the main problems in this process is to define a complete set of quantum numbers; i.e., to discover *all* the quantum numbers. In the following we discuss *how the quantum numbers have been assigned* and other properties of fundamental particles. (See also the tables in App. 1.)

10.1 Assignment of Space-Time Quantum Numbers for "Stable"[1] Particles

a. Photon

Rest mass is zero and spin 1. It belongs to the [0,1] representation of the inhomogeneous Lorentz group: The component of spin in the direction of motion is always ± 1; i.e., spin is directed either parallel or antiparallel to the direction of motion in any frame. As we have seen this is a relativistically invariant statement only for zero-mass particles.[2] The antiparticle of a photon

---

[1] The word "stable particle" is also used for the relatively long-lived mesons and hyperons decaying via electromagnetic and weak interactions.

[2] E. P. Wigner, *Rev. Mod. Phys.*, **29**, 255 (1957); E. P. Wigner in *Jublilee of Relativity Theory*, Helv. Physica Acta, Suppl. IV (Basel: Birkhäuser, 1956), p. 210. See also L. Bass and E. Schrödinger, *Proc. Roy. Soc.* (London), **A232**, 1 (1955).

is again a photon. Photons can carry any amount of orbital angular momentum, which determines the multipolarity of the radiation.

Under proper Lorentz transformations alone, particles with zero mass have only one direction of polarization, regardless of spin the second direction of polarization is due to parity or reflection symmetry, whereas massive particles with spin S have $(2S + 1)$ directions of polarization under proper Lorentz transformations alone.

b. Leptons

There are eight leptons $\nu_e, \bar{\nu}_e; \nu_\mu, \bar{\nu}_\mu; e^-, e^+; \mu^-, \mu^+$, all spin $\frac{1}{2}$. The electron-antineutrino has been postulated in β-decay:

$$n \to p + e^- + \bar{\nu}_e$$

as the missing particle from energy-momentum conservation. Its spin must be half if n, p, e have spin $\frac{1}{2}$. [See the discussion after Eq. (2.65).] It has been actually discovered much later by the process[3]

$$\bar{\nu}_e + p \to n + e^+.$$

The process

$$\bar{\nu}_e + n \to p + e^-$$

does not take place,[4] which shows that ν and $\bar{\nu}$ are different. Neutrino and antineutrino belong to $[0,\frac{1}{2}]$ representation of the Poincaré group, differing in their spin orientations: neutrino spin is along the direction of motion, the antineutrino spin opposite or symbolically:

$$\nu \; , \quad \bar{\nu}.$$

The assignment when to use ν when $\bar{\nu}$ in the above reaction is determined by an additive quantum number the *Lepton number L*, which has the value $+1$ for ν, -1 for $\bar{\nu}$. (See Sec. 10.2.)

The muon neutrino has been predicted[5] theoretically to explain the absence of reactions like $\mu \to 3e$, $\mu \to e + \gamma$, $k \to \mu e$, etc. It has been recently discovered.[6] The neutrinos (antineutrinos) from

$$\pi^+ \to \mu^+ + \nu,$$
$$\pi^- \to \mu^- + \bar{\nu},$$

are scattered from neucleons. About 30 events of the type

$$\bar{\nu} + p \to n + \mu^+$$

[3] C. L. Cowan, F. Reines, F. B. Harrison, H. W. Kruse, and A. D. McGuire, *Science*, **124**, 103 (1956).

[4] C. O. Meuhlhause and S. Oleska, *Phys. Rev.*, **105**, 1322 (1957). For failure to observe double β-decay $2n \to 2p + 2e^-$ which would be possible if $\bar{\nu}_e + n \to p + e^-$, see C. L. Cowan, F. B. Harrison, I. M. Langar, and F. Reines, *Nuovo Cimento*, **3**, 649 (1956) C. L. Cowan and F. Reines, *Phys. Rev.*, **106**, 825 (1957).

[5] K. Nishijima, *Phys. Rev.*, **108**, 907 (1957).

[6] G. Darby, J-M. Gaillard, K. Goulianos, L. M. Lederman, V. Mistry, M. Schwartz, and J. Steinberger, *Phys. Rev. Letters*, **9**, 36 (1962).

are observed but none of the type

$$\bar{\nu} + p \to n + e^+.$$

This implies

$$\nu_e \neq \nu_\mu.$$

The μ-meson was observed first in cosmic rays,[7] and was later shown to arise from the decay of π-mesons.[8]

c. π-Mesons

Spin 0; charge triplet π^+, π^-, π^0.

Spin of π^+: Consider the reactions

$$\pi^+ + d \to p + p,$$
$$p + p \to \pi^+ + d.$$

If the principle of detail balancing holds, the ratio of the total cross sections averaged over spin states of these two processes, at the same center-of-mass energy, depends only on the densities of final states and spin-weight factors $2S_\pi + 1$, $2S_d + 1$. Deuteron spin is 1; and one infers $S_\pi = 0$.[9] (See Exercise 1.)

Intrinsic Parity of π^-: The reaction $\pi^- + d \to n + n$ is observed.[10] π^- has spin 0 and is absorbed from an S-state of the $\pi^- d$ mesic atom. Thus $\pi^- d$ system has $J = 1$ and a parity equal to the intrinsic parity of π^- with respect to (np) system. The final state, because of the Pauli principle, is one of the states

$$^1S_0, \ ^3P_{0,1,2}, \ ^1D_2, \dots.$$

Because of conservation of angular momentum it must be $^3P_1$, which has a parity of -1. Consequently Parity $(\pi^- d) = -$Parity (nn), if parity is conserved in the process.

Parities can also be inferred from charge conjugation C, for CP seems to be conserved (see later).

The mass of pions has been measured first from the energy spectrum of gamma rays in the reaction:

$$\pi^- + p \to n + \gamma.$$

Neutral pions were directly observed by bombarding Be with γ-rays; the π^0 are detected by the two photons in which they decay.[11] Consider the two processes

$$\pi^- p \to n\gamma$$
$$\to n\pi^0 \to n + 2\gamma.$$

[7] C. D. Andersen and S. H. Neddermeyer, *Phys. Rev.*, **51**, 884 (1938); **54**, 88 (1938).

[8] C. M. G. Lattes, H. Muirhead, G. P. S. Occhialini, and C. E. Powell, *Nature*, **159**, 694 (1947).

[9] W. F. Cartwright, C. Richman, M. N. Whitehead, and H. A. Wilcox, *Phys. Rev.*, **81**, 677 (1953).

[10] W. K. H. Panofski et al., *Phys. Rev.*, **81**, 865 (1951).

[11] J. Steinberger, W. K. H. Panofski, and J. S. Steller, *Phys. Rev.*, **78**, 802 (1950).

The first process is electromagnetic, the second is a strong interaction; the ratio of the cross sections of the two processes is therefore an interesting quantity:

$$\text{Panofski ratio} = \frac{\sigma(\pi^- p \to \pi^0 n)}{\sigma(\pi^- p \to n\gamma)}.$$

The experimental value of the ratio is[12] 1.62 ± 0.06.

The decay of π^0 is electromagnetic, most predominantly into 2γ; one estimates[13]

$$\frac{\pi^0 \to e^+ + e^- + \gamma}{\pi^0 \to 2\gamma} \cong \frac{1}{80}.$$

The most recent values for the π^0 lifetime is[14]

$$\tau = 1.9^{+1.3}_{-.8} \times 10^{-16} \text{ sec}.$$

The spin and parity of π^0 can be inferred from the decay $\pi^0 \to 2\gamma$. The final amplitude is a function of the relative momentum k of two photons and the polarization vectors ϵ_1, ϵ_2 satisfying $\mathbf{k} \cdot \epsilon_1 = 0$. A spin 1 particle cannot decay into 2γ,[15] for the only vector (spin 1) final state is of the form $A\epsilon_1 \times \epsilon_2$, which is excluded by Bose statistics, i.e., symmetry under $\epsilon_1, \mathbf{k}_1 \to \epsilon_2, \mathbf{k}_2$. For π^0-spin equal to zero the final amplitude is of the form $A\epsilon_1 \cdot \epsilon_2$ if π^0 is scalar, $A\epsilon_1 \times \epsilon_2 \cdot \mathbf{k}$ if π^0 is pseudo scalar. The parity can therefore be determined by measuring the polarization of the two γ rays.

d. K-Mesons

The first event identified in emulsion was

$$K^+_{\pi3} (\equiv \tau^+) \to \pi^+ + \pi^+ + \pi^-.$$

Also the modes $K^+_{\pi3}(\tau^+) \to \pi^0 + \pi^0 + \pi^+$ have been identified. Other three-body decays are $K^+_{\mu3} \to \mu^+ + \pi^0 + \nu$, $e^+\pi^0\nu$ and the two-body decays
$$\underset{(e3)}{}$$

$$K^+_{\mu2} \to \mu^+ + \nu; \quad K^+_{e2} \to e^+ + \nu.$$

Interestingly, one has also mesons decaying into 2π:

$$K^+_{\pi2}(\equiv \theta^+) \to \pi^0 + \pi^-,$$
$$K^0_{\pi2}(\equiv \theta^0) \to \pi^+ + \pi^-. \quad (V \text{ events.})$$

The negative K-mesons interact very strongly with nuclei; their decay can only be observed in flight (see App. 1).

All these various decay modes were soon recognized to originate from a particle of the same mass, with a small difference in mass among the charge

[12] N. P. Samios, in *Proceedings of Rochester Conference* (New York: Wiley, 1960), p. 35.
[13] R. H. Dalitz, *Proc. Roy. Soc.*, **A64**, 667 (1951).
[14] H. Shwe, F. M. Smith, and W. H. Barkas, *Phys. Rev.*, **125**, 1024 (1962).
[15] C. N. Yang, *Phys. Rev.*, **77**, 242 (1950); L. Landau, *Doklady*, **60**, 207 (1948). See also Chap. 13, Eqs. (13.26)ff.

multiplets: $m(K^-)/m(K^+) = 0.998 \pm 0.013$. Also the lifetimes and excitation functions were approximately the same. But the existence of 2π and 3π decays gave rise to the so-called θ-τ *puzzle*:

Consider $\theta^+ \to \pi^+ + \pi^0$; let J be the angular momentum of the two pions in the c.o.m. system. The intrinsic parity of 2π is $(-1)^2 = +1$, the orbital parity $(-1)^J$. Because θ^+ decays at rest, the spin of θ^+ is also J and intrinsic parity $(-1)^J$. If parity is conserved, the spin and parity assignment of θ is $(J, (-1)^J)$, i.e., $(0, +), (1, -), (2, +), \ldots$. Now consider $\tau^+ \to \pi^+ + \pi^+ + \pi^-$.

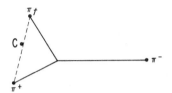

Figure 10.1   The three-pion system.

Let C be the c.o.m. of two π^+ (Fig. 10.1), and **P** relative momentum of the two π^+ with respect to C, **k**-momentum of π^- with respect to C; and ℓ_p, ℓ_k angular momenta associated with **p** and **k**. Parity of the final state is $(-1)^3(-1)^{\ell_p + \ell_k}$. Conservation of angular momentum implies that if the spin of π is zero, then $\ell_k = \ell_p$, because the lowest value of J is $|\ell_p - \ell_k|$ and this has to be zero. The conservation of parity gives τ the assignment $(0, -)$. Thus, if spin of τ is zero, then either τ and θ are different or parity is not conserved. If spin of τ is ≥ 1 one has to study the angular distribution of the pions, but the conclusion is the same.[16]

If in the τ decay there is a π^- emitted with zero energy, then the spin of τ must be even irrespective of parity conservation, for by Bose statistics the total angular momentum is even.

Spin of K: The absence of $K^+ \to \pi^+ + \gamma$ points to K spin to be zero, because this process is forbidden only for this case. Also $K^+ \to \mu^+ + \nu$ behaves like $\pi^+ \to \mu^+ + \nu$; μ^+ is fully polarized in both cases.[17] Furthermore, the existence[18] of $K^0 \to \pi^0 + \pi^0$ implies by Bose statistics an even spin value for K.

e. Nonconservation of Parity

The answer to the question of equality of the τ- and θ-particles hinges on the conservation of parity. One must therefore look into this question. The atomic and nuclear spectroscopic measurements show that electromagnetic

[16] R. H. Dalitz, *Phil. Mag.*, **44**, 1068 (1952).

[17] C. Combes, B. Cork, W. Gailbraith, G. Lamberton, and W. Wentzel, *Phys. Rev.*, **108**, 1348 (1957); see also G. Backenstoss et al., *Phys. Rev. Letters*, **6**, 415 (1961).

[18] J. Brown et al., *Phys. Rev. Letters*, **3**, 51 (1959).

interactions and so-called strong interactions (i.e., interaction conserving isospin) conserve parity—e.g., the double scattering of protons.[19] The possibility of parity violations in the (decay) reactions involving leptons was pointed out by Lee and Yang,[20] and then experimentally observed, first in the β-decay[21] of polarized Co^{60}: $Co^{60} \rightarrow Ni^{60} + e^- + \bar{\nu}$, then in both π- and μ-decays and in μ-captive: $\mu^- + p \rightarrow n + \nu$.[22] In the first case the angular distribution of the electrons showed a pronounced asymmetry favoring a direction opposite to the spin of the Co^{60} nucleus. In the second case,

$$\pi^\pm \rightarrow \mu^\pm + \begin{bmatrix} \nu \\ \bar{\nu} \end{bmatrix}, \; \mu^\pm \rightarrow e^\pm + \nu + \bar{\nu},$$ the electrons are observed to be emitted

asymmetrically, predominantly in the backward direction with respect to the direction of $\mu^\pm$. These asymmetries demonstrate directly, and independent of any theory, the violation of parity in these reactions. These are indications that in our R-amplitudes we have a sum of terms with both $\eta_p = +1$ and -1; one measures the existence of pseudo-scalar terms.

The τ-θ puzzle can be solved if the parity is not conserved in the K-decay; there is, however, the rather unlikely possibility that τ and θ are different and that parity is conserved.

f. The CP-Symmetry

The experiments mentioned above show clearly that the simple space-reflection invariance does not hold. For the spin of Co, e.g. (or the current in the coil producing the magnetic field to polarize Co), together with Co-source form a plane of symmetry, but the electrons are emitted in an asymmetrical way (Fig. 10.2).

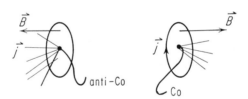

Figure 10.2 CP symmetry.

We can restore the symmetry if we postulate that the mirror image of matter is really antimatter, the electrons are replaced by positrons, or, more generally, particles are replaced by antiparticles. In this case the mirror image of the Co^{60} experiment, e.g., which is not the same as its original, would be just the

[19] O. Chamberlain et al., *Phys. Rev.*, **105**, 288 (1957).

[20] T. D. Lee and C. N. Yang, *Phys. Rev.*, **104**, 254 (1957).

[21] C. Wu et al., *Phys. Rev.*, **105**, 1413 (1957).

[22] M. Garwin, L. Lederman, and M. Weinrich, *Phys. Rev.*, **105**, 1415 (1957); J. L. Friedman and V. Telegdi, *Phys. Rev.*, **105**, 1681 (1957). For above, see A. Astburry et al., *Phys. Rev. Letters*, **3**, 476 (1959).

experiment done with anti-Co. This is the CP-invariance.[23] It is remarkable that *improper Lorentz transformations seem to be coupled with the internal properties of matter*, whereas the proper Lorentz transformations do not.

g. Neutral K-Mesons

We shall see in the next section that the *K*-particles can be assigned to a nonzero value of a new internal quantum number, the hypercharge *Y*, which is conserved in strong interactions. Therefore the antiparticles must have the opposite value of the hypercharge. In particular, $K^0 \neq \bar{K}^0$. But this leads to the following difficulty: Under charge conjugation K^0 is transformed into $\bar{K}^0$. Consider now the decay $K^0 \rightarrow \pi^+ + \pi^-$. The final state with $\ell = 0$ is C- and CP-invariant, but the initial state is not. Gell-Mann and Pais[24] have postulated that the observed K^0 and $\bar{K}^0$ are mixtures of states with CP $= \pm 1$, assuming that the weak decay reactions conserves CP. (Originally they used *C* alone, but since *C* is violated, CP must be used.) If we introduce

$$K_1^0 = \frac{1}{\sqrt{2}}(K^0 + \bar{K}^0), \quad \text{CP} = +1,$$
$$K_2^0 = \frac{1}{\sqrt{2}}(K^0 - \bar{K}^0), \quad \text{CP} = -1. \tag{10.1}$$

Then K_1 can decay into 2π, but K_2 cannot, if CP holds. Hence K_1 and K_2 must have different lifetimes. The strangeness conservation at the production point implies that we have at the beginning a K^0, e.g., in

$$\pi^- + p \rightarrow \Lambda + K^0.$$

The short-lived part of the mixture, $K_1^0 \sim 10^{-10}$ sec, decays and one observes far away, $K_2^0 \sim 6.10^{-6}$ sec; K_1^0, K_2^0 do not have a definite value of hypercharge, but K^0 and $\bar{K}^0$ do have a definite hypercharge.

Experimentally, the particles found far away seemed to decay into 3π, $\ell\pi\nu$, $\pi\mu\nu$ but not into 2π, which confirms the above hypothesis.[25] (However, see further below.) Because the long-lived K_2^0-particle is a mixture of hypercharge ± 1, there has been also much experimental work to detect the effect of $Y = -1$ component, e.g., on the reaction[26]

$$K_2^0 + p \rightarrow \Xi^0 + K^+, \quad \Lambda + \pi^+ + \pi^0; \quad \Lambda + \pi^+, \quad \Sigma^0 + \pi^+.$$

On the other hand, the $Y = +1$ component of K_2^0 gives rise to reactions of the type $K_2^0 + p \rightarrow K^+ + n$, which has also been observed. The regeneration of K_1^0 is also possible by $K_2^0 + p \rightarrow K_1^0 + p$.

---

[23] L. Landau, *Nucl. Phys.*, **3**, 127 (1957); A. Salam, *Nuovo Cimento*, **5**, 229 (1957); T. D. Lee, C. N. Yang, and R. Oehme, *Phys. Rev.*, **106**, 340 (1957).

[24] M. Gell-Mann and A. Pais, *Phys. Rev.*, **97**, 1387 (1955).

[25] M. Bardon, K. Lande, and M. L. Lederman, *Ann. Phys.*, **5**, 156 (1958).

[26] H. Martin, L. Leipuner, W. Chinowsky, F. Shively, and R. Adair, *Phys. Rev. Letters*, **6**, 283 (1961).

h. Possible CP or T Violation

The above analysis based on Eq. (10.1) turned out to be not quite correct. Recently, the decay of the long-lived K_2^0 into two pions, $\pi^+\pi^-$, has been observed[27] with a branching ratio of about 2.10^{-3} with respect to all other decay modes of K_2^0 and with

$$\frac{K_2^0 \to \pi^+\pi^-}{K_1^0 \to \pi^+\pi^-} \simeq 4 \times 10^{-6}.$$

Thus, assuming that the basic superposition principle of quantum mechanics holds, the observed long- and short-lived combinations of K^0 and $\bar{K}^0$, which have simple exponential decay laws, are different than those in Eq. (10.1):

$$\begin{aligned} |L\rangle &= p|K^0\rangle + q|\bar{K}^0\rangle, \\ |S\rangle &= r|K^0\rangle + s|\bar{K}^0\rangle, \end{aligned} \tag{10.2}$$

$|p|^2 + |q|^2 = |r|^2 + |s|^2 = 1$. The CPT-invariance implies $r = p$, $s = -q$.

Although other proposals have been put forward, the most direct explanation of the above experiment is the violation of CP. Which part of the interaction does violate CP remains to be established.[28]

i. Nucleons and Hyperons

Nucleons:

$$n, p, \bar{n}, \bar{p}. \quad \text{Spin } \tfrac{1}{2}.$$

Antiproton has been discovered in nucleon-nucleon collisions at high energies $N + N \to N + N + \bar{N} + N$. The threshold energy for this process is $6M^2 \approx 5.6$ Bev, which is further reduced to 4.3 Bev due to the motion of nucleons in target nuclei.[29]

Hyperons:

$$\Lambda^0, \Sigma^{\pm,0}, \Xi^-, \Xi^0. \quad \text{All spin } \tfrac{1}{2} \text{ (see below).}$$

The Λ^0-particle was found in the reaction $\Lambda^0 \to p + \pi^-$ as a so-called *V*-event with a unique *Q*-value of 37 Bev. Soon other decays have been observed in emulsions, cloud, or bubble chambers: $\Sigma^+ \to \pi^0 + p$ or $\pi^+ + n$ (and *not* $\pi^0 + \bar{p}$); $\Sigma^0 \to \Lambda^0 + \gamma$; $\Xi^- \to \pi^- + \Lambda^0$, and more recently $\Xi^0 \to \Lambda^0 + \pi^0$.

The Spins of the Hyperons: Consider the process

$$\begin{aligned} \pi^- + p &\to \Lambda + K^0 \\ &\to p + \pi^-, \end{aligned}$$

[27] J. H. Christenson, J. W. Cronin, V. L. Fitch, and R. Turlay, *Phys. Rev. Letters*, **13**, 138 (1964).

[28] For a recent review of all the possibilities see the review papers by C. Prentki and by J. S. Bell and J. Steinberger in the *Proceedings of Oxford International Conference on Elementary Particles*, Rutherford High Energy Laboratory, January 1966.

[29] O. Chamberlain, E. Segré, C. Wiegand, and T. Ypsilantis, *Phys. Rev.*, **100**, 947 (1955).

with Λ's produced in the forward and backward direction.[30] The orbital angular momentum along this direction is zero, hence the spin component $m_\Lambda = \pm\frac{1}{2}$. This does not prove yet that $S_\Lambda = \frac{1}{2}$. Now one looks at the decay of Λ and the angular distribution of decay products (Fig. 10.3).

Figure 10.3   Spin-measurement of Λ.

The angular distribution is isotropic for $S_\Lambda = \frac{1}{2}$; it is $(1 + 3\cos^2\theta)$ for $S_\Lambda = \frac{3}{2}$, and $(1 - 2\cos^2\theta + 5\cos^4\theta)$ for $S_\Lambda = \frac{5}{2}$, etc.

The experiment indicates[31] $S_\Lambda = \frac{1}{2}$. The method can also be applied to

$$\pi^+ p \to \Sigma^+ + K^+.$$

Another method is to look at the process

$$K^- + p \to Y + \pi \quad (Y \text{ either } \Lambda \text{ or } \Sigma).$$

If K^- is captured in this process from an s-state, then again the conservation of the component of angular momentum along the direction of outgoing hyperon implies $m_Y = \pm\frac{1}{2}$. Consequently one can look at the angular distribution of the decay of the hyperon. There is a strong argument that K^--p capture is from an s-state[32]; and the experimental result implies[33] $S_\Sigma = \frac{1}{2}$.

The spin of Ξ has not yet been determined. All antihyperons, except $\bar{\Xi}^0$ have been experimentally observed, most recently $\bar{\Xi}^+$.[34]

j. Relative Intrinsic Parities

We have seen in Chap. 5 that the intrinsic parities of the particles are not uniquely determined: If there are additive quantum numbers, q, then we can assign any parity of the form $\eta e^{i\varphi q}$ for all φ. In strong interactions we now know such additive quantum numbers, N, Y, I_3, and we will show that only certain relative parities are meaningful.

[30] R. Adair, *Phys. Rev.*, **100**, 1540 (1955).

[31] P. Eisler et al., *Nuovo Cimento*, **7**, 222 (1958).

[32] T. Day, J. Sucher, and G. Snow, *Nuovo Cimento*, **14**, 637 (1959); *Phys. Rev.*, **119**, 1100 (1960).

[33] L. Alvarez, *Proceedings of the Ninth International Conference on High Energy Physics* (Moscow: USSR Academy of Sciences, 1960), Vol. 1, p. 471.

[34] H. L. Brown et al., *Phys. Rev. Letters*, **8**, 255 (1962); *ibid.*, 257 (1962).

The parity conservation in low-energy nuclear physics is well established. For example, by slow polarized neutron capture,[35]

$$n + Cd^{113} \to Cd^{114*} \to Cd^{114} + \gamma;$$

i.e.,

$$(\text{spin } \tfrac{1}{2}, +) \to (1+) \to (0+),$$

and the relative amplitude of the wrong parity state to the correct parity state is of the order of 10^{-4} (in cross section, 10^{-8}). In pion physics we have seen that we can only determine the relative parity of π with respect to nucleons.

For strange particles we have also restrictions. Because the decays $\Lambda \to p\pi$, $K \to 2\pi$ do not conserve parity, ΛN or $K\pi$ relative parities are not defined. Consider the reaction $\pi^- + p \to \Lambda + K^0$ which conserves parity. (If parity is not conserved it is possible to find Λ longitudinally polarized, which could be detected by asymmetry in the Λ decay which is not found.) We have therefore a meaningful Λ-K^0 relative parity, but there is no way of separating Λ- and K-parities, which is due to associated production, or to hypercharge conservation (see next section). If at threshold the Λ-K system is in an s-state, then the Λ-K relative parity is even or odd, depending whether the π^--p system is in a p-state or an s-state, respectively. Similarly, we have a Σ-K relative parity which is equivalent to a Σ-Λ relative parity if we combine it with the K-Λ relative parity. On the other hand, the Ξ-parity does not depend on K-Λ and Σ-Λ parities. For in the reaction

$$\pi^- + p \to K^0 + K^0 + \Xi^0$$

the parities of K's compensate and we have only Ξ-N relative parity. Or, more conveniently, consider the reaction

$$\Xi^- + p \to \Lambda + \Lambda$$

occurring in the s-state of Ξ^--p system. The Λ-Λ system, by Pauli principle, is in the states $^1S_0$, $^3P_{0,1,2}$, $^1D_2, \ldots$. If $J = 1$, the final state is $^3P_1$ which has negative parity, so Ξ-p relative parity must be odd; if $J = $ even, the parity is even, in which case the initial state cannot be in $^3S_1$. (This process is very similar to the one discussed earlier of the parity determination of π in $\pi^- d \to mn$.)

Thus, we have altogether the following relative parities among the strongly interacting stable particles:

$$\pi N, \ K\Lambda, \ \Sigma\Lambda, \ \Xi N.$$

The relative parity of ΛN or $K\Xi$ is not defined; it can be assigned (Table 10–1).

Table 10–1
Relative Parities

$N\Lambda$	$+$	Assigned
$N\pi$	$-$	Measured
$NK(K\Lambda)$	$-$	,,
$N\Sigma(\Lambda\Sigma)$	$+$	,,
$N\Xi$		

[35] R. Haas, L. B. Leipuner, and R. K. Adair, *Phys. Rev.*, **116**, 1221 (1959).

10.2   Assignment of "Internal" Quantum Numbers

a. Charge, Baryon Number, Lepton Number

The *electric charge* Q is the best known internal quantum number. It gives rise to a *superselection rule*; i.e., not only is the charge absolutely and additively conserved in all reactions, but we cannot form pure quantum mechanical states consisting of states with different values of charge and with definite phase relations between them.

Charge conservation and similarly the conservation of the *baryon number* N and *lepton number* L arise from, or explain, the absolute stability of the particles. Thus, electron and position are stable because there are no other lighter charged particles, and charge is conserved. (In the frame in which the decaying particle is at rest the mass of the decaying particle must be larger than or equal to the sum of the masses of decay it produces.) Similarly, proton is absolutely stable. To account for it we introduce the quantum number N and the fact that there are no other lighter particles with $N = 1$ and that N is absolutely conserved.[36] The stability of the neutrino is accounted for by the lepton number conservation, or the fact that there are no lighter particles with half integer spin (see Table 10–2). We recall the theorem (Chap. 4) that, as a result of relativistic invariance, the number of fermions in any reaction must be even.

Table 10–2

Absolutely Stable Particles

d	
$p(\bar{p})$	Lightest particle with $N \neq 0$
$e^-(e^+)$	Lightest particle with $Q \neq 0$
$\nu(\bar{\nu})$	{ Lightest fermion { Lightest particle with $L \neq 0$
γ	Cannot decay into $\nu + \bar{\nu}$ by the conservation of angular momentum
—	No spin zero, stable particle

Lepton Number L.   We have already mentioned that ν and $\bar{\nu}$ are distinguished by their leptonic numbers. The consistent assignment of the lepton number L to other leptons is shown in Table 10–3. With this assignment L is absolutely

Table 10–3

Leptonic Number L

Particle	ν	$\bar{\nu}$	e^-	e^+	μ^-	μ^+
L	$+1$	-1	$+1$	-1	$+1$	-1

[36] The baryon conservation law was first postulated by E. C. G. Stueckelberg, *Helv. Phys. Acta*, **11**, 299 (1938). See also E. P. Wigner, *Proc. Nat. Acad. Sci.*, **38**, 449 (1952). For lepton conservation law, see G. Marx, *Acta Phys. Hung.*, **3**, 55 (1953); A. B. Zeldovitch, *Dokl. Akad. Nauk. SSSR*, **91**, 1317 (1953); E. J. Konopinski and H. M. Mahmoud, *Phys. Rev.*, **92**, 1045 (1953).

conserved. We must have then

$$\pi^+ \to \mu^+ + \nu; \quad \pi^- \to \mu^- + \bar{\nu}; \quad \mu^+ \to e^+ + \nu_e + \bar{\nu}_\mu.$$

The decays $\mu \to e + 2\nu$ or $e + 2\bar{\nu}$ are forbidden. Part of the conservation of the lepton number is contained in charge conservation, part in the conservation of evenness of the fermion number.

Because ν_e and ν_μ are different and one reacts only with electrons, the other with muons, we could introduce two kinds of lepton numbers—*electronic lepton number* L_e and *muonic lepton number* L_μ, which are separately conserved (Table 10-4). Reactions like $\nu_\mu + p \to p + e^- + \mu^+ + \nu_e$ can distinguish between separate L_e, L_μ conservation and L and $(-1)^{L_e}$ conservation.

Table 10–4

L_e	+1	−1	L_μ	+1	−1
	e^-	e^+		μ^-	μ^+
	ν_e	$\bar{\nu}_e$		ν_μ	$\bar{\nu}_\mu$

b. Charge Independence and Isospin

After the discovery of the neutron it was postulated by Heisenberg[37] that so far as nuclear forces are concerned, n and p are two different states of the same particle. Then the equality of p-p and n-p forces was deduced in scattering experiments[38] (also the equality of n-n forces with a smaller accuracy). This behavior could be well understood by the meson theory of Yukawa[39] according which the nuclear forces between any pair of nucleons are transmitted by the same mesons.

Without the electromagnetic effect and Pauli principle, all nuclei composed of the same number of nucleons should therefore show the same nuclear energy levels. The Pauli principle eliminates some of the energy levels. For example, the ground state of d is $3S_1$; this state is not allowed for H^2 or n^2. And, because for the known strength of the nuclear forces, there is only one bound state; there are no stable or metastable H^2 or n^2. Or, consider the nuclei with $A = 6$. The energy levels with or without the Pauli principle are shown in Fig. 10.4. All the low-lying energy levels of B^6 and H^6 are eliminated so that no such stable or metastable nuclei can exist.

The isotopic spin quantum number is introduced to label the degeneracy of states of a given A, in analogy to the two-valuedness of the atomic energy levels which gave rise to the spin quantum number. The members of an isotopic spin multiplet have the same J and parity; they differ only in charge. So far as nuclear forces are concerned, the energy levels are independent of I_3, but the electrostatic interactions increase the energy of states with higher

[37] W. Heisenberg, *Z. Physik.*, **77**, 1 (1932).
[38] G. Breit and E. Wigner, *Phys. Rev.*, **50**, 850 (1936); B. Cassen and E. Condon, *Phys. Rev.*, **50**, 846 (1936).
[39] H. Yukawa, *Proc. Math. Soc. Japan*, **17**, 48 (1935).

number of protons and decrease those with a higher number of neutrons—an effect which can be taken into account (Fig. 10.5).

Except for very small effects the charge independence seems to be well established in light nuclei.[40]

In pion and strange-particle physics the direct tests are not very accurate.[41] Let us remark here the difference between *charge independence* and *charge symmetry*. The latter means $I_3 \rightarrow -I_3$ (a rotation of 180° around the first

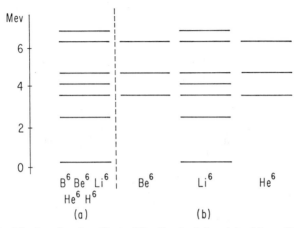

Figure 10.4 Nuclear levels: effect of Pauli principle—(a) without Pauli principle, (b) with Pauli principle.

(or second) axis in the isospace); the former implies all rotations in isospace, e.g., also the exchange.

Pions, kaons, and hyperons occur in charge multiplets with very small mass differences between the members of the multiplets. We can therefore associate to them an isospin quantum number. But now it must be experimentally tested that charge independence holds. For this purpose any consequence of the isotopic spin amplitudes derived in Chap. 4 may be used. For example, the K-N system has only two independent amplitudes corresponding to total isospin 0 and 1, and we can immediately derive the equality of the following amplitudes (spin parts being equal, or averaged over spins):

$$R(K^+p \rightarrow K^+p) = R(K^0n \rightarrow K^0n)$$
$$R(K^+n \rightarrow K^+n) = R(K^0p \rightarrow K^0p)$$
$$R(K^+n \rightarrow K^0p) = R(K^0p \rightarrow K^+n) \qquad (10.3)$$
$$R(K^+n \rightarrow K^+n) + R(K^+n \rightarrow K^0p) = R(K^+p \rightarrow K^+p)$$
$$R(K^0p \rightarrow K^0p) + R(K^0p \rightarrow K^+n) = R(K^0n \rightarrow K^0n).$$

[40] For a survey, see D. H. Wilkinson, *Nature*, **172**, 576 (1953); W. Burcham, *Progr. Nucl. Phys.*, **4**, 171 (1953).

[41] A. M. Sachs et al., *Phys. Rev.*, **119**, 1716 (1960). The discrepancy in the binding energy of hypernuclei, $_\Lambda He^4$ and $_\Lambda H^4$ can be explained by electro-magnetic mixing of particles with different isospin. B. W. Downs, *Nuovo Cimento*, **43**, 454 (1966).

Only the last two equations test charge independence; the first three are also true under charge symmetry alone. The experimentally observed quantities are proportional to $|R|^2$. Consider the fourth relation $R_n + R_{CE} = R_p$.

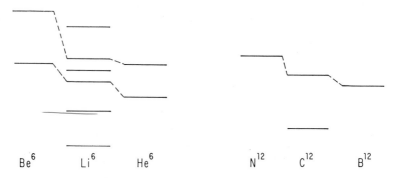

Be^6 Li^6 He^6 N^{12} C^{12} B^{12}

Figure 10.5   Nuclear levels: effect of Coulomb interaction.

Because R is a complex number, we can represent it as shown in Fig. 10.6. Hence, by triangular inequality, we have

$$|R_n| + |R_{CE}| \geqslant |R_p| \geqslant ||R_n| - |R_{CE}||$$

or, in terms of cross sections,

$$\sqrt{\sigma_n} + \sqrt{\sigma_{CE}} \geqslant \sqrt{\sigma_p} \geqslant |\sqrt{\sigma_n} - \sqrt{\sigma_{CE}}|$$

and two more inequalities for the other sides of the triangle. These relations may be used to test charge independence.

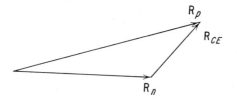

Figure 10.6.

Many other tests of charge independence have been proposed.[42]

In all these considerations, electromagnetic interactions and mass differences are neglected. For example, the various πN cross sections can be fitted in terms of two parameters, $R^{(3/2)}$ and $R^{(1/2)}$; from Eq. (4.14) we obtain

[42] D. Feldman, *Phys. Rev.*, **103**, 254 (1956); T. D. Lee, *Phys. Rev.*, **99**, 337 (1955); Y. Yamaguchi, *Progr. Theor. Phys.*, **19**, 662 (1958).

Process	**Amplitude $R^{\alpha_3 \alpha_4}_{\alpha_1 \alpha_2}$ in Terms of R^I**
$\pi^+ p \rightarrow \pi^+ p$ $\pi^- n \rightarrow \pi^- n$	$R^{1\frac{1}{2}}_{1\frac{1}{2}} = R^{3/2}$
$\pi^- p \rightarrow \pi^- p$ $\pi^+ n \rightarrow \pi^+ n$	$R^{-1\frac{1}{2}}_{-1\frac{1}{2}} = \frac{1}{3}[R^{3/2} + 2R^{1/2}]$
$\pi^- p \rightarrow \pi^0 n$ $\pi^+ n \rightarrow \pi^0 p$	$R^{0\frac{1}{2}}_{-1\frac{1}{2}} = \frac{\sqrt{2}}{3}[R^{3/2} - R^{1/2}]$
$\pi^0 p \rightarrow \pi^0 p$ $\pi^0 n \rightarrow \pi^0 n$	$R^{0\frac{1}{2}}_{0\frac{1}{2}} = \frac{1}{3}[2R^{3/2} + R^{1/2}]$

(10.4)

Other tests are based on the comparison of reactions and branching ratios. Examples:

(1)
$$\frac{\sigma(pp \rightarrow d + \pi^+)}{\sigma(np \rightarrow d + \pi^0)} = 2. \qquad (10.5)$$

[Note that d has $I = 0$ ($Q = I_3 + 1$).]

(2)
$$\frac{\sigma(K^- d \rightarrow \Sigma^- p)}{\sigma(Kd \rightarrow \Sigma^- n)} = 2. \qquad (10.6)$$

c. Relation between Isospin, Baryon Number N, and Charge

Proton and neutron can be combined into an isotopic spin doublet: Proton $I_3 = +\frac{1}{2}$, neutron $I_3 = -\frac{1}{2}$. Of course the introduction of I-spin is meaningful only if it is conserved in some instances. This is the case in so-called strong interactions. Because the charge of proton and neutron are $+1$ and 0, respectively, we have the relation

$$Q = I_3 + \tfrac{1}{2}.$$

In the case of N nucleons, because Q and I_3 are additive, we find

$$Q_{\text{tot}} = I_{3_{\text{tot}}} + \frac{N}{2}.$$

For each I, $I_3 = +I, \ldots, -I$, and the charges of the $(2I + 1)$ members of the multiplets are $I + N/2, \ldots, -I + N/2$. We may call $N/2$ the *center of charge* of the nucleon system. For antinucleons, $\bar{p}$ has $I_3 = -\frac{1}{2}$, $\bar{n}$ has $I_3 = +\frac{1}{2}$, hence $Q = I_3 + \frac{1}{2}$. Or, if we interpret N as *the number of nucleons minus the number of antinucleons*, we have the general equation

$$Q = I_3 + \frac{N}{2} \qquad (10.7)$$

valid now for any nucleon-antinucleon system. We thus obtain an additive quantum number, baryon number N, which is $+1$ for nucleons and -1 for antinucleons. This quantum number is indeed useful, because of the stability of protons. Reactions like $p \rightarrow e^+ + \gamma$, $p \rightarrow e^+ + \nu + \bar{\nu}$ have never been observed. (Proton lifetime has been shown to exceed 10^{21} years.[43]) They are

[43] G. Backenstoss et al., *Nuovo Cimento*, **16**, 749 (1960).

forbidden by lepton-number conservation, but we can also use the baryon-number conservation. In $n \rightarrow p + e^- + \bar{\nu}$, again both say the same thing. But, of course, there are processes involving only baryons or leptons, in which case we have to use baryon- or lepton-number conservation, respectively. We then have the assignments

$$\text{Baryon number } N \begin{array}{|cccc} p & n & \bar{p} & \bar{n} \\ 1 & 1 & -1 & -1 \end{array}. \tag{10.8}$$

Two identical nucleons (*pp* or *nn*) have, by the Pauli principle, an antisymmetric amplitude; they are symmetric under the interchange of isotopic spins. The *n-p* system can be symmetric or antisymmetric in spin and momenta, similarly in isospin. But with the introduction of isospin, we can consider the nucleons to be identical. Therefore the amplitude must be antisymmetrical under the interchange of two nucleons (change of momenta, spin, and isospin). This is a *generalized Pauli principle*; accordingly the *pp*, *nn*, and *np* in $I = 1$ states are ^1S, ^1D; ^3P, ^3F, while *np* in $I = 0$ states are ^3S, ^3D; ^1P, ^1F.

In the case of electrons the isotopic spin is not defined. If we consider also for this case the charge as an internal degree of freedom and apply the generalized Pauli principle we must have an antisymmetric amplitude for the two-electron system. Let η^C be the phase factors under the exchange of charge (charge conjugation, or particle-antiparticle conjugation), ℓ and S the angular momentum and spin states, then

$$(-1)^\ell (-1)^{S+1} \eta_1^C \eta_2^C = -1.$$

For two electrons or two positrons we get the usual Pauli principle, ($\eta_1 \eta_2 = 1$), but for $(e^+ - e^-)$ system we have

$$\eta_1^C \eta_2^C = (-1)^{\ell+S}.$$

Consider, as an application, the decay of positronium into *n* photons. The charge conjugation parity of *n* photons is $(-1)^n$. If *C* is conserved we have $(-1)^{\ell+S} = (-1)^n$. Therefore, positronium in ^3S-state decays into an odd number of photons (3γ), in ^1S-state into an even number of photons (2γ). Decay of ^3S-state into 2γ is also forbidden by angular momentum conservation.[15]

d. *Strangeness or Hypercharge Quantum Number*

The hyperons together with the *K*-mesons showed a remarkable property: They were produced with large cross sections in scattering experiments; but they have relatively a very long lifetime ($10^{-8} - 10^{-10}$ sec) so that they can be identified as particles; and moreover they decay into π, *N*, and other hyperons or kaon. It was also found that these new or *strange particles* were produced in association with at least one other strange particle. (*Associated production.*) It follows from here that the production and decay processes must be quite different. A new approximative selection rule must prevent the decay from occuring, whereas in association with other particles in production, the conservation law is exactly satisfied. This is the so-called *strangeness* scheme of Gell-Mann and Nishijima.[44] We introduce a new additive quantum number, called the *strangeness number*, which is conserved in production processes but which is violated in decay reactions. To pions and nucleons we associate zero strangeness, because they decay into leptons and protons. If one now considers some of the observed processes one easily arrives at the following *strangeness assignments*:

$$
\begin{array}{c|ccccccc}
\text{Particle} & K^+ & K^0 & \Lambda^0 & \Sigma^{\pm,0} & \Xi^{-,0} & \pi & N \\
\hline
\text{Strangeness } S & 1 & 1 & -1 & -1 & -2 & 0 & 0
\end{array}
\tag{10.9}
$$

The antiparticles K^-, $\bar{K}^0$, $\bar{\Lambda}^0$, $\bar{\Sigma}$, $\bar{\Xi}$ have the opposite strangeness. All production processes should satisfy $\Delta S = 0$, and all decay processes $|\Delta S| = 1$; indeed they do. For example, the process $\pi^- + p \to \Lambda^0 + K^0$ is allowed, but $\pi^- + n \to \Lambda^0 + K^-$ is not. The decay $\Sigma^0 \to \Lambda^0 + \gamma$ does violate the $\Delta S = 1$ rule; but it is an electromagnetic process and does not belong to the same category. The above scheme also explains a striking difference between K^- and $K^+ : K^-$ can be absorbed: $K^- + p \to (\Lambda, \Sigma) + \pi$, whereas K^+ can make at low energies only elastic scattering until pion production occurs, $K^+ + p \to K^+ + n + \pi^+$ or $K^0 + p + \pi^+$.

There is also a more theoretical approach to the strangeness quantum number. The hyperons, being heavier than nucleons, finally decay into protons and leptons. In both decay and production the nucleon number N is conserved, if we associate to all hyperons the nucleon or baryon number 1 and to antihyperons the baryon number -1. Now we ask whether we can assign isotopic spin to strange particles and what would be the relation between Q and I_3 given in Eq. (10.7).

We associate to pions and kaons which enter into the production processes the baryon number 0 and, anticipating the charge independence of these processes, isotopic spin 1 and $\frac{1}{2}$ mesons, respectively. For pions, we have thus $Q = I_3$, for $K^{+,0}$ mesons; $Q = I_3 + \frac{1}{2}$, for K^-, $\bar{K}^0$; $Q = I_3 - \frac{1}{2}$. In the case of hyperons, we have a singlet Λ^0 with $I = 0$, a triplet Σ with $I = 1$ and a doublet Ξ with $I = \frac{1}{2}$. The relation between Q and I_3 for these is $Q = I_3$, $Q = I_3$, and $Q = I_3 - \frac{1}{2}$ ($I_3 = \frac{1}{2}$ is Ξ^0, $-\frac{1}{2}$ is Ξ^-). If we now compare these relations with the table of strangeness above we can write a single equation valid for any number of pions, nucleons, and strange particles:

$$
\begin{aligned}
Q &= I_3 + \tfrac{1}{2}(S + N) \\
&= I_3 + Y/2.
\end{aligned}
\tag{10.10}
$$

[44] M. Gell-Mann, *Phys. Rev.*, **92**, 833 (1953); T. Nakao and K. Nishijima, *Progr. Theor. Phys.*, **10**, 581 (1953).

Because N is always conserved, the so-called *hyperon charge Y* is equivalent to strangeness; it is more convenient to use Y with the assignments:

Particle	π	N	$K^{+,0}$	Λ^0	Σ	Ξ
Y	0	1	1	0	0	−1

$$\text{(10.11)}$$

Actually Σ^0 has been predicted on the basis of the above treatment and found later experimentally; so is Ξ^0. Also a particle with $I = 0$, $Y = 0$ would fit into this scheme.

e. Classification of Interactions according to Conservation Laws

We can summarize our discussion of assignment of quantum numbers and various types of interactions in Table 10–5.

Table 10–5

	LORENTZ INVARIANCE E, P, J	MULTIPLICA- TIVE QUANTUM NUMBERS				ADDITIVE QUAN- TUM NUMBERS					ISO- TOPIC SPIN I
		P	C	T	CP	Q	N	L	Y	I_3	
Strong interactions	✓	✓	✓	✓	✓	✓	✓	✓	✓	✓	✓
EM interactions	✓	✓	✓	✓	✓	✓	✓	✓	✓	✓	×
Weak interactions	✓	×	×	✓	✓	✓	✓	✓	×	×	×
Gravitation	✓										

The *weak interactions have additional features and symmetries not shown in the above table.* We have already noted a possible new quantum number distinguishing the two types of neutrino. On the other hand, the Q, N, L conservation does not characterize all weak interactions. For example, the following reactions consistent with these laws have not been observed:

$$\mu^- \rightarrow 2e^- + e^+,$$
$$\mu^+ + p \rightarrow e^- + p; \quad \mu^- + n \rightarrow e^- + n,$$
$$K^0 \rightarrow \mu^+ + e^-.$$

Phenomenologically, this is explained by allowing only certain types of amplitudes (or certain types of "currents" in the Lagrangian theory) illustrated schematically in Fig. 10.7.

Only weak reactions connecting the sides of the tetrahedron are possible, together with all CPT equivalent and analytically continued reactions. Various phenomenological rules

$$\left[\text{such as } |\Delta I| = \tfrac{1}{2} \text{ and } \frac{\Delta S}{\Delta Q} = +1 \text{ rule} \right]$$

have also been introduced.

There is a different kind of symmetry in weak interactions not found in other interactions. In β-decay and in μ-decay it is observed experimentally that one has a unique spin basis function in the R-amplitude, at least at low energies. In other words the form of the amplitude is much simpler than that required by relativistic invariance alone, which must be due to an additional symmetry requirement. In field theory the situation is explained by the so-called chirality invariance, and the corresponding amplitude is the V-A amplitude (Exercise 14).

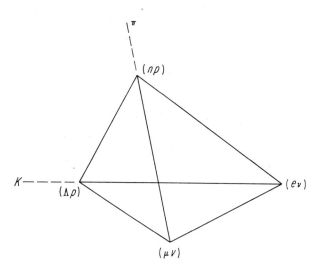

Figure 10.7   Puppi triangle.

f. G-Parity (Isospin Parity)

This is a useful, but not new, quantum number in the study of pion, baryon, and antibaryon systems.[45] It combines simultaneous invariance under particle-antiparticle conjugation and isotopic spin invariance:

$G \equiv$ Particle-antiparticle conjugation $\times$ rotation by $180°$ around the second axis in the isotopic spin space,

$$G = D^S(C)D^I(C)D^I\left(\exp\left(i\frac{\sigma_2}{2}\pi\right)\right), \qquad (10.12)$$

for outgoing particles, and the conjugate operators for the incoming particles. If we have C- and I-invariance, we have also automatically G-invariance. The first two terms in G change particle into antiparticle; the last term changes the third component of the isotopic spin again, according to $e^{i\pi\frac{\sigma_2}{2}}$ for $I = \frac{1}{2}$.

---

[45] L. Michel, *Nuovo Cimento*, **10**, 319 (1953); T. D. Lee and C. N. Yang, *Nuovo Cimento*, **3**, 749 (1956); C. J. Goebel, *Phys. Rev.*, **103**, 258 (1956).

We thus obtain

$$G: \quad \pi^+ \to -\pi^+; \quad \pi^- \to -\pi^-; \quad \pi^0 \to -\pi^0,$$
$$p \to \bar{n}, \quad n \to -\bar{p},$$
$$\Lambda \to \bar{\Lambda}, \quad \text{etc.}$$

On the other hand, because G is a discrete transformation, its representations are one-dimensional phase factors η_G—one for each particle. The pions have the G-parity $\eta_G = -1$. Note that under charge conjugation only neutral particles have a definite η_G. For baryons we do not have a definite η_G, but for baryon-antibaryon system we have. Quite generally, η_G has a definite value for systems with $N = 0$ and $S = 0$ (all additive quantum numbers zero).

The G-parity and the corresponding selection rules for the baryon-antibaryon systems is obtained as follows. We have seen in Sec. 4.7 that the intrinsic parity of baryon-antibaryon system (same kind) is odd. If we think the baryon and the antibaryon to be the same particle differing by η_G and use a further generalized Pauli principle (analogous to the case of positronium discussed above) for fermions, we obtain

$$(-1)(1-)^{I+L+S}\eta_G\bar{\eta}_G = 1,$$

where L and S are the orbital angular momentum and total spin of the baryon-antibaryon system. The G-parity of the system is therefore

$$\eta_G\bar{\eta}_G = (-1)^{I+L+S}.$$

In the decay of such a system into n pions we must have, by conservation of G-parity,

$$(-1)^{I+L+S} = (-1)^n, \tag{10.13}$$

which shows that $B\bar{B}$-system in $^1S_0$ state can decay into at least three pions in $I = 1$ or at least four pions in $I = 0$ state. Similarly $^3S_1$ can decay into at least two pions in $I = 1$ and at least three pions in $I = 0$ state, etc. [See Table in Ref. 45(2).]

As a further application of G-invariance, one can easily deduce that an even number of pions cannot go into an odd number of pions via strong interactions (Exercise 13).

g. Mass Differences

We shall refer to the mass differences between the members of an isotopic multiplet as the *electromagnetic mass differences*. For only if these mass differences are neglected we have an exact isospin invariance commuting with the Lorentz invariance. These mass differences are small. An important number is the neutron-proton mass difference:

$$\Delta m = m_n - m_p = 1.294 \text{ Mev} = 0.09 \, m_\pi,$$
$$\frac{\Delta m}{m} = 0.138 \text{ per cent.}$$

Other electromagnetic mass-differences are shown in Table 10–6.

Table 10–6

Electromagnetic Mass Differences

Δm	Mev	IN UNITS OF m_π	IN UNITS OF m_e	$\dfrac{\Delta m}{m}$, per cent
$m_n - m_p$	1.2933 ± 0.0001	0.0095	2.52	0.138
$m_{\Sigma^-} - m_{\Sigma^0}$	4.86 ± 0.007	0.036	9.5	0.406
$m_{\Sigma^0} - m_{\Sigma^+}$	3.04 ± 0.09	0.0225	5.95	0.255
$m_{\Xi^-} - m_{\Xi^0}$	6.5 ± 1.0	0.048	12.60	0.49
$m_{\pi^\pm} - m_{\pi^0}$	4.6056 ± 0.0055	0.034	9.00	3.4
$m_{K^0} - m_{K^\pm}$	3.90 ± 0.25	0.029	7.61	0.79

For baryons, the negatively charged member of the multiplet is always the heaviest, the positively charged member the lightest. In the case of mesons, charged pions are heavier, whereas charged kaons are lighter than their neutral counterpart.

10.3   Quantum Numbers of the Resonant States

We are quite familiar with the connection between the resonances and excited states of systems in atomic and nuclear physics. For example, $\gamma + H \to H^* \to H + \gamma$, or $n + A \to A^*$ (compound nucleus) $\to a + B$. We could not understand atomic and nuclear physics if we knew the ground structures alone. Therefore, the study of particle resonances is fundamental in the understanding of the structure of elementary particles.

The instability of the resonant states can be understood qualitatively in the same way as in nuclear physics. The compound system is formed but is in an unfavorable configuration to be completely stable.

The salient feature of strong interactions which differs them from other interactions is the existence of many resonances.

We want to emphasize the following features concerning the resonant states:

1. One can associate to them definite quantum numbers, spin, isospin, charge, hypercharge, baryon number.
2. These resonant states in strong interactions are characterized by their shorter lifetime ($\sim 10^{-22}$ sec); they decay, therefore, again via strong interactions; that is to say, all the conservation laws of strong interactions are satisfied also in the decay, in contrast to the electromagnetic and weak decay of the other particles. Because definite quantum numbers can be assigned to these resonances, they differ from other particles only quantitatively.

We now discuss in some detail how one assigns quantum numbers to resonant states.

a. Pion-Nucleon Resonances ($N = 1$, $Y = 1$)

The earliest known resonances are those observed in the π-N system, the $S = 0$, $N = +1$ resonances. They have been observed in scattering and in photo-pion production reactions. The first one is the resonance at 1236 Bev with half-width $\Gamma/2 \simeq 60$ Bev. A definite I-spin can be associated to this state as follows: The reaction $\pi^+ p \to \pi^+ p$ shows the resonance predominantly; this state has $I = \frac{3}{2}$; in a lesser degree we see the same resonance in $\pi^- p \left\langle \begin{smallmatrix} \pi^- p \\ \pi^0 n \end{smallmatrix} \right.$. According to Eq. (10.4) we have

$$\frac{\sigma(\pi^+ p \to \pi^+ p)}{\sigma(\pi^- p \to \pi^- p \text{ and } \pi^- p \to \pi^0 n)} = 1 \bigg/ \left(\frac{1}{9} + \frac{2}{9}\right) = 3, \qquad (10.14)$$

which is in agreement with the experiment. But π^- p-scattering has some $I = \frac{1}{2}$ component. The pure $I = \frac{1}{2}$ state

$$\sigma^{(I = \frac{1}{2})} = \frac{3}{2}[\sigma(\pi^- p) - \frac{1}{3}\sigma(\pi^+ p)] \qquad (10.15)$$

does not show this resonance (Fig. 10.8). We conclude that the 1236 Bev state has $I = \frac{3}{2}$, and we have additional evidence for charge independence. This resonance is well accounted for by the Chew-Low static model (see Chap. 12). Its spin is $J = \frac{3}{2}$; its decay is 100 per cent into the πN-channel. It is a p-wave resonance, hence parity $+$.

The $I = \frac{3}{2}$ curve shows another broad resonance at 1922 Bev with $\Gamma/2 \approx$ 95 Bev; its spin is $\frac{7}{2}$, parity $+$. There is also a small bump at 1650 Bev, which is probably not a true resonant state.[46]

In the $I = \frac{1}{2}$ channel we have two distinct resonances. One is at 1512 Bev with $\Gamma/2 \approx 65$ Bev, and is also known from photoproduction reactions; the angular distribution and polarization of the recoil protons determine the spin and parity of this state to be $(\frac{3}{2}, -)$ $(0, \frac{3}{2})$. The other $I = \frac{1}{2}$ resonance is at 1688 Bev with $\Gamma/2 \approx 50$ Bev whose spin is again determined from photoproduction experiments to be $\frac{5}{2}$; it is a $F\frac{5}{2}$ state, i.e., parity $+$. (A classification of π-N resonances is given in Chap. 12.)

We also remark in connection with Fig. 10.8 that $\pi^- p$ and $\pi^+ p$ cross sections seem to approach the same constant at very high energies (Pomeranchuk-limit); see previous chapter.

Other π-N resonances are shown in Table 1–3, App. 1.

b. Pion Resonances ($N = 0$, $Y = 0$)

The existence of an $I = 1$, π-π resonance and $I = 0$, 3π-resonance has been used in the analysis of the electron-nucleon scattering experiment measuring the form factors of neutron and proton.[46a]

[46] J. C. Brisson et al., *Nuovo Cimento*, **19**, 210 (1961).
[46a] W. R. Frazer and J. R. Falco, *Phys. Rev.*, **117**, 1609 (1960).

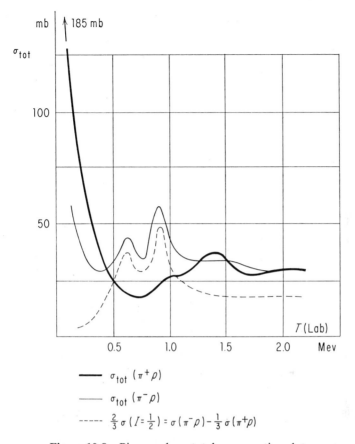

Figure 10.8 Pion-nucleon total cross-section data.

Directly, the 2π-resonance has been observed in the reactions[47]

$$\pi^- + p \to \pi^+ + \pi^- + n$$
$$\to \pi^+ + \pi^0 + p$$

for π^- momentum, 1.9 Bev/c. If the 2π form a resonant state, then we have a two-body reaction, and the center of mass energy of the two-pion system should show a sharp peak. Indeed the barycentric total energy of two pions shows a sharp peak at about $m = 760$ Bev with a half-width $\Gamma/2 \approx 60$ Bev for both $\pi^+\pi^-$ and $\pi^+\pi^0$, with a branching ratio $(\pi^-\pi^+n)/(\pi^-\pi^0p) = 1.8 \pm 0.03$. This is the ρ-meson state. The isospin can only be $I = 1$ or 2. The above branching ratio, and the fact that in $\pi^+p \to \pi^+\pi^+n$; $\pi^+p \to \pi^+\pi^0p$ the resonance is observed in $\pi^+\pi^0$ and not in $\pi^+\pi^+$, implies $I = 1$. According to Bose statistics applied to two pions, the angular momentum

---

[47] A. Erwin et al., *Phys. Rev. Letters,* **6**, 628 (1961).

must then be odd. The spin and parity assignments of ρ is $(1,-)$; it is a charged vector meson in the language of field theory.

The three-pion resonance has been observed in $p\bar{p}$ annihilation:[48]

$$\bar{p} + p \to \pi^+ + \pi^+ + \pi^- + \pi^- + \pi^0.$$

The pions have been grouped in triplets $+ + -$, $- - +$, $+ + 0$, $- - 0$, and $+ - 0$, and their barycentric energy (effective mass) has been plotted. Only the $+ - 0$ state shows a sharp resonance at 790 Bev with $\Gamma \approx 12$ Bev. The isotopic spin is $I = 0$. Independently this ω^0-particle has been observed in[49]

$$\pi^+ + d \to p + p + \pi^+ + \pi^- + \pi^0,$$

and in[50]

$$\bar{p} + p \to 3\pi^+ + 3\pi^- + \pi^0.$$

The spin-parity analysis of ω^0 is rather complicated; the present evidence indicates that it is $(1-)$, a neutral vector meson.

A third very sharp pion resonance is definitely established—the η-meson at about 550 Bev with a half-width $\Gamma/2 < 5$ Bev, which has definitely[51] $I = 0$:

$$\pi^+ + d \to p + p + \eta^0 \to p + p + \pi^+ + \pi^- + \pi^0.$$

The spin of η has been determined to be zero.[52] The G-parity of η is $+1$; thus its decay into 3π is electromagnetic. Other important decay modes of η are $\gamma\gamma$, $\pi^0 2\gamma$, and $\pi^+\pi^-\gamma$ (see App. 1). Because of these decay properties, η can be considered to be a "stable" particle. Another "stable" particle has been predicted on the basis of symmetry considerations (see Sec. 10.4) and then discovered. It is the Ω^--particle decaying into $\Xi\pi$ and $\Lambda\bar{K}$ with a lifetime of about 1.0×10^{-10} sec. The hypercharge of Ω^- is -2.

There is one other resonance decaying predominantly into two pions—namely, the f-meson with a mass of about 1253 Bev, width $\Gamma/2 \sim$ Bev, and $I(J^{PG}) = 0(2^{++})$. The resonances ρ, ω, η, f combined with pions give rise to new resonances, and so on, whose quantum numbers are presently being determined (see App. 1).

c. Pion-Kaon Resonances ($N = 0$, $Y = \pm 1$)

The first such resonance has been observed in the reactions[53]

$$K^- + p \to K^-\pi^0 p$$
$$\to \bar{K}^0\pi^- p$$

at K^- laboratory momentum of 1150 Bev/C. The measurements are easier

[48] B. Maglic, L. Alvarez, A. Rosenfeld, and M. Stevenson, *Phys. Rev. Letters*, **7**, 178 (1961).

[49] A. Pevsner et al., Aix-en-Province Conference on Elementary Particles, 1961.

[50] N. Xuong and G. Lynch, *UCRL–9857*.

[51] A. Pevsner et al., *Phys. Rev. Letters*, **7**, 421 (1961).

[52] A. Pevsner et al., *Phys. Rev. Letters*, **9**, 127 (1962); C. Alff et al., *Phys. Rev. Letters*, **9**, 322, 325 (1962).

[53] M. Alston et al., *Phys. Rev. Letters*, **6**, 300 (1961).

for the second system. The total barycentric energy of $\bar{K}^0\pi^-$ shows a peak at 890 Bev with a half-width of $\Gamma/2 \approx 25$ Bev. The ratio of $(\bar{K}^0\pi^-)/(K^-\pi^0)$ is expected to be $\frac{1}{2}$ for $I = \frac{3}{2}$ and 2 for $I = \frac{1}{2}$ for the $(K - \pi)$ state; the observed ratio 1.4 ± 0.4 favors $I = \frac{1}{2}$ for this K^* resonance.

The positive counterparts of K^* have also been observed in[54]

$$\pi^- + p \to \Sigma^- + K^{*+} \to \Sigma^- + K^0 + \pi^+$$
$$\to \Sigma^- + K^+ + \pi^0$$

and also in[55]

$$K^+ + p \to K^{*0} + N_{33}^{*++} \to K^+ + \pi^- + p + \pi^+.$$

To determine the spin, the Adair analysis is applied, in the first and last reactions, to the decay products of K^*. The first reaction gives $J < 2$, the last one $J \geqslant 1$. Hence the spin must be $J = 1$; the relative parity is negative.[55] Other πK and KK resonances are listed in App. 1.

d. Pion-Hyperon Resonances ($N = 1$, $Y = 0$, -1)

The π-Λ resonance Y_1^* was first established in[56]

$$K^- + p \to \Lambda + \pi^+ + \pi^-$$

at 1150 Bev/C $- K^-$ laboratory momentum. If one plots the kinetic energies of π^+ and π^- in the barycentric system, one obtains Fig. 10.9, which shows

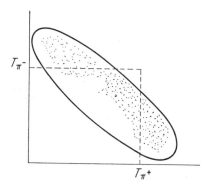

Figure 10.9   Evidence of Y_1^*-resonance in $K^-p \to \Lambda\pi^+\pi^-$ (schematic).

that most π^+ and π^- have definite energies; they must come from two-body decays via

$$K^- + p \to Y_1^{*+} + \pi^- \to (\Lambda + \pi^+) + \pi^-$$
$$\to Y_1^{*-} + \pi^+ \to (\Lambda + \pi^-) + \pi^+.$$

Thus one obtains a mass of 1385 Bev and a half-width of about 25 Bev for Y_1^*.

[54] W. Walker, Aix-en-Province Conference (September, 1961).
[55] W. Chinowski et al., *Phys. Rev. Letters*, **9**, 330 (1962).
[56] M. Alston et al., *Phys. Rev. Letters*, **5**, 520 (1960).

It has been found also in K^-p reactions at other energies and in the following reactions[57-59]:

$$K^- + d \to Y_1^{*-} + p \to \Lambda + \pi^- + p,$$

$$K_2^0 + p \begin{array}{c} \nearrow Y_1^{*0} + \pi^+ \\ \searrow Y_1^{*+} + \pi^0 \end{array} \Biggr\} \to \Lambda + \pi^0 + \pi^+,$$

$$K^- + \mathrm{He}^4 \to \mathrm{He}^3 + Y_1^{*-} \to \mathrm{He}^3 + \Lambda + \pi^-.$$

Spin-parity determination gives $\frac{3}{2}^+$.

There is a second distinct resonance at 1405 Bev, $\Gamma/2 \approx 29$ Bev with $I = 0$, which is observed in the reactions[60]

$$K^- + p \to \Sigma^+\pi^-\pi^+\pi^-, \Sigma^-\pi^+\pi^-\pi^+, \Sigma^0\pi^0\pi^-\pi^+, \Lambda\pi^0\pi^+\pi^-.$$

The peaking shows only in $(\Sigma^+\pi^-)$ and $(\Sigma^-\pi^+)$ systems; $(\Sigma^+\pi^+)$, $(\Sigma^-\pi^-)$ do not show a peaking, nor the last $(\Lambda\pi)$ system. There is also a peak in the $(\Sigma^0\pi^0)$ system. The previously found resonance Y_0^{1*} cannot decay into $\Sigma^0\pi^0$. Consequently the new resonance must be distinct from Y_1^{0*}; it is called Y_0^*.

Further resonances at 1660 Bev (Y_1^*), 1520 Bev (Y_0^*), and at 1815 Bev (Y_0^*) have been established.

No resonances with $N = 1$, $Y = 2$ (e.g., in K^+p-system) have been found so far.

In the KN-system the K^-p cross section shows a resonance at 1815 Bev[61] but the K^-n reaction does not. K^-n has $I = 1$ but K^-p has $I = 0$ [the $I = 0$ cross section is $2\sigma(K^-p) - \sigma(K^-n)$]. Spin parity assignment is $\frac{5}{2}^+$.

Resonances in $\pi\Xi$ systems have also been reported.[62]

We have given a brief account of how the resonance states have been discovered in order to give an idea of the assignment of quantum numbers. Many more such resonance states have been established. (See tables in App. 1, for the state of affairs as of August 1966.) It is clear that we have to do here with the many excited states of strongly interacting particles (hadrons) analogous to the excited states of nuclei, and we must look for new methods to bring order to this multitude of particles. One such method is to look for bigger multiplets than the isospin multiplets, another is the families of Regge trajectories.

10.4 Higher Symmetry of Particles

We have seen that charge multiplets can be described by the ray representations of the rotation group in the three-dimensional isotopic spin space.

[57] H. Martin et al., *Phys. Rev. Letters*, **6**, 283 (1961).
[58] O. Dahl et al., *Phys. Rev. Letters*, **6**, 142 (1961).
[59] M. Block et al., *Nuovo Cimento*, **20**, 724 (1961).
[60] M. Alston et al., *Phys. Rev. Letters*, **6**, 698 (1961).
[61] V. Cook et al., *Rev. Mod. Phys.*, **33**, 389 (1961).
[62] L. Bertanza et al., *Phys. Rev. Letters*, **9**, 180 (1962).

Thus $I = \frac{1}{2}, 1, \frac{3}{2}$ corresponds to two-, three-, four-, etc., dimensional irreducible ray representations of this group. Because there are more than one multiplet with the same I and because there are new quantum numbers like N, Y, L, the "internal symmetry" must be a larger one. In recent years there has been a great deal of effort to include all baryons and all mesons with the same spin and parity into groups, a new kind of multiplet structure. The mass differences are now much larger than those of charge multiplets, which are thought to be caused by electromagnetic interactions. One can then differentiate between an idealized symmetry, neglecting all mass differences (the so-called *broken symmetry*), and the symmetry that remains when mass differences are included. Furthermore, it is possible that in scattering at very high energies and momentum transfer the symmetries may take a different and much simpler form. Finally, one should distinguish between the symmetry group that gives the multiplet structure and the symmetry group of the S-matrix.

An attractive idea is to consider three fundamental particles, and all others as being built up from them. This number 3 is necessary to obtain the quantum numbers Q, N, Y, and I with $Q = I_3 + Y/2$. Various models differ in the way quantum numbers are assigned to these basic three "objects." In the Sakata model[63] one takes the physical, n,p; in the *octet model* one takes three objects with fractional quantum numbers in such a way that the particles in the eight-dimensional representation have the observed quantum numbers[64]; in the Goldhaber model,[65] Λ, K^+, K^0.

For the leptons one can take, e.g., μ^-, e^-, ν. It is not necessary to consider some existing particles as more fundamental; one can take three "materia prima" fields, unobserved, whose possible forms we do observe. In fact, it is better to think of these three basic "fields" as mathematical objects (spinors) out of which higher-dimensional realized representations of the symmetry groups are constructed.

One is then led to a generalization of the isotopic spin group in the sense that one now considers the 3×3 unitary group SU_3 of which the quantum mechanical isospin group SU_2 is a subgroup. The states of the irreducible representations of this group will now be labeled by the quantum numbers I, I_3, and Y. In the transformation equation of our R- or M-functions we will have now the representations $D(I, I_3, Y, \ldots)$ of SU_3 instead of $D^{(I)}(u)$. The group SU_3 has irreducible representations of dimensionality 1, 3, 6, 8, 10, 15, 21, 24, 27, 28, ...

[63] S. Sakata, *Progr. Theor. Phys.*, **16**, 686 (1956); M. Ikeda, S. Ogawa, and Y. Ohnuki, *Progr. Theor. Phys.*, **22**, 715 (1959); W. Thirring, *Nucl. Phys.*, **10**, 97 (1959); J. E. Wess, *Nuovo Cimento*, **15**, 52 (1960); Y. Yamaguchi, *Prog. Theor. Phys.*, Suppl. **11**, 1 (1959); ibid., **11**, 37 (1959); *Prog. Theor. Phys.*, **23**, 882 (1960); A. Salam and J. Ward, *Nuovo Cimento*, **20**, 419 (1961).

[64] M. Gell-Mann, *Phys. Rev.*, **125**, 1066 (1962); Y. Ne'eman, *Nucl. Phys.*, **26**, 222 (1961).

[65] M. Goldhaber, *Phys. Rev.*, **101**, 437 (1953).

Groups other than SU_3, as possible symmetry groups, generalizing the isotopic spin group have been considered,[66] but SU_3 seems to be the most successful one. On the other hand, there are simpler and perhaps more physical ways of stating the SU_3 symmetry: One says that the permutation symmetry of three identical fermions and a continuous conservation law such as the charge conservation law give the same result as the SU_3 symmetry.[67] Another way is that SU_3 invariance is essentially equivalent to SU_2 invariance of the two fundamental objects n and p, plus the permutation invariance $n \leftrightarrow \Lambda$, which establishes again the symmetry of the three basic objects.

In the SU_3 symmetry, scalar mesons and baryons are assigned to an eight-dimensional representation, the $\frac{3}{2}^+$ baryon resonances to a 10-dimensional representation, and the nine vector mesons to a singlet and an octet, as shown below in the so-called weight diagram of the group SU_3. The assignment of the $\frac{3}{2}^-$ and other resonant states is not yet definitely established.

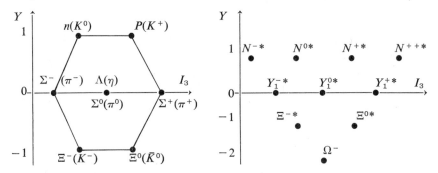

A higher symmetry such as SU_2 does not only order the particles into multiplets, but also allows one to predict relations between the properties of these particles. If one postulates how, e.g., the magnetic moment or even the mass, should transform under the transformations of SU_2, one can write the most general form of these quantities and fit the constants from the experiment.[68]

The invariance of the S-matrix under SU_3 can be also treated along the lines developed in Chap. 4 for SU_2, and the general form of invariant amplitudes and crossing matrices can be constructed.[69] However, the postulate

[66] For a review of possible higher symmetry groups in strong interactions see E. Behrends, J. Dreitlein, C. Fronsdal, and B. W. Lee, *Rev. Mod. Phys.*, **34**, 1 (1962); D. Speiser and J. Tarski, *J. Math. Phys.*, **4**, 588 (1963).

[67] See, e.g., Y. Yamaguchi, *Phys. Rev. Letters*, **9**, 281 (1964); J. Schechter, Y. Ueda and S. Okubo, *Ann. Phys.*, **32**, 424 (1965). There is a similar result already for SU_2; the permutation symmetry S_2 for two fermions plus charge conjugation leads to SU_2; K. M. Case, R. Karplus, and C. N. Yang, *Phys. Rev.*, **101**, 874 (1956).

[68] See M. Gell-Mann and Y. Ne'eman (eds.), *The Eightfold Way* (New York: Benjamin, 1965), for a collection of papers dealing with these questions.

[69] E. Branscomb, Thesis, Syracuse University 1963 (unpublished). For other methods, see Ref. 68.

that the S-matrix is invariant under SU_3 does *not* seem to agree well with experiment.[70] Thus, as we mentioned above, one has probably to distinguish between the symmetry of an internal dynamics, which gives rise to a multiplet structure, and the symmetry of the scattering of the members of multiplets.

An even larger multiplet structure than that of SU_3 is possible. For example, one can mix the spin J with the internal quantum numbers I, Y and put all the spin $\frac{1}{2}$ and spin $\frac{3}{2}$ positive parity baryons together and all negative parity mesons together into multiplets of the group SU_6, the so-called supermultiplets.[71]

The relevant representations of SU_6 are a 35-dimensional representation containing eight scalar and nine vector mesons, a 56-dimensional representation containing eight spin $\frac{1}{2}$ baryons and ten spin $\frac{3}{2}$ baryons, possible singlets, and one other possible 35-dimensional positive parity meson multiplet. An important success of the SU_6 symmetry is the prediction, under reasonable assumptions, of the neutron-proton magnetic moment ratio of $-\frac{2}{3}$. Again the invariance of the S-matrix under SU_6 is not well satisfied experimentally, because it contains SU_3 as a subgroup exactly as before.

From the point of view of the scattering matrix, the higher symmetries, beyond SU_2 (I-spin) and Y, can be interpreted as a particular way of parametrization of the S-matrix. For the S-matrix, invariant under Lorentz group, $SU_2(\bar{I})$ and Y can be systematically written as a sum of terms which are, respectively, SU_6 and SU_3 invariant, with other terms which break the symmetry, so that the exact symmetry limits correspond to the dominance or importance of these terms.[72]

Problems and Further Developments

1. Consider the pion absorption in $\pi^+ + d \to p + p$, and the pion production in $p + p \to \pi^+ + d$. Show that at the same value of the center-of-mass energy one has

$$\frac{\sigma_{\text{production}}}{\sigma_{\text{absorption}}} = \frac{3(2S_\pi + 1)p_\pi^2}{2p_p^2}, \tag{10.16}$$

where p_π and p_p are momenta in the center-of-mass frame of the pion and the proton, respectively.

2. Show that the np-system with $I = 1$ cannot be in ${}^3S$, ${}^3D$, ${}^1P$, ${}^1F$ states.

3. Name two particles that can interact only elastically below the threshold for the production of three particles.

[70] For a review of comparison of scattering experiments with SU_3 see, for example, Y. Harari, in *International Seminar on High Energy Physics*, Trieste (Vienna: International Atomic Energy Agency, 1965).

[71] The approximate supermultiplet SU_4 combining the SU_2 of isospin and SU_2 of spin has been used in nuclear physics: E. P. Wigner, *Phys. Rev.*, **51**, 105 (1937). For SU_6, see F. Gürsey and L. Radicati, *Phys. Rev. Letters*, **13**, 173 (1964), and B. Sakita, *Phys. Rev.*, **136**, B1756 (1964).

[72] For this separation, see A. O. Barut in *International Seminar on High Energy Physics*, Trieste (Vienna: International Atomic Energy Agency, 1965).

4. For the KN-system, derive the equality of the isotopic spin amplitudes shown in Eq. (10.3).

5. Derive Eqs. (10.4) to (10.6).

6. Consider $NN \to NN\pi$. Write down all possible amplitudes in terms of the total I-spin amplitudes. [L. Van Hove, R. E. Marshak, and A. Pais, *Phys. Rev.*, **88**, 1211 (1952); A. Rosenfeld, *Phys. Rev.*, **96**, 139 (1954).]

7. Show that

(i)
$$\frac{p + d \to \text{He}^3 + \pi^0}{p + d \to \text{H}^3 + \pi^+} = \frac{1}{2}. \tag{10.17}$$

(Note that H^3: $[I = \frac{1}{2}, I_3 = -\frac{1}{2}]$ and He^3: $[I = 0, I_3 = \frac{1}{2}]$. Experimental agreement within 10 per cent as of 1960:

(ii)
$$\frac{K^- d \to \text{He}^3 \Sigma^-}{K^- d \to \text{H}^3 \Sigma^0} = 2. \tag{10.18}$$

8. Evaluate $K_2^0 p \to K_1^0 p$ regeneration cross sections in terms of the $K^0 p$ and $\bar{K}^0 p$ scattering amplitudes. [D. Luers, L. Mitra, W. Willis, and S. Yamamoto, *Phys. Rev. Letters*, **7**, 255 (1961).]

9. Discuss the consequences of parity conservation in $N\bar{N} \to 2\pi$ and $N\bar{N} \to 3\pi$.

10. Show that for any internal symmetry group independent of the Lorentz group all members of a multiplets have the same parity, mass, and spin.

11. Show that for $NN \to NN$ and $N\bar{N} \to N\bar{N}$ the total spin is conserved; i.e., there are no $S = 0 \to S = 1$ transitions.

12. Derive the consequences of CPT-invariance on the short- and long-lived decay combinations of K^0 and $\bar{K}^0$ shown in Eq. (10.2). Derive the isospin amplitudes for $|L\rangle \to 2\pi$ and $|s\rangle \to 2\pi$. [Compare J. S. Bell and J. Steinberger, *Proceedings of Oxford Conference on Elementary Particles* (London: Oxford U.P., 1965).]

13. Show that a system of even number of pions cannot go via strong interactions into a system of odd number of pions. (Use G-invariance.)

14. Assume that the spinorial "current elements" of the S-matrix shown in Table 4–3 [Eq. (4.38)] are of the type V-A only. Show that the spinorial amplitude for the scattering of two spin $\frac{1}{2}$ particles is of the form

$$M = A(s,t)\sigma^\mu \otimes \sigma_\mu. \tag{10.19}$$

Discuss crossing properties of this amplitude. Apply Eq. (10.19) to the μ-decay, $\mu \to e + \nu + \bar{\nu}$, assuming A to be constant at low energies. Find lifetime and the decay spectrum.

15. Consider π-decay, $\pi \to e + \nu$ (or $\mu + \nu$). Apply the same V-A "current element" to the lepton pair, find the amplitude and lifetime. Find same for $K \to \pi + \ell + \nu$.

16. Discuss selection rules in the η-decay.

17. Derive isospin branching ratios of $\Lambda\pi^0 \to \Sigma^0\pi^0, \Sigma^+\pi^-, \Sigma^-\pi^+$.

CHAPTER 11

Pion-Pion Scattering

Because all processes are related to each other by unitarity, no scattering problem can be completely treated independent of the others. Approximately, however, the effect of certain other processes can be neglected. The simplest approximations are based on single particle states in all channels. The pion-pion problem, because of the low mass, is basic to all strong interactions, and so we begin with this problem.

11.1 Kinematics

We shall denote the pion mass by μ, isospin $I = 1$, isospin components by $I_3 = Q = \alpha_1, \ldots, \alpha_4$. The R-amplitude has the form [see Eq. (4.6)]

$$R \equiv M^{\alpha_1 \alpha_2}_{\alpha_3 \alpha_4} = A(s,t,u)C^{\alpha_1 \alpha_2}C_{\alpha_3 \alpha_4} + B(s,t,u)\delta^{\alpha_1}_{\alpha_3}\delta^{\alpha_2}_{\alpha_4} + C(s,t,u)\delta^{\alpha_2}_{\alpha_3}\delta^{\alpha_1}_{\alpha_4}. \quad (11.1)$$

Using Eq. (4.9), we obtain amplitudes belonging to total isotopic spin values $I = 0, 1, 2$:

$$\begin{aligned} A^0 &= 3A + B + C, \\ A^1 &= B - C, \\ A^2 &= B + C. \end{aligned} \quad (11.2)$$

The scalar functions A, B, C are functions of the invariants only. We use the usual invariants $s = (k_1 + k_2)^2$, $t = (k_1 - k_3)^2$, $u = (k_1 - k_4)^2$, all k's being physical energy-momentum vectors. From Eq. (11.1) we can easily obtain the crossing relations between the amplitudes. The interchange of particles 3 and 4 implies $t \leftrightarrow u$, hence

$$\begin{aligned} A(s,t,u) &= A(s,u,t), \\ B(s,t,u) &= C(s,u,t). \end{aligned} \quad (11.3)$$

Similarly, the interchange of particles 2 and 3 ($k_2 \leftrightarrow -k_3$) implies $s \leftrightarrow t$:

$$\begin{aligned} A(s,t,u) &= B(t,s,u), \\ C(s,t,u) &= C(t,s,u), \end{aligned} \quad (11.3')$$

and the interchange of particles 2 and 4 ($k_2 \leftrightarrow -k_4$) implies $s \leftrightarrow u$,

$$A(s,t,u) = C(u,t,s),$$
$$B(s,t,u) = B(u,t,s). \tag{11.3''}$$

Mathematically these crossing relations express the symmetry of the amplitudes. For example, Eq. (11.3) implies the symmetry with respect to the line s-s' (Fig. 11.1); A is symmetric with respect to this line, its values being

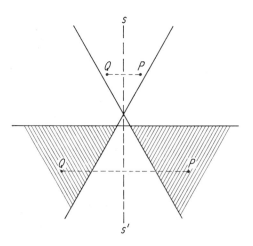

Figure 11.1   Symmetry of the π-π amplitude.

equal at points P and Q, whereas the values of B at P are equal to those of C at Q. This symmetry holds even at unphysical points; in particular, B in t-channel is equal to C in the symmetric point (with respect to s-s') of the u-channel. Other crossing relations have similar interpretation. It is convenient to keep the order of argument s, t, u fixed once and for all in the form $A(s,t,u)$ and let the domains of these variables distinguish the three channels, I, II, III.

The "forces" between the two pions are isospin dependent; we expect, in general, two pions in $I = 0$, 1, or 2 states to interact differently. (The charge independence is expressed by the I-spin conservation.) This difference of forces will be expressed by the different behavior of amplitudes A^0, A^1, and A^2.

Because the interchange $t \leftrightarrow u$ is equivalent to an interchange of $\cos\theta \to -\cos\theta$ in the center-of-mass frame, we see from Eq. (11.3) that $A(s,t,u)$ is even in $\cos\theta$ and $B + C$ is also even in $\cos\theta$, whereas $B - C$ is odd. Therefore it follows from Eq. (11.2) that A^0 and A^2 are even, whereas A^1 is odd in $\cos\theta$. Thus, in the partial wave expansions of these amplitudes,

$$A^I(s,t) = \sum (2\ell + 1)A^I(s,\ell)P_\ell(\cos\theta), \quad I = 0, 1, 2; \tag{11.4}$$

only even values of ℓ appear for $I = 0, 2$, but only odd values of ℓ for $I = 1$. This can be expressed by the rule

$$\ell + I = \text{even},$$

or   (11.5)

$$(-1)^{\ell+I} = 1,$$

and is the generalized Pauli principle for two pions with space parity $(-1)^\ell$ and charge parity $(-1)^I$. The other symmetry relations can be interpreted as the Pauli principle in the other crossed channels.

We use the normalization, Eq. (7.26), such that for $4\mu^2 < s < 16\mu^2$, the unitarity relation can be expressed as

$$A^I(s,\ell) = \sqrt{\frac{s}{s - 4\mu^2}} \, e^{i\delta_\ell^I(s)} \sin \delta_\ell^I(s)$$

$$= \sqrt{\frac{\nu + \mu^2}{\nu}} \, e^{i\delta_\ell^I} \sin \delta_\ell^I, \qquad (11.6)$$

with $\nu = q^2 = $ center-of-mass momentum square, and from Eq. (7.25) we have for the differential cross section

$$\frac{d\sigma}{d\Omega} = \frac{1}{s} |A(s,\theta)|^2$$

$$= \frac{1}{s} \left| \sum_\ell (2\ell + 1) A(s,\ell) P_\ell(z) \right|^2 .$$

On the other hand, the unitarity

$$\text{Im} A^I(s,\ell) = \sqrt{\frac{s - 4\mu^2}{s}} |A^I(s,\ell)|^2$$

gives the optical theorem

$$\sigma_{\text{tot}} = \frac{4\pi}{s} \sqrt{\frac{s}{s - 4\mu^2}} \, \text{Im} A(s, \theta = 0). \qquad (11.7)$$

The threshold for $2\pi, 4\pi, 6\pi, 8\pi, \ldots$, intermediate, states are at $s = 4\mu^2, 16\mu^2, 36\mu^2, \ldots$, or at $\nu = q^2 = 0, 3\mu^2, 8\mu^2, 13\mu^2, 24\mu^2, \ldots$. In the range $0 \leqslant \nu \leqslant 3\mu^2$ the phase shifts are real as a result of unitarity.

For $s > 16\mu^2$ ($\nu > 3\mu^2$) it is sometimes convenient to write *phenomenologically*

$$\text{Im} A^I(s,\ell) = \sqrt{\frac{s - 4\mu^2}{s}} |A^I(s,\ell)|^2 R^I(s,\ell) \qquad (11.8)$$

or

$$\text{Im} \frac{1}{A^I(s,\ell)} = -\sqrt{\frac{s - 4\mu^2}{s}} R^I(s,\ell), \qquad (11.9)$$

where $R^{(I)}$ is the ratio of the total to elastic partial-wave cross section and expresses phenomenologically the effect of inelastic processes on the elastic cross section.

11.2   Analyticity of the Partial-Wave Amplitudes

Consider the partial-wave projections [inverse of Eq. (11.4)]:

$$A^I(s,\ell) = \frac{1}{2} \int_{-1}^{+1} dz \, A^I(s,z) P_\ell(z). \tag{11.10}$$

We can determine the singularities of $A(s,\ell)$ in s (for fixed physical ℓ for the time being) from those of $A(s,z)$. The singularities of $A(s,\ell)$ will depend on the singularities $A(s,z)$. Let us assume the validity of double-dispersion relation for $A(s,t)$: i.e.,

$$A(s,t,u) = \frac{1}{\pi^2} \int ds' \, dt' \, \frac{a_{st}(s',t')}{(s'-s)(t'-t)} + \frac{1}{\pi^2} \int ds' \, du' \, \frac{a_{su}(u',s')}{(s'-s)(u'-u)}$$

$$+ \frac{1}{\pi^2} \int dt' \, du' \, \frac{a_{tu}(t',u')}{(t'-t)(u'-u)}, \tag{11.11}$$

similarly for $B(s,t,u)$ and $C(s,t,u)$. [All integrals ranging between $4\mu^2$ and ∞.] The crossing relations imply that out of nine spectral functions only two are independent, one of which is a symmetric function of s and t:

$$\rho^{(1)}(s,t) \equiv a_{st}(s,t) = a_{su}(t,s) = b_{st}(t,s) = b_{tu}(s,t)$$

$$= c_{su}(s,t) = c_{tu}(t,s), \tag{11.12}$$

$$\rho^{(2)}(s,t) = \rho^{(2)}(t,s) = a_{tu}(s,t) = b_{su}(s,t) = c_{st}(s,t).$$

It follows from these relations that

$$\rho_{tu}^I(t,u) = (-1)^I \rho_{tu}^I(u,t),$$

and similar relations can be obtained for the other spectral functions.

The boundary of the ρ-curves have been determined in Chap. 7. They are given by the curves

$$t = 16\mu^2 \, \frac{s}{s - 4\mu^2} \qquad \text{for} \quad t > s$$

and $\tag{11.13}$

$$s = 16\mu^2 \, \frac{t}{t - 4\mu^2} \qquad \text{for} \quad s > t.$$

Finally we give another equivalent expression for the partial-wave amplitudes derived in Chap. 9, Eq. (9.24), from Eq. (11.10); i.e.,

$$A(s,\ell) = \frac{1}{s - 4\mu^2} \int_{-(s-4\mu^2)}^{0} dt \, A(s,t,u) P_\ell \left(1 + \frac{2t}{s - 4\mu^2} \right)$$

and the above double-dispersion relations for $A(s,t,u)$. This expression is

$$A(s,\ell) = \frac{1}{\pi} \int_{z_0}^{\infty} dz \, [A_2(s,z) + (-1)^\ell A_3(s,z)] Q_\ell(z). \tag{11.14}$$

Here the absorptive parts of the amplitudes A_2 and A_3 are integrals of ρ's along the lines $t = $ const. and $u = $ const., respectively;

$$A_2(s,t) = \frac{1}{\pi} \int_{4\mu^2}^{\infty} ds' \frac{\rho_{st}^{(1)}}{s' - s} + \frac{1}{\pi} \int_{4\mu^2}^{\infty} du' \frac{\rho_{tu}^{(2)}}{u' - (4\mu^2 - t - s)}, \quad (11.15)$$

$$A_3(s,t) = \frac{1}{\pi} \int_{4\mu^2}^{\infty} ds' \frac{\rho_{su}}{s' - s} + \frac{1}{\pi} \int_{4\mu^2}^{\infty} dt' \frac{\rho_{tu}}{t' - (4\mu^2 - u - s)}. \quad (11.16)$$

We see from these last formulas that A_2 has a cut in s from $4\mu^2$ to ∞ and one from $-\infty$ to the boundary of the ρ_{tu} spectral function. Similarly, A_3 has a cut in s from $4\mu^2$ to ∞ and one from $-\infty$ to the boundary. In addition

$$Q_\ell(1 + 2t/(s - 4\mu^2))$$

has a cut from $s = -\infty$ to $s = -(t - 4\mu^2)$.

Figure 11.2 shows the lines $t = $ const. and $u = $ const. along which the integrations in A_2 and A_3 are to be taken. The branch points in A_2 and A_3 are given by the intersection of these lines with the spectral regions. The left-hand cut of Q_ℓ extends farthest to the right.

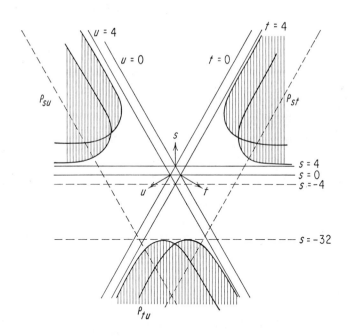

Figure 11.2 π-π spectral regions.

Furthermore, A_2 and A_3 have branch points corresponding to inelastic spectral function ρ_{st} and ρ_{tu}. Thus, these left-hand branch points correspond to the normal threshold singularities in the crossed channels.

It follows therefore from Eq. (11.14) that the partial-wave amplitudes $A(s,\ell)$, ℓ = physical, have two cuts—one from $s = 4\mu^2$ to ∞, the *physical* or *right-hand* cut; the other from $s = -\infty$ to $s = 0$, the left-hand cut (Fig. 11.3).

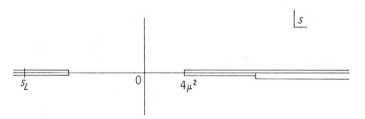

Figure 11.3   Cuts of the partial-wave amplitudes in the s-plane.

For $0 < s < 4\mu^2$ the partial-wave amplitude is real, so it is a real analytic function, single-valued in the cut plane as indicated.[1]

We note for further reference that if we had taken ℓ in Eq. (11.14) to be arbitrary the cut of $Q_\ell[1 + (2t/s - 4\mu^2)]$ would run from $s = -\infty$ to $s = 4\mu^2$, and $A(s,\ell)$ would not be a real analytic function.

We shall refer to the left-hand cut coming from Q_ℓ as the *projection cut* which begins at $s = 0$, and the cut coming from $\rho_{(s,t)}$ as the *spectral cut*. The discontinuity across the first cut can be evaluated from the discontinuity of $Q_\ell(z)$. Thus, the partial-wave amplitudes in this spinless case have a rather simple singularity structure.

11.3   Approximate Solutions of Partial-Wave Amplitudes

The unitarity equation (11.8), or

$$\frac{1}{2i}[A(s_+,\ell) - A(s_-,\ell)] = \sqrt{\frac{s - 4\mu^2}{s}}\, A(s_+,\ell)A(s_-,\ell)R(s,\ell), \quad (11.17)$$

gives us an expression for the discontinuity across the right-hand physical cut; $R(s,\ell) = 1$ for $s < 16\mu^2$. If we also knew the discontinuity across the left-hand cut *and* the asymptotic behavior of $A(s,\ell)$ for large $|s|$ we could immediately determine the partial-wave amplitudes. If $A(s,\ell) \to 0$ for $|s| \to \infty$ we can write the dispersion relations

$$A(s,\ell) = \frac{1}{\pi}\int_{-\infty}^{0} ds' \frac{\text{disc. } A(s',\ell)}{s' - s} + \frac{1}{\pi}\int_{4\mu^2}^{\infty} ds' \frac{\text{disc. } A(s',\ell)}{s' - s}. \quad (11.18)$$

If $A(s,\ell) \xrightarrow[|s| \to \infty]{} C_s$ we need one subtraction in these dispersion relations, and so on.

---

[1] It is interesting to note that in potential scattering with a Yukawa potential one obtains directly from the Schrödinger equation a physical cut from $q^2 = 0$ to ∞ and a left-hand cut from $q^2 = -\infty$ to $q^2 = -\frac{1}{4}\mu^2$ (relativistically $q^2 = -\mu^2$). For a cutoff potential the left-hand cut moves to $-\infty$ but the amplitude has an essential singularity at ∞. (See references in Chap. 7.)

In detailed calculations it will be convenient to separate the right and left cuts of the amplitude by the so-called *N/D method*.[2] We write

$$A(s,\ell) = \frac{N(s,\ell)}{D(s,\ell)} \tag{11.19}$$

in such a way that the function N has the left cut of A only and the function D has the right cut only. Therefore, we have

$$\text{disc. } A(s,\ell) = \frac{1}{D(s,\ell)} \text{disc. } N(s,\ell), \qquad s < 0,$$

and, for $s > 4\mu^2$,

$$\text{disc. } A(s,\ell) = N \frac{-\text{disc. } D(s,\ell)}{D(s_+)D(s_-)} = -\frac{1}{N}|A(s,\ell)|^2 \text{ disc. } D(s,\ell) \tag{11.20}$$

or

$$\text{disc. } \frac{1}{A(s,\ell)} = \frac{1}{N(s,\ell)} \text{disc. } D(s,\ell); \qquad s > 4\mu^2.$$

Having obtained the discontinuities of N and D we can write separate dispersion relations for them and obtain the coupled integral equations:

$$N(s,\ell) = A(s_0,\ell) + \frac{s - s_0}{\pi} \int_{-\infty}^{0} ds' \frac{D(s',\ell) \text{ disc. } A(s',\ell)}{(s' - s)(s' - s_0)}$$

and

$$D(s,\ell) = 1 - \frac{s - s_0}{\pi} \int_{4\mu^2}^{\infty} ds' \sqrt{\frac{s' - 4\mu^2}{s'}} R(s',\ell) \frac{N(s',\ell)}{(s' - s)(s' - s_0)}, \tag{11.21}$$

where we have used one subtraction and normalized Eq. (11.19) in such a way that at $s = s_0$ (the subtraction point, not yet chosen):

$$D(s_0,\ell) = 1.$$

One of the most important advantages of the N/D method is the fact that the poles of the amplitude $A(s,\ell)$ can be described by the zeros of $D(s,\ell)$, and consequently they do not appear in the dispersion relations, Eq. (11.21). Thus the question whether a particle or a resonance should be introduced as a pole in the dispersion relations from the beginning, or should arise as a result of dynamical calculations, is avoided. (See in this connection the Levinson's theorem, Exercise 7.)

How do we determine the unknown discontinuity across the left cut in the first equation? If we were talking about a problem with no crossing, to be specific with $\rho_{tu} \equiv 0$, then the left-hand cut is entirely due to projection with Q_ℓ in Eq. (11.15), and the discontinuity of Q_ℓ is known. Thus disc. A for $s < 0$ can be evaluated in terms of A_2 and A_3, which themselves can be evaluated from the spectral functions ρ_{st} and ρ_{su} by Eq. (11.16). The potential

---

[2] The π-π problem in this form was first formulated by G. F. Chew and S. Mandelstam, *Phys. Rev.*, **119**, 467 (1960).

scattering with exchange potential is of this type; for a simple direct potential, even ρ_{su} is identically zero.

In the general case we have also to evaluate the discontinuity across the spectral cut.

a. Evaluation of Left-Hand Discontinuity

We start from Eq. (11.14) [in units such that $\mu = 1$]:

$$A^I(s,\ell) = \frac{2}{(s-4)^2} \left[\frac{1}{\pi} \int_{4\mu^2}^{\infty} dt \, A_2^I(s, t, 4 - s - t) Q_\ell\left(1 + \frac{2t}{s-4}\right) \right.$$
$$\left. + \frac{1}{\pi}(-1)^\ell \int_4^{\infty} du \, A_3^I(s, 4 - s - u, u) Q_\ell\left(1 + \frac{2u}{s-4}\right) \right].$$

In the range $-32 < s < 0$, A_2 and A_3 are real, the imaginary part of $A(s,\ell)$ is due to that of Q_ℓ. The cuts of Q_ℓ (i.e., nonzero imaginary part) runs from

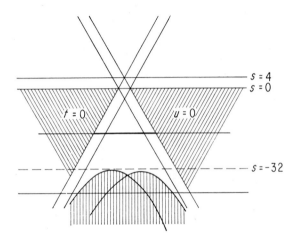

Figure 11.4.

$t = 0$ to $u = 0$ (Fig. 11.4). Thus, because the discontinuity of Q_ℓ is $(\pi/2)P_\ell$ (by Neumann formula), we find

$$\text{Im} A^I(s,\ell) = \frac{1}{s-4} \left[\int_4^{-(s-4)} dt \, A_2^I(s, t, 4 - s - t) P_\ell\left(1 + \frac{2t}{s-4}\right) \right.$$
$$\left. + (-1)^\ell \int_4^{-(s-4)} du \, A_3^I(s, 4 - s - t, u) P_\ell\left(1 + \frac{2u}{s-4}\right) \right],$$

$$-32 < s < 0. \quad (11.22)$$

In the interval $-32 < s < 0$ the above function is real, but it becomes complex for $s < -32$ because A_2 and A_3 are complex inside the spectral region, as indicated in Fig. 11.4.

This implies a singularity for the function ImA^I at the point $s = s_L = -32$ where the spectral function begins.

For $s < -32$, the discontinuity consists then of two terms:

$$\text{disc. } A^I(s,\ell)|_{s<s_L} = \frac{2}{s-4}\frac{1}{\pi}\int_4^\infty dt' \, P_\ell\left(-1 - \frac{2t'}{s-4}\right) P \int_{s_B(t')}^{-\infty} \frac{ds'}{s'-s}$$

$$\times \, [\rho_{tu}(t', 4 - s - t') \pm \rho_{tu}(4 - s - t', t')]$$

$$+ \int_{t_L(s)}^{t_R(s)} dt' \, \text{Re}\left[Q_\ell\left(-1 - \frac{2t'}{s-4}\right)\right]$$

$$\times \, \{\rho_{tu}(t', 4 - s - t') \pm \rho_{tu}(4 - s - t', t')\}.$$

The second term vanishes for physical ℓ-values because of the symmetry

$$ReQ_\ell(z) = (-1)^{\ell+1} \, ReQ_\ell(-z).$$

But this does not mean that the point $s = s_L$ is not a singular point. It is in fact a singular point, as shown earlier, even for physical ℓ-values, and we have

$$ImA^I(s,\ell)|_{s<s_L} = \frac{1}{s-4}\int_4^{-(s-4)} dt \, P_\ell\left(1 + \frac{2t}{s-4}\right)$$

$$\times \, [ReA_2^I(s, t', 4 - s - t') + (-1)^\ell ReA_3^I(s, 4 - s - t', t')]. \tag{11.22'}$$

This equation is not correct without the real parts written before A_2 and A_3 and is not the analytic continuation of Eq. (11.22).[3] In other words, we get two branch points by taking the discontinuity of Q_ℓ.

Neglecting first the I-spin complication (i.e., for $I = 0$ bosons), we have a single-amplitude symmetric in all three indices. This implies in particular, that $(-1)^\ell = 1$. Now Eq. (11.22) requires the knowledge of A_2 and A_3 in the region between $u = 0$ and $t = 0$; we know, A_2 and A_3 in their respective physical regions (Fig. 11.4). However, we can continue these functions analytically from the physical regions to the required unphysical region by the Legendre expansion:

$t > 4\mu^2$:

$$A_2(s, t, 4 - s - t) = \sum_{\ell'} (2\ell' + 1) \, ImA(t,\ell')P_{\ell'}\left(1 + \frac{2s}{t-4}\right).$$

$u > 4\mu^2$:

$$A_3(s, 4 - s - u, u) = \sum_{\ell''} (2\ell'' + 1) \, ImA(u,\ell'')P_{\ell''}\left(1 + \frac{2s}{u-4}\right).$$

Here ℓ' and ℓ'' have the interpretation of angular momenta in crossed

---

[3] E. Jones and V. Teplitz, *Nuovo Cimento*, **31**, 1079 (1964).

channels. These series converge as long as A_2 and A_3 have no singularities, i.e., again up to $s = -32$. We have then in this region

$$ImA(s,\ell) = \frac{2}{s-4} \int_4^{-(s-4)} dt\, P_\ell\left(1 + \frac{2t}{s-4}\right)$$

$$\times \sum_{\ell'} (2\ell' + 1)\, ImA(t,\ell')P_{\ell'}\left(1 + \frac{2s}{t-4}\right) + u\text{-term};$$

$$-32 < s < 0.$$

In the region of integration $ImA(t,\ell')$ itself is given by unitarity in the t-channel.

With I-spin the crossing relations are more complicated. Here A_2^I is a linear combination of the quantities $\tilde{A}_2^{I'}$ in the t-channel so that we take in the region of the t-channel the physical quantities $\tilde{A}_2^{I'}$, then pass to A_2^I, and then continue it analytically to the region of a thick solid line (Fig. 11.4). We then have

$$A_2^I(s, t, 4 - s - t) = \beta^{II'} \tilde{A}_2^{(I')}(t, s, 4 - s - t),$$
$$A_3^I(s, 4 - s - t, u) = (-1)^\ell \tilde{A}_3^I(s, u, 4 - s - t)$$
$$= (-1)^\ell \beta^{II'} \tilde{A}_3^{(I')}(u, s, 4 - s - t), \qquad (11.23)$$

where β is the crossing matrix for the interchange of the first two indices:

$$\beta^{II'} = \begin{bmatrix} \frac{1}{3} & 1 & \frac{5}{3} \\ \frac{1}{3} & \frac{1}{2} & -\frac{5}{6} \\ \frac{1}{3} & -\frac{1}{2} & \frac{1}{6} \end{bmatrix}. \qquad (11.24)$$

This isotopic-spin crossing matrix can be obtained from Eq. (11.3) or from the general formulas of Chap. 4.

We can now combine the two terms in Eq. (11.22) if we change the dummy index u on the second term into t. The absorptive part A_2 in the t-channel can again be written itself as a Legendre series:

$$A_2^{(I')}(t, s, 4 - s - t) = \sum_{\ell'=0}^{\infty} (2\ell' + 1)\, ImA^{(I')}(t,\ell')P_{\ell'}\left(1 + \frac{2s}{t-4}\right), \qquad (11.25)$$

so that the left-hand side is actually the analytic continuation into $u > 0$, s fixed, of $ImA(t > 4)$ in the t-channel. Hence we finally get

$$ImA^I(s,\ell)\big|_{-32<s<0} = \frac{2}{s-4} \int_4^{-(s-4)} dt\, P_\ell\left(1 + \frac{2t}{s-4}\right) \sum_{I',\ell'} \beta^{II'}(2\ell' + 1)$$

$$\times ImA^{I'}(t,\ell')P_{\ell'}\left(1 + \frac{2s}{t-4}\right). \qquad (11.26)$$

At this point we shall derive the *threshold behavior of the partial-wave amplitude,* which we can use to our advantage in the approximate calculations. For this purpose we rewrite Eq. (11.14) in the form

$$A^I(s,\ell) = \frac{4}{s-4}\frac{1}{\pi}\int_4^\infty dt\, A_2^I(s, t, 4 - s - t)Q_\ell\left(1 + \frac{2t}{s-4}\right)$$

$$(11.14')$$

where

$$A_2^I(s, t, 4 - s - t) = \sum_{I'}\beta^{II'}\sum_{\ell'}(2\ell' + 1)ImA^{I'}(t,\ell')P_\ell\left(1 + \frac{2s}{t-4}\right).$$

$$(11.15)$$

We see now from Eq. (11.14') that, for small $(s - 4)$,

$$Q_\ell\left(1 + \frac{2t}{s-4}\right) = Q_\ell\left(\frac{2t}{s-4}\right) \approx \left(\frac{2t}{s-4}\right)^{-\ell-1},$$

because

$$Q_\ell(z) \xrightarrow[|z|\to\infty]{} \frac{1}{z^{\ell+1}}.$$

Hence

$$A(s,\ell) \xrightarrow[(s-4)\text{small}]{} (s - 4)^\ell \frac{4}{\pi 2^{\ell+1}}\int_4^\infty dt\, \frac{A_2(s, t, 4 - s - t)}{t^{\ell+1}};\quad (11.25'')$$

i.e., at threshold the ℓth partial-wave goes to zero as $(s - 4)^\ell$.

We remark that the final equation Eq. (11.26) could also be obtained from Eq. (11.10), namely from

$$A(s,\ell) = \frac{1}{s-4}\int_{-(s-4)}^0 dt\, P_\ell\left(1 + \frac{2t}{s-4}\right)A(s,t,u).\quad (11.27)$$

Here P_ℓ is real, and $ImA(s,\ell)$ comes therefore from $ImA(s,t,u)$, which can be obtained from the fixed-energy dispersion relation

$$A(s,t,u) = \frac{1}{\pi}\int_4^\infty dt'\, \frac{A_2(s, t', 4 - t' - s)}{t' - t}$$

$$+ \frac{1}{\pi}\int_4^\infty du'\, \frac{A_3(s, 4 - u' - s, u')}{u' - u}.\quad (11.28)$$

In the region of integration of Eq. (11.27) both A_2 and A_3 are real (but discontinuous); moreover, A_2 and A_3 vanish for $t < 4\mu^2$ and $u < 4\mu^2$, respectively, and again we get Eq. (11.22). Note that in the *s-plane,*

$$ImA(s,t,u) = -A_2(s,t,u) - A_3(s,t,u).$$

Having obtained the left-hand discontinuity in the region $s_L < s < 0$, we go back to the N/D method and separate the N integral as follows:

$$N^I(s,\ell) = A(s_0,\ell) + \frac{s - s_0}{\pi} \int_{s_L}^0 ds' \frac{D(s',\ell)}{(s' - s_0)(s' - s)}$$

$$\times \left[\frac{2}{s - 4} \frac{1}{\pi} \int_4^{-(s-4)} dt\, P_\ell \left(1 + \frac{2t}{s - 4} \right) \right.$$

$$\times \left. \sum_{I',\ell'} \beta^{II'}(2\ell' + 1)\, ImA^{I'}(t,\ell')P_{\ell'}\left(1 + \frac{2s}{t - 4} \right) \right]$$

$$+ \frac{s - s_0}{\pi} \int_{-\infty}^{s_L} ds' \frac{D(s',\ell)}{(s' - s_0)(s' - s)}\, \text{disc. } A(s',\ell)|_{s < s_L}. \qquad (11.29)$$

In the last term, disc. $A(s',\ell)$ is still unknown. It can only be obtained by an analytic continuation from the crossed channels, in some other way than the partial-wave expansion. We shall, however, now go over to approximations and discuss how this last term can be approximated.

b. Pole Approximation of the Far-Away Left-Hand Cut

In the last term of Eq. (11.29) the spectral function ρ_{tu} contributes. Because s_L is rather far away from the physical region, we try to approximate the last integral by poles.

For this purpose let us make in the last term a change of variables, $s' = -1/x$, $ds' = dx/x^2$, so that it becomes

$$\frac{s - s_0}{\pi} \int_0^{x_L = -(1/s_L)} \frac{dx}{x} \frac{D(-x^{-1},\ell)\, \text{disc. } A(-x^{-1},\ell)}{[(1/x) + s_0](1 + xs)}.$$

We can now make a polynomial approximation of the integrand in $0 < x < x_L$ by putting

$$\frac{1}{1 + xs} = \sum_i \frac{G_i(x)}{1 + x_i s}.$$

For example, a two-pole approximation corresponds to replacing $1/(1 + xs)$ by a straight line, Fig. 11.5. We then obtain

$$\frac{s - s_0}{\pi} \sum_i \frac{1}{1 + x_i s} \int_0^{x_L} \frac{dx}{x} \frac{D(-x^{-1},\ell)\, \text{disc. } A(-x^{-1},\ell)}{[(1/x) + s_0]} = (s - s_0) \sum_i \frac{F_i}{s + s_i}.$$

Each pole is then characterized by two parameters, s_i and F_i. In the next section we apply this approximation to an actual problem—the calculation of pion resonances.

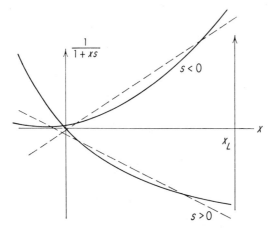

Figure 11.5.

11.4   An Example: Self-Consistent Calculation of the ρ-Meson

Our equations should give us the important features of low energy pion-pion interactions. Experimentally two pions interact strongly in the $I = 1$ state and weaker in the $I = 0$ and $I = 2$ states. In the $I = 1$ state there is a resonant state at 760 Bev with $J = 1$, the ρ-meson. (See Chap. 10.)

Because the left-hand cut discontinuity (i.e., the "forces") is given by the amplitude in crossed channel, and because the important aspect of the crossed-channel amplitude is the ρ-meson, we could take as the crossed-channel amplitude the contribution of the ρ-meson alone and ask if this could reproduce the ρ-meson in the original channel. This would be an approximate self-consistent calculation of the ρ-meson.[4,5] In this approximation the

---

[4] This approximation was first done by F. Zachariasen, *Phys. Rev. Letters*, **7**, 112, 268 (E)(1961), using a Feynman amplitude (Fig. 11.6)

$$N^0 = \frac{g^2}{m_\rho^2 - t}$$

as a zeroth-order approximation in an iterative N/D method. $N_\ell^{(0)} = N$ (Feynman). Then to first-order

$$D^{(1)} = 1 - \frac{s - s_0}{\pi} \int_4^\infty ds' \sqrt{\frac{s - 4}{s}} \frac{N^{(0)}}{(s' - s)(s' - s_0)},$$

and one requires $Re\,D(s = m_\rho^2) = 0$ and $Im\,D^{(1)}(s = m^2) = $ const. g^2. We have two equations and two unknowns, m_ρ^2 and g^2. One has of course to include factors due to the fact that ρ is vector meson, and one obtains

$$m_\rho^2 \approx 350 \text{ Bev.}$$

[5] A different approximation was made by L. Balász, *Phys. Rev.*, **128**, 1939 (1962), which is essentially the one discussed in the text. See also F. Zachariasen and F. Zemach, *Phys. Rev.*, **128**, 849 (1962) for the effect of ω-meson in these calculations.

ρ-meson is thought to be due to the exchange of ρ-meson itself in the crossed channel. We shall therefore insert the ρ-meson in the crossed channel and require that it produces the same resonance in the original channel.

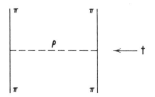

Figure 11.6   Feynman diagram for Born term.

Let us then approximate the $\ell = 1$ partial-wave amplitude in the crossed channel by a zero-width resonance, i.e.,

$$Im A'(t, \ell' = 1) = \pi(t_R - 4)\Gamma\delta(t - t_R).$$

Then by Eq. (11.25'), with $\beta^{11} = \tfrac{1}{2}$ and $P_1(z) = z$,

$$A_2(s, t, 4 - s - t) = \tfrac{3}{2}\pi\Gamma(t_R - 4)\delta(t - t_R)\cdot\left(1 + \frac{2s}{t - 4}\right);$$

by Eq. (11.14'),

$$A'(s,\ell) = 3\Gamma\,\frac{t_R - 4 + 2s}{s - 4}\,Q_\ell\!\left(1 + \frac{2t_R}{s - 4}\right), \qquad (11.30)$$

so that the partial wave in the s-channel is expressed in terms of two parameters, t_R and Γ, the position and the width of the ρ-meson. On the other hand the N-equation gives

$$N(s,\ell) = A(s_0,\ell) + \frac{s - s_0}{\pi}\int_{s_L}^{4 - t_R} ds'\,\frac{D(s',\ell)}{(s' - s_0)(s' - s)}\,Im A(s',\ell)$$

$$+ \frac{s - s_0}{\pi}\int_{-\infty}^{s_L} ds'\,\frac{D(s',\ell)}{(s' - s_0)(s' - s)}\,Im A(s',\ell).$$

If we choose $s_L = 4 - t_R$ (i.e., $t_R < 36$), the second term drops altogether. We then approximate the last term by two poles whose positions are chosen a priori. The result is not very sensitive to the choice of these positions in the range $4 < s \lesssim 36$. We then have

$$\left.\begin{aligned} N(s,1) &= A(s_0,1) + (s - s_0)\left[\frac{F_1}{s + s_1} + \frac{F_2}{s + s_2}\right] \\[2mm] D(s,1) &= 1 - \frac{s - s_0}{\pi}\int_4^\infty ds'\,\sqrt{\frac{s' - 4}{s'}}\,\frac{N(s',\ell)}{(s' - s)(s' - s_0)} \end{aligned}\right\}. \qquad (11.31)$$

We can also choose the subtraction point s_0; but again one has to verify that the result is not very sensitive to this choice. There remains then three constants, $A(s_0,1)$, F_1, and F_2, which can be determined by requiring that $A(s_0,1)$

and its derivative $A'(s_0, 1)$ as calculated from Eqs. (11.30) and (11.31) respectively, are equal, and that

$$A[(s - 4), \ell = 1] = 0,$$

because the partial-wave amplitudes $A(s, \ell)$ go to zero as $(s - 4\mu^2)^\ell$ when $s \to 4\mu^2$.

These conditions determine $A(s_0)$, F_1, and F_2 as a function of t_R and Γ. Now, finally, we require that the solution Eq. (11.31) in the s-channel has also a resonance at $s = t_R$ with width parameter Γ. The position of the resonance is fixed by the condition

$$Re D(s = t_R, 1) = 0. \tag{11.32}$$

To find the width we first form

$$\frac{1}{D(s)} = \frac{1}{\left[D(t_R) + (s - t_R) \dfrac{dD}{ds}\Big|_{t_R} \right]} = \frac{1}{\dfrac{dD}{ds}\Big|_{t_R} \left[(s - t_R) + \dfrac{D(t_R)}{\{dD/ds\}_{t_R}} \right]}$$

$$\cong \frac{1}{\dfrac{dD}{ds}\Big|_{t_R} \left[(s - t_R) + i \dfrac{Im D(t_R)}{(dRe D/ds)_{t_R}} \right]}; \quad \frac{d}{ds}[Im D]\Big|_{t_R} \ll \frac{d}{ds} Re D$$

$$\cong \frac{[dRe D/ds]_{t_R}}{s - t_R + i \dfrac{\Gamma}{2}}.$$

Let us put, in the neighborhood of resonance (Fig. 11.7),

$$Re D(s) = -\frac{s - s_R}{t_R - s_0},$$

then

$$\frac{dRe D(s)}{ds}\Big|_{t_R} = -\frac{1}{t_R - s_0}.$$

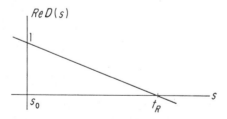

Figure 11.7 Approximation of $D(s)$ near the resonance.

On the other hand, from unitarity we have

$$Im D(s) = -\sqrt{\frac{s - 4}{s}}\, N(s), \quad s > 0.$$

Hence

$$\frac{\Gamma'}{2} = \frac{Im D(t_R)}{dReD/ds|_{t_R}} = \sqrt{\frac{t_R - 4}{t_R}}\, N(t_R)(t_R - s_0).$$

We now insert these quantities into the amplitude

$$ImA(s) = -\frac{\sqrt{(s-4)/s}\, N^2(s)}{(ReD)^2 + \frac{s-4}{s} N^2(s)}, \quad s > 0.$$

In the neighborhood of the resonance we can also put

$$N(s) = \frac{s-4}{t_R - 4} N(t_R)$$

and obtain

$$ImA(s) = \frac{\left(\frac{s-4}{s}\right)^{1/2} \frac{(s-4)^2}{(t_R-4)^3} \frac{t_R}{4} \Gamma'^2}{(s - t_R)^2 + \frac{(s-4)^3}{s(t_R-4)^3} \frac{t_R}{4} \Gamma'^2}.$$

If we define

$$\Gamma^2 = \frac{t_R}{4(t_R - 4)^3} \Gamma'^2,$$

we get

$$ImA(s) = \frac{a^2}{(s - t_R)^2 + b^2}$$

$$a^2 = \left(\frac{s-4}{s}\right)^{1/2}(s-4)^2\Gamma^2; \quad b = \frac{(s-4)^{3/2}\Gamma^2}{\sqrt{s}}.$$

A zero-width approximation to this resonance form is obtained by letting

$$ImA(s) \simeq c\delta(s - t_R).$$

We determine c such that

$$\int_4^\infty ds\, \frac{a^2}{(s-t_R)^2 + b^2} = c \int ds'\, \delta(s' - t_R),$$

which gives

$$c = \pi(s-4)\Gamma\delta(s - t_R) = \pi\frac{a^2}{b},$$

which is exactly the form we had assumed at the outset in the t-channel; thus that the second resonance condition is

$$ImA'(s,1) = -\frac{N(s,1)\, Im D(s,1)}{|D|^2} = \pi(s-4)\Gamma\delta(s - t_R). \qquad (11.33)$$

As a numerical example,[5] we take two poles at

$$s_1 = -21 \quad \text{and} \quad s_2 = -196$$

and choose the subtraction point equal to the point of comparison:

$$s_0 = -4.$$

We then have the three conditions

$$N(4) = A(-4) + 8\left[\frac{F_1}{4 + s_1} + \frac{F_2}{4 + s_2}\right] = 0, \tag{I}$$

$$N(-4) = A(-4) = \frac{\frac{3}{2}\Gamma(t_R - 12)}{-8} Q_1\left(1 + \frac{2t_R}{-8}\right), \tag{II}$$

and

$$\left(\frac{N}{D}\right)'\bigg|_{s=-4} = N'(-4) - D'(-4)A(-4)$$

$$= \frac{d}{ds}\left[\frac{\frac{3}{2}\Gamma(t_R - 4 + 2s)}{s - 4} Q_1\left(1 + \frac{2t_R}{s - 4}\right)\right]_{s=-4}. \tag{III}$$

In Condition (III) we have to insert the quantities

$$N'(-4) = \frac{F_1}{-4 + s_1} + \frac{F_2}{-4 + s_2},$$

$$D'(-4) = -\frac{1}{\pi}\int_4^\infty ds' \sqrt{\frac{s' - 4}{s'}} \frac{N(s')}{(s' + 4)^2}$$

$$= -[A(-4)K(-4,-4) + F_1 K(-4,s_1) + F_2 K(-4,s_2)]$$

where we have introduced the auxiliary function

$$K(x,y) = \frac{1}{\pi}\int_4^\infty ds' \sqrt{\frac{s' - 4}{s'}} \frac{1}{(s' - x)(s' - y)} = \frac{\gamma(x) - \gamma(y)}{x - y}$$

with

$$\gamma(x) = \frac{1}{\pi}\int_4^\infty ds' \sqrt{\frac{s' - 4}{s'}} \frac{1}{s' - x}.$$

This last integral is divergent, and we make one subtraction:

$$\gamma_0(x) = \gamma(x) - \gamma(4) = (x - 4)\int_4^\infty \frac{ds'}{\pi} \sqrt{\frac{s' - 4}{s'}} \frac{1}{(s' - s)(s' - 4)}.$$

Then

$$K(x,y) = \frac{1}{x - y}[\gamma_0(x) - \gamma_0(y)],$$

and we get

$$\gamma_0(x) = \frac{1}{\pi}\sqrt{\frac{x - 4}{x}} \log\frac{\sqrt{x - 4} - \sqrt{x}}{\sqrt{x - 4} + \sqrt{x}}.$$

The function $\gamma_0(x)$ has square-root branch points at $x = 4$ (cut from 4 to ∞) and at $x = 0$ (cut from $-\infty$ to 0) and a logarithmic branch point at $x = 4$ (cut from $-\infty$ to 4).

We are interested in its determination for $s < 0$, which is given by

$$\gamma_0(x) = Re\gamma_0(s) = \frac{2}{\pi}\sqrt{\frac{-s+4}{-s}}\log\frac{\sqrt{4-s}-\sqrt{-s}}{2}, \quad s < 0.$$

We obtain the following numerical values:

$$K(-4,-4) = 0.02996,$$

$$K(-4,-21) = 0.0174,$$

$$K(-4,-196) = 0.004875.$$

With these numbers we can solve the conditions (I), (II), (III) for the three quantities $A(-4)$, F_1, and F_2 in terms of t_R and Γ. We then go to the resonance conditions, Eqs. (11.32) and (11.33), to determine t_R and Γ.

The result of these calculations is

$$t_R \cong 17.6\mu^2 \text{ (585 Mev)},$$

$$\Gamma \cong 125 \text{ Mev.}$$

It is interesting that a single pole approximation gives a too-low mass value, $t_R \approx 350$ Mev. (Exercise 1.)

More detailed calculations have been made by taking into account a D-wave resonance in the $I = 0$ state again in zero-width approximation, and the inelastic effects have been included in a rough way by taking a model function for the inelasticity factor $R(s,\ell)$. These approximations seem to bring the value of t_R closer to experiment.[6] In particular, the inelastic effects seem to reduce the width of the resonance without much affecting the position.

Clearly these crude approximations can be improved, but at the expense of complicated numerical calculations.

Recent investigations show that the above results are not very sensitive to the choice of the subtraction point, but are extremely sensitive to the choice of the matching or comparison point.[7]

11.5   Further Approximations in the $\pi\pi$-Problem

A great many other approximations have been performed in the problem.[8] Essentially one has to solve the fundamental coupled integral equations (11.21) with the left-hand discontinuity given by Eq. (11.26). This is, of course, not a complete set of equations because the inelasticity factor $R(s,\ell)$ is

[6] L. Balasz, *Phys. Rev.*, **129**, 872 (1963); *Phys. Rev. Letters*, **10**, 170 (1963).

[7] M. L. Mehta and P. K. Srivastava, *Phys. Rev.*, **137**, B423 (1965).

[8] G. F. Chew and S. Mandelstam, Ref. 2, and *Nuovo Cimento*, **19**, 752 (1961); J. Ball and D. Wong, *Phys. Rev. Letters*, **7**, 390 (1961); D. Wong, *Phys. Rev.*, **126**, 1220 (1962); B. H. Bransden and J. Moffat, *Nuovo Cimento*, **21**, 505 (1961) and **23**, 598 (1962); *Phys. Rev. Letters*, **6**, 708 (1961) and **8**, 145 (1962); V. V. Serebyakov and D. V. Shirkov, *JETP*, **15**, 425 (1962).

unknown and because Eq. (11.26) is not valid for $s < -32$. But with $R \cong 1$ these coupled integral equations would give us more information than the simple approximation in Sec. 11.4.

11.6 "Bootstrap" Approximations

To what extent is the bootstrap approximation (discussed in Sec. 11.4 for the ρ-meson) a general feature of the strongly interacting particles? The basic intuitive idea here is that the strongly interacting particles are bound together by forces due to the same or other strongly interacting particles. And this idea is expressed in a natural way by the crossing symmetry and analyticity of the amplitudes. In order for the idea to be practically successful, certain states in the crossed channels have to contribute the dominant part of the forces necessary for binding the two particles. Otherwise, if too many states play a role, nothing is gained, for we know from unitarity that all amplitudes are coupled to each other and determine each other. Also, the same particle can occur as bound state in many different situations so that the question as to which are the constituent strongly interacting particles is meaningful only in the case of so-called composite particles like deuteron. In this case many properties of the deuteron can be explained on the basis that it is composed of a neutron and a proton, indicating that the contribution of other states like $2N + \pi$, $2N + 3\pi$, $2N + N\overline{N}, \ldots$, is small. However, a tightly bound state like π is not simply made up by the $N\overline{N}$ system. The bootstrap approximations in other situations are fairly good: In the case of ρ-meson, ρ and ω contributions explain the major part of the binding phenomenon. Another important example is the reciprocal role played by nucleon and the $I = \frac{3}{2}$, $J = \frac{3}{2}$ resonance N^* (1236 Bev): N^* is to a good approximation a $\pi - N$ bound state, bound mainly by the exchange of N itself in the u-channel, similarly N by the exchange of N^* (see Chap. 12). To see how successful the approach is in detail we refer to specialized review papers.[9]

The bootstrap idea does not exclude the possibility that the strongly interacting particles have more fundamental and other type of constituents bound together by extremely strong forces. For example, in the case of nuclei, we can use nuclei themselves as constituents, like α-particles or more fundamental nucleons. Or, in atomic physics, wave functions of atoms can be expanded in principle in terms of the wave functions of other atoms.

Problems and Further Developments

1. Repeat the ρ-meson bootstrap calculation by taking a single pole at $s = s_1$ to approximate the faraway part of the left-hand cut.

2. N/D *Method and Levinson's theorem:* Let $A_\ell(E) = N_\ell(E)/D_\ell(E)$ with the

---

[9] See, e.g., F. Zachariasen, "Lectures on Bootstrap," *Pacific International Summer School of Physics*, Honolulu, 1965; B. Udgaonkar, in *International Seminar on High Energy Physics, Trieste* (Vienna: International Atomic Energy Agency, 1965).

cut of $D_\ell(E)$ in E-plane shown in Fig. 11.8. Consider the following contour integral:

$$\mathcal{J} = \frac{1}{2\pi i} \oint_C dE_\ell \frac{1}{D_\ell} \frac{dD_\ell}{dE}$$

$$= \frac{1}{2\pi i} \int_0^\infty dE \text{ disc.} \left[\frac{d}{dE} (\log D_\ell) \right]$$

$$= \frac{1}{2\pi i} \int_0^\infty dE \frac{d}{dE} [\log D_\ell(E + i0) - \log D_\ell(E - i0)]$$

$$= -\frac{1}{2\pi i} \int_0^\infty dE \, 2\pi i \delta_\ell(E)$$

$$= \frac{1}{\pi} [\delta(0) - \delta(\infty)].$$

Here one has assumed that $\dfrac{d}{dE} [\log D_\ell(E)]$ vanishes at infinity for complex E, and used the fact that on the real axis

$$s_\ell = e^{2i\delta_\ell} = \frac{D_\ell^*}{D_\ell} = \frac{D_\ell(E - i0)}{D_\ell(E + i0)},$$

or

$$\delta_\ell(E) = \frac{1}{2i} \log s_\ell$$

$$= \frac{1}{2i} [\log D_\ell(E - i0) - \log D_\ell(E + i0)].$$

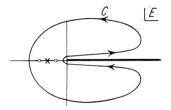

Figure 11.8.

On the other hand, the contour integral $\mathcal{J}$ is equal to the number of zeros of D_ℓ, n_B minus the number of poles of D_ℓ, n_P. Thus

$$\delta(0) - \delta(\infty) = \pi(n_B - n_P),$$

which is the Levinson's theorem. The zeros of D_ℓ give the bound states, the poles of D_ℓ do not correspond to any singularities of the S-matrix. These poles, however, have to be present in the dispersion relation for D_ℓ, Eq. (11.21). [N. Levinson, *Matt. Fys. Medd. Dansk Vis. Selsk.*, **25**, no. 9 (1949); R. Warnock, *Phys. Rev.*, **131**, 1320 (1963).]

3. Consider the vector meson ω as a bound state of π and ρ and perform a self-consistent calculation similar to that of ρ. [Compare M. L. Mehta, *Phys. Rev.*, **134**, B1377 (1964).]

4. Obtain the total-isospin amplitudes, Eq. (11.2).

CHAPTER 12

$\pi N \rightarrow \pi N$ and $\pi\pi \rightarrow N\bar{N}$ Scattering

The interactions of pions and nucleons is one of the most important problems of strong interactions. In contrast to pion-pion scattering a large number of direct experimental information is available both at low and high energies. We shall also see explicitly the effect of spin. Most of the results in this chapter apply equally well to other spin 0-spin $\frac{1}{2}$ scattering problems such as $KN \rightarrow KN$, $\pi\Lambda \rightarrow \pi\Sigma$, etc.

12.1 Kinematics

We denote the masses of nucleons and antinucleons by m, those of pions by μ. Mass differences between isospin multiplets are neglected. The *physical* momenta k_i and isospin indices α_i are denoted as shown in Fig. 12.1.

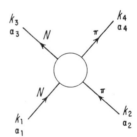

Figure 12.1 Labeling of momenta and isospin indices.

The three channels are denoted as follows:

$$\begin{array}{llll}
s\text{-channel:} & s = (k_1 + k_2)^2, & \pi + N \rightarrow \pi + N, & \\
t\text{-channel:} & t = (k_1 - k_3)^2, & N + \bar{N} \rightarrow \pi + \pi, & (12.1) \\
u\text{-channel:} & u = (k_1 - k_4)^2, & \pi + N \rightarrow \pi + N. &
\end{array}$$

a. Isospin Amplitudes

There are two isospin amplitudes corresponding to two values of total

226

isospin. We introduce the isospin amplitudes R^+, R^- by [see Eqs. (4.14) and (4.15)]

$$R^{\alpha_1\alpha_2}_{\alpha_3\alpha_4} = R^+ \delta^{\alpha_1}_{\alpha_3}\delta^{\alpha_2}_{\alpha_4} + R^-(-1)^{\alpha_3}\varepsilon^{\alpha_1 n}_{-\alpha_3}\rho^{n\alpha_2}_{\alpha_4}. \tag{12.2}$$

In the s-channel, the connection between $R^\pm$ and $R^{\frac12,\frac32}$ is, from Eq. (4.9),

$$\begin{aligned}R^{\frac12} &= R^+ + 2R^-,\\ R^{\frac32} &= R^+ - R^-.\end{aligned} \tag{12.3}$$

In the t-channel the total I-spin takes values 0 and 1 and we find

$$\begin{aligned}R^0 &= \sqrt{6}\,R^+,\\ R^1 &= 2R^-.\end{aligned} \tag{12.4}$$

The u-channel is the same as the s-channel as far as isotopic spin is conserved, and we obtain

$$\begin{aligned}R^{\frac12} &= R^+ - 2R^-,\\ R^{\frac32} &= R^+ + R^-.\end{aligned}$$

b. s-Channel Spin Amplitudes

The spin amplitudes, assuming parity conservation can be written in terms of the two positive-parity basis functions discussed in Chap. 4,

$$M = AY_1 + BY_3$$

where

$$Y_1 = \frac{1}{m}(k_1 + k_3)\cdot\sigma,$$

$$Y_2 = \frac{1}{2}\left(n\cdot\sigma + \frac{k_3\cdot\sigma}{m}\,n\cdot\tilde{\sigma}\,\frac{k_1\cdot\sigma}{m}\right), \tag{12.5}$$

and

$$n = \frac{1}{\mu}(k_2 + k_4).$$

Hence the R-amplitudes are

$$R = AR_1 + BR_3, \tag{12.6}$$

with

$$R_1 = \left(\frac{k_3\cdot\tilde{\sigma}}{m}\right)^{\frac12}Y_1\left(\frac{k_1\cdot\tilde{\sigma}}{m}\right)^{\frac12} = \frac{1}{m}(k_3\cdot\tilde{\sigma}k_1\cdot\sigma)^{\frac12} + \frac{1}{m}(k_3\cdot\sigma k_1\cdot\tilde{\sigma})^{\frac12},$$

$$R_2 = \frac{1}{2}\left[\left(\frac{k_3\cdot\tilde{\sigma}}{m}\right)^{\frac12}n\cdot\sigma\left(\frac{k_1\cdot\tilde{\sigma}}{m}\right)^{\frac12} + \left(\frac{k_3\cdot\sigma}{m}\right)^{\frac12}n\cdot\tilde{\sigma}\left(\frac{k_1\cdot\sigma}{m}\right)^{\frac12}\right]. \tag{12.6'}$$

In the s-channel all the k's in Eq. (12.6') are physical. We now evaluate these covariant expressions in the center-of-mass frame of the s-channel; i.e.,

$$k_1 = (E,\mathbf{q}),\quad k_2 = (\omega,-\mathbf{q}),\quad k_3 = (E,\mathbf{q}'),\quad k_4 = (\omega,-\mathbf{q}'),$$

with

$$q^2 = q'^2,\quad \mathbf{q} = q\hat{\mathbf{q}};\quad \text{total energy } W = E + \omega = \sqrt{s} \tag{12.7}$$

and obtain after some calculation

$$R_1 = \frac{1}{m} [(E + m) - (E - m)\boldsymbol{\sigma} \cdot \hat{\mathbf{q}}' \boldsymbol{\sigma} \cdot \hat{\mathbf{q}}],$$

$$R_2 = \frac{1}{m\mu} [(E + m)(W - m) + (E - m)(W + m)\boldsymbol{\sigma} \cdot \hat{\mathbf{q}}' \boldsymbol{\sigma} \cdot \hat{\mathbf{q}}].$$
(12.8)

Or, from Eq. (12.6),

$$R = \frac{E + m}{m} \left(A + \frac{W - m}{\mu} B \right) + \frac{E - m}{m} \left(-A + \frac{W + m}{\mu} B \right) \boldsymbol{\sigma} \cdot \hat{\mathbf{q}}' \boldsymbol{\sigma} \cdot \hat{\mathbf{q}}$$
(12.9)
$$= f_1 + f_2 \boldsymbol{\sigma} \cdot \hat{\mathbf{q}}' \boldsymbol{\sigma} \cdot \hat{\mathbf{q}},$$

where we have put

$$f_1 = \frac{E + m}{m} \left(A + \frac{W - m}{\mu} B \right),$$

$$f_2 = \frac{E - m}{m} \left(-A + \frac{W + m}{\mu} B \right).$$
(12.10)

Note also that

$$E = \frac{W^2 + m^2 - \mu^2}{2W}; \qquad E \pm m = \frac{1}{2W} [(W \pm m)^2 - \mu^2]. \quad (12.11)$$

The elastic $\pi N - \pi N$ cross section is given by [see Eq. (3.11)]

$$\frac{d\sigma}{d\Omega} = \frac{|G|^2}{(2\pi)^2} \frac{m^2 \mu^2}{s}$$

with

$$R = (2\pi)^4 \delta(P_i - P_f)G$$

or

$$\frac{d\sigma}{d\Omega} = \frac{m^2 \mu^2}{s} \sum_{\text{spin}} |f_1 + f_2 \boldsymbol{\sigma} \cdot \hat{\mathbf{q}}' \boldsymbol{\sigma} \cdot \hat{\mathbf{q}}|^2,$$
(12.12)

where we have incorporated some factor (2π) into the scalar amplitudes A, B. Now for an initially unpolarized beam we have to average over the initial spins, then the right-hand side of Eq. (12.12) must be multiplied by a factor $\frac{1}{2}$. Obviously we could also put the factors $m^2 \mu^2/s$ into the f's. Equation (12.12) holds for each isospin amplitude separately so that we have the amplitudes $f_1^\pm$ and $f_2^\pm$.

The scalar functions $A^\pm(s,t,u)$, $B^\pm(s,t,u)$, or $f_1^\pm$, $f_2^\pm$ represent the physical amplitude in the s-channel if the arguments s, t, u take values in the region of this channel; similarly for the other two channels. The values of s, t, u for the three channels in their respective centers of mass are given on the next page.

s-channel [Eq. (12.7)]:

$$s = W^2 = (E + \omega)^2 = [(q^2 + m^2)^{\frac{1}{2}} + (q^2 + \mu^2)^{\frac{1}{2}}]^2,$$
$$t = -2q^2(1 - \cos \theta),$$
$$u = 2m^2 + 2\mu^2 - W^2 + 2q^2(1 - \cos \theta),$$
$$s + t + u = 2m^2 + 2\mu^2,$$

(12.13)

$$q^2 = \frac{1}{4W^2} [(W + m)^2 - \mu^2][(W - m)^2 - \mu^2].$$

t-channel:

$$k_1 = (E,\mathbf{q}), \quad k_2 = (-\omega,-\mathbf{q}'), \quad k_3 = (-E,\mathbf{q}), \quad k_4 = (\omega,-\mathbf{q}')$$

(12.14)

$$[E = \omega, \quad q^2 \neq q'^2],$$

whence

$$t = 4(q'^2 + \mu^2) = 4(q^2 + m^2) = 4E^2 = 4\omega^2,$$
$$u = -q^2 - q'^2 - 2qq' \cos \theta,$$
$$s = -q^2 - q'^2 + 2qq' \cos \theta.$$

(12.15)

u-channel:

$$k_1 = (E,\mathbf{q}), \quad k_2 = (-\omega,-\mathbf{q}'), \quad k_3 = (-E,-\mathbf{q}'), \quad k_4 = (-\omega,+\mathbf{q}'),$$

(12.16)

$$[E \neq \omega, \quad q^2 = q'^2],$$

whence

$$u = (E + \omega)^2 = [(q^2 + m^2)^{\frac{1}{2}} + (q^2 + \mu^2)^{\frac{1}{2}}]^2 = W^2,$$
$$s = 2m^2 + 2\mu^2 - W^2 + 2q^2(1 + \cos \theta),$$
$$t = -2q^2(1 + \cos \theta).$$

(12.17)

Note that the center-of-mass momenta q and q' are different in different channels, so that when it is necessary to distinguish them we shall write $q_s, q_t, q_u, \ldots$. The physical regions of the three channels are shown in Fig. 12.2 and are characterized by the inequalities:

s-channel:
$$s \geqslant (m + \mu)^2, \quad t \leqslant 0, \quad su \leqslant (m^2 - \mu^2)^2.$$

u-channel:
$$u \geqslant (m + \mu)^2, \quad t \leqslant 0, \quad su \leqslant (m^2 - \mu^2)^2.$$

(12.18)

t-channel:
$$t \geqslant 4m^2, \quad su \geqslant (m^2 - \mu^2)^2.$$

Equation (6.13) gives the first column of Eq. (12.18) plus the relation

$$stu \geqslant (m^2 - \mu^2)t.$$

(12.18′)

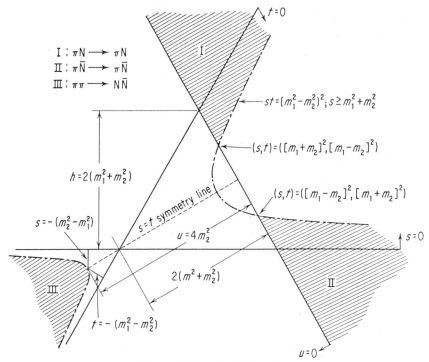

Figure 12.2 Physical regions.

c. t-Channel Spin Amplitudes

In the t-channel we can use the same basic Eq. (12.5); but now the vectors $(-k_3)$ and $(-k_2)$ are the physical momenta. Thus

$$M = A\frac{1}{m}[k_1 - (-k_3)]\cdot\sigma + \frac{B}{2}\left[n'\cdot\sigma - \frac{(-k_3)\cdot\sigma}{m}n'\cdot\tilde{\sigma}\frac{k_1\cdot\sigma}{m}\right], \quad (12.19)$$

$$n' = \frac{1}{\mu}[k_4 - (-k_2)].$$

In other words, $M(k_4, -k_3; k_1, -k_2)$ is the physical amplitude in the region where $k_4 - k_3 = k_1 - k_2$ is physical or $k_1 + k_3 = k_2 + k_4$—i.e., the energy-momentum conservation of the t-channel. Then

$$R = A\frac{1}{m}[(-k_3\cdot\tilde{\sigma}k_1\cdot\sigma)^{1/2} - (-k_3\cdot\sigma k_1\cdot\tilde{\sigma})^{1/2}]$$

$$+ \frac{1}{2m}B[(-k_3\cdot\tilde{\sigma})^{1/2}n'\cdot\sigma(k_1\cdot\sigma)^{1/2} - (-k_3\cdot\sigma)^{1/2}n'\cdot\tilde{\sigma}(k_1\cdot\sigma)^{1/2}]. \quad (12.20)$$

Using the center-of-mass values, Eq. (12.14), and the equalities in this frame,

$$\left(-\frac{k_3\cdot\tilde{\sigma}}{m}\right)^{1/2} = \left(\frac{k_1\cdot\sigma}{m}\right)^{1/2} = \frac{1}{\sqrt{2}}\left[\left(\frac{E+m}{m}\right)^{1/2} + \left(\frac{E-m}{m}\right)^{1/2}\sigma\cdot\hat{\mathbf{q}}\right],$$

$$n'\cdot\sigma = -\frac{2}{\mu}\boldsymbol{\sigma}\cdot\mathbf{q}'; \quad n'\cdot\tilde{\sigma} = \frac{2}{\mu}\boldsymbol{\sigma}\cdot\mathbf{q}',$$

we obtain

$$R = A\frac{2}{m}\,\boldsymbol{\sigma}\cdot\mathbf{q} - B\frac{2}{\mu m}\left[E\boldsymbol{\sigma}\cdot\mathbf{q}' - \frac{1}{E+m}\,\mathbf{q}\cdot\mathbf{q}'\boldsymbol{\sigma}\cdot\mathbf{q}\right], \qquad (12.21)$$

or

$$R = \frac{2}{m}\left[\left(A + B\frac{\bar{\mathbf{q}}\cdot\bar{\mathbf{q}}}{\mu(E+m)}\right)\boldsymbol{\sigma}\cdot\mathbf{q} - B\frac{E}{\mu}\,\boldsymbol{\sigma}\cdot\mathbf{q}'\right],$$

or, finally,

$$R = h_1\boldsymbol{\sigma}\cdot\mathbf{q} + h_2\boldsymbol{\sigma}\cdot\mathbf{q}', \qquad (12.21')$$

where

$$h_1 = \frac{2}{m}\left[A + \frac{B}{\mu}\frac{\mathbf{q}\cdot\mathbf{q}'}{E+m}\right],$$

$$h_2 = -\frac{2}{m}B\frac{E}{\mu}. \qquad (12.22)$$

Again we have two sets of amplitudes $h_i^\pm$ for each total isotopic spin value.
The differential cross section of $\pi\pi \to N\bar{N}$ is given by

$$\frac{d\sigma}{d\Omega} = \sum_{\text{spin}} \frac{|G|^2}{(2\pi)^2}\frac{m^2\mu^2}{4E^2}\frac{q}{q'}$$

$$= \sum_{\text{spin}} m^2\mu^2(2\pi)^{-10}\frac{1}{t}\left(\frac{q}{q'}\right)|h_1\boldsymbol{\sigma}\cdot\mathbf{q} + h_2\boldsymbol{\sigma}\cdot\mathbf{q}'|^2. \qquad (12.23)$$

The u-channel is the same as the s-channel.

d. Helicity Amplitudes and Partial-Wave Amplitudes in the s-Channel

The spinor indices of the R amplitudes are the third component of the spins of all particles with respect to a fixed direction z. If we measure the spin

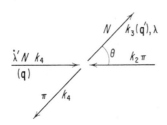

Figure 12.3 Helicities in the center-of-mass frame; s-channel.

of each particle with respect to its own direction of motion we obtain the helicity amplitudes. They will be seen to be more convenient from the point of analytic continuation in energy as well as angular-momentum variables.

(1) Helicity Amplitudes in the s-Channel. In the center-of-mass frame we denote the momenta and the helicities as shown in Fig. 12.3. Let λ and $\dot{\lambda}$ be the helicities of the outgoing and incoming nucleon respectively. Then the helicity amplitudes, using the general formulas of Chap. 4, are given by

$$H_{\lambda\dot{\lambda}} = D^{(\frac{1}{2},0)}\left[\exp\left(-i\theta\frac{\sigma_2}{2}\right)\right]^{\alpha}_{\lambda} R_{\alpha\dot{\lambda}}, \tag{12.24}$$

where we have now "rotated" the spinor index of k_3 from the z-direction ($=$ direction of $\mathbf{q}$) to the direction of $\mathbf{q}'$. Or, with Eq. (12.9),

$$H_{\lambda\dot{\lambda}} = [e^{-i\theta\frac{\sigma_2}{2}}]^{\alpha}_{\lambda}(f_1 + f_2\boldsymbol{\sigma}\cdot\hat{\mathbf{q}}'\boldsymbol{\sigma}\cdot\hat{\mathbf{q}})_{\alpha\dot{\lambda}}.$$

Now if α is the angle of a vector a with respect to z we have the identity, in matrix form,

$$\exp\left(-i\alpha\frac{\sigma_2}{2}\right)\boldsymbol{\sigma}\cdot\mathbf{a} = \sigma_3 a \exp\left(-i\alpha\frac{\sigma_2}{2}\right) \tag{12.25}$$

$$= 2\lambda a \, d^{\frac{1}{2}}(\theta),$$

where λ takes the values $\pm\frac{1}{2}$ and where we used the rotation matrices d^J, defined by

$$D^{(J,0)}(e^{-i\theta\frac{\sigma_2}{2}}) = d^J(\theta). \tag{12.26}$$

Thus we get

$$H_{\lambda\dot{\lambda}} = (f_1 + 4\lambda\dot{\lambda}f_2) \, d^{\frac{1}{2}}_{\lambda\dot{\lambda}}(\theta)$$

$$= Z(\lambda,\dot{\lambda}) \, d^{\frac{1}{2}}_{\lambda\dot{\lambda}}(\theta). \tag{12.27}$$

Because of the relation

$$d^{\frac{1}{2}}(\theta) = e^{-i\sigma_2\frac{\theta}{2}} = \begin{pmatrix} \cos\dfrac{\theta}{2} & -\sin\dfrac{\theta}{2} \\[2mm] \sin\dfrac{\theta}{2} & \cos\dfrac{\theta}{2} \end{pmatrix} \tag{12.28}$$

there are two distinct helicity amplitudes:

$$H_{\frac{1}{2},\frac{1}{2}} = H_{-\frac{1}{2},-\frac{1}{2}} = (f_1 + f_2)\cos\frac{\theta}{2} \equiv \varphi_1,$$

$$H_{-\frac{1}{2},\frac{1}{2}} = -H_{\frac{1}{2},-\frac{1}{2}} = (f_1 - f_2)\sin\frac{\theta}{2} \equiv \varphi_2. \tag{12.29}$$

Thus $(f_1 + f_2)$ is essentially the amplitude for transitions of equal helicity and $(f_1 - f_2)$ that of opposite helicities between initial and final nucleons. We have also, from Eq. (12.24),

$$f_{\frac{1}{2}} = \frac{1}{2}\left[\frac{H_{\frac{1}{2},\frac{1}{2}}}{\cos\dfrac{\theta}{2}} \pm \frac{H_{\frac{1}{2},-\frac{1}{2}}}{\sin\dfrac{\theta}{2}}\right]. \tag{12.30}$$

(2) Partial-Wave Amplitudes in s-Channel. We now introduce the total angular momentum J through the expansion

$$H_{\lambda\dot{\lambda}} = \frac{1}{2q}\sum_{J}(2J + 1)h_{\lambda\dot{\lambda}}(s) \, d^{J}_{\lambda\dot{\lambda}}(\theta), \tag{12.31}$$

where, because λ, $\hat{\lambda}$ are $\pm\frac{1}{2}$, J takes all positive half-integer values. This expansion generalizes the Legendre expansion to spinor functions of θ. A transition with definite helicities specified is a linear combination of all such transitions with different J's. The inverse of Eq. (12.26),

$$h_{\lambda\hat{\lambda}}^J(s) = \tfrac{1}{2}q \int_{-1}^{+1} dz H_{\lambda\hat{\lambda}} d_{\lambda\hat{\lambda}}^J, \tag{12.32}$$

gives the amplitudes for both definite helicities and definite total angular momentum. To obtain these we insert Eq. (12.27) into Eq. (12.32) and get

$$h_{\lambda\hat{\lambda}}^J = \frac{q}{2} \int_{-1}^{+1} dz(f_1 + 4\lambda\hat{\lambda}f_2)\, d_{\lambda\hat{\lambda}}^{\frac{1}{2}}(\theta)\, d_{\lambda\hat{\lambda}}^J(\theta). \tag{12.33}$$

The product of two d-functions can be expanded in a Clebsch-Gordan series:

$$d_{\lambda\mu}^s\, d_{\alpha\beta}^s = \sum_I [\ell sI]^{\lambda\alpha}[\ell sI]^{\mu\beta}\, d_{\lambda+\alpha,\mu+\beta}^I. \tag{12.34}$$

In our case only two values of I occur, hence

$$h_{\lambda\hat{\lambda}}^J = \frac{q}{2} \int_{-1}^{+1} dz\, (f_1 + 4\lambda\hat{\lambda}f_2)\{[\tfrac{1}{2}, J, J - \tfrac{1}{2}]^{\lambda\lambda}[\tfrac{1}{2}, J, J - \tfrac{1}{2}]^{\hat{\lambda}\hat{\lambda}}\, d_{2\lambda,2\hat{\lambda}}^{J-\frac{1}{2}}$$
$$+ [\tfrac{1}{2}, J, J + \tfrac{1}{2}]^{\lambda\lambda}[\tfrac{1}{2}, J, J + \tfrac{1}{2}]^{\hat{\lambda}\hat{\lambda}}\, d_{2\lambda,2\hat{\lambda}}^{J+\frac{1}{2}}\}. \tag{12.35}$$

We can interpret the appearance of $J - \frac{1}{2}$, $J + \frac{1}{2}$ as the possible orbital angular-momentum ℓ-values, as will be more clear below.

The Clebsch-Gordan coefficients and the d-functions which so occur have the following values:

$$[\tfrac{1}{2}, J, J - \tfrac{1}{2}]^{\frac{1}{2},\frac{1}{2}} = -\frac{(J - \frac{1}{2})^{\frac{1}{2}}}{(2J + 1)^{\frac{1}{2}}} = [\tfrac{1}{2}, J, J - \tfrac{1}{2}]^{-\frac{1}{2},-\frac{1}{2}},$$
$$[\tfrac{1}{2}, J, J + \tfrac{1}{2}]^{\frac{1}{2},\frac{1}{2}} = \frac{(J + \frac{3}{2})^{\frac{1}{2}}}{(2J + 1)^{\frac{1}{2}}} = [\tfrac{1}{2}, J, J + \tfrac{1}{2}]^{-\frac{1}{2},-\frac{1}{2}}, \tag{12.36}$$

and

$$d_{11}^{J-\frac{1}{2}} = \frac{P'_{J-\frac{1}{2}} - P'_{J-\frac{3}{2}} + (J - \frac{1}{2})^2 P_{J-\frac{1}{2}}}{(J - \frac{1}{2})(J + \frac{1}{2})},$$
$$d_{-1,1}^{J-\frac{1}{2}} = d_{1,-1}^{J-\frac{1}{2}} = \frac{(1 + \cos\theta)P'_{J-\frac{1}{2}}}{(J - \frac{1}{2})(J + \frac{1}{2})} - P_{J+\frac{1}{2}}. \tag{12.37}$$

Inserting these relations and the identities,

$$P'_{J+1}(z) - P'_{J-1}(z) = (2J + 1)P_J(z),$$
$$zP'_J(z) - P'_{J-1}(z) = JP_J(z), \tag{12.38}$$
$$P'_{J+1}(z) - zP'_J(z) = (J + 1)P_J(z),$$

where the primes are derivatives with respect to the argument z; we get finally

$$h_{(\frac{1}{2},-\frac{1}{2})}^J = \frac{q}{2} \int_{-1}^{+1} dz\, (f_1 \pm f_2)(P_{J-\frac{1}{2}} \pm P_{J+\frac{1}{2}}). \tag{12.39}$$

(3) Amplitudes with Definite Orbital Angular Momentum. It is clear that given the total angular momentum J, the orbital angular momentum can take the values $\ell = J - \frac{1}{2}$ and $\ell = J + \frac{1}{2}$. Because parity is conserved we have two independent transitions:

$$J - \tfrac{1}{2} \to J - \tfrac{1}{2},$$
$$J + \tfrac{1}{2} \to J + \tfrac{1}{2}.$$

To obtain the corresponding partial-wave amplitudes we form the linear combinations:

$$f_{J-\frac{1}{2},+} \equiv a^J_{J-\frac{1}{2},J-\frac{1}{2}} \equiv h^J_{\frac{1}{2},\frac{1}{2}} + h^J_{\frac{1}{2},-\frac{1}{2}} = q \int_{-1}^{+1} dz \, [f_1 P_{J-\frac{1}{2}} + f_2 P_{J+\frac{1}{2}}]$$

$$= 2q[f_1(J - \tfrac{1}{2}) + f_2(J + \tfrac{1}{2})].$$

$$f_{J+\frac{1}{2},-} \equiv a^J_{J+\frac{1}{2},J+\frac{1}{2}} \equiv h^J_{\frac{1}{2},\frac{1}{2}} - h^J_{\frac{1}{2},-\frac{1}{2}} = q \int_{-1}^{+1} dz \, [f_2 P_{J-\frac{1}{2}} + f_1 P_{J+\frac{1}{2}}]$$

$$= 2q[f_2(J - \tfrac{1}{2}) + f_1(J + \tfrac{1}{2})].$$

(12.40)

We thus have two sets of partial-wave amplitudes:

$$f_1(J \pm \tfrac{1}{2}), \quad f_2(J \pm \tfrac{1}{2}),$$

or

$$A_{J\pm\frac{1}{2}}, \quad B_{J\pm\frac{1}{2}},$$

$$f_1(J \pm \tfrac{1}{2}) = \frac{E + m}{m} \left[A_{J\pm\frac{1}{2}} + \frac{W - m}{\mu} B_{J\pm\frac{1}{2}} \right],$$

$$f_2(J \pm \tfrac{1}{2}) = \frac{E - m}{m} \left[-A_{J\pm\frac{1}{2}} + \frac{W + m}{\mu} B_{J\pm\frac{1}{2}} \right],$$

(12.41)

where

$$A_{J\pm\frac{1}{2}}(s) = \frac{1}{2} \int_{-1}^{1+} dz \, A(s,z) P_{J\pm\frac{1}{2}}(z),$$

(12.42)

and similarly for B. Because $A_{J\pm\frac{1}{2}}$, $B_{J\pm\frac{1}{2}}$ depend only on $s = W^2$, we obtain, from Eqs. (12.42) and (12.11), the symmetry relation

$$f_{1,\ell}(W) = -f_{2,\ell}(-W); \quad \ell = J - \tfrac{1}{2}, J + \tfrac{1}{2};$$

hence

$$f_{J-\frac{1}{2},+}(W) = -f_{J+\frac{1}{2},-}(-W).$$

(12.43)

We remark that the Eq. (12.39) could also be obtained more simply from Eq. (12.32) by using the identities

$$d^J_{\frac{1}{2},\frac{1}{2}} = \frac{\cos \dfrac{\theta}{2}}{J + \frac{1}{2}} [P'_{J+\frac{1}{2}} - P'_{J-\frac{1}{2}}] = d^J_{-\frac{1}{2},-\frac{1}{2}};$$

$$d^J_{-\frac{1}{2},\frac{1}{2}} = \frac{\sin \dfrac{\theta}{2}}{J + \frac{1}{2}} [P'_{J+\frac{1}{2}} + P'_{J-\frac{1}{2}}] = -d^J_{\frac{1}{2},-\frac{1}{2}},$$

(12.44)

and the individual values of H given by Eq. (12.39). The procedure above, however, is more general and shows the appearance of ℓ-values, $\ell = J \pm \frac{1}{2}$. To emphasize this last point we expand the scalar amplitudes f_1 and f_2 into Legendre series:

$$f_i(s,z) = \sum_{\ell=0}^{\infty} (2\ell + 1)f_i(s,\ell)P_\ell(z); \quad i = 1, 2.$$

This expansion of the scalar amplitudes into the Legendre series gives a precise definition of orbital angular momentum in the presence of spin. Then

$$h_{\lambda\lambda}^J = \frac{q}{2} \sum_\ell (2\ell + 1)[f_{1,\ell}(s) + 4\lambda\dot\lambda f_{2,\ell}(s)] \int_{-1}^{+1} dz \, d_{\lambda\lambda}^J \, d_{\lambda\lambda}^{\frac{1}{2}} \, d_{00}^\ell. \quad (12.44')$$

If we combine the three d-functions we see that only two values of ℓ occur in the sum, namely $\ell = J - \frac{1}{2}$ and $\ell = J + \frac{1}{2}$. Because there can be no interference between the amplitudes $f_{J-\frac{1}{2},+}$ and $f_{J+\frac{1}{2},-}$, we expect them to satisfy uncoupled unitarity condition. This will be shown in the next sections.

e. Helicity and Partial-Wave Amplitudes for t-Channel

(i) Helicity Amplitudes. Let the nucleon helicity be denoted by λ, the antinucleon helicity by $\dot\lambda$. Now N and $\bar N$ have the same center-of-mass momentum q. In order, therefore, to keep the helicities apart, we first evaluate $H_{\lambda\dot\lambda}$ in a general frame with $k_3 = (E,\mathbf{q}_3)$, $-k_1 = (E,\mathbf{q}_1)$, $k_2 = (\omega,\mathbf{q}_2)$, $-k_4 = (\omega,\mathbf{q}_4)$. Because we are using the analytically continued s-channel basis, the spinor indices of R in t-channel are $R_{m_3,-m_1}$ (see Chap. 4), so that

$$H_{\lambda,-\dot\lambda} = U_3^{-1}RU_1$$

$$= U_3^{-1}\left\{ \frac{A}{2}\left(\left[\sqrt{\frac{E+m}{m}} - \hat{\mathbf{q}}_3\cdot\boldsymbol\sigma\sqrt{\frac{E-m}{m}}\right]\left[\sqrt{\frac{E+m}{m}} + \hat{\mathbf{q}}_1\cdot\boldsymbol\sigma\sqrt{\frac{E-m}{m}}\right] \right.\right.$$

$$- \left[\sqrt{\frac{E+m}{m}} + \hat{\mathbf{q}}_3\cdot\boldsymbol\sigma\sqrt{\frac{E-m}{m}}\right]$$

$$\left. \times \left[\sqrt{\frac{E+m}{m}} - \hat{\mathbf{q}}_1\cdot\boldsymbol\sigma\sqrt{\frac{E-m}{m}}\right] \right)$$

$$+ \frac{B}{4\mu}\left(\left[\sqrt{\frac{E+m}{m}} - \hat{\mathbf{q}}_3\cdot\boldsymbol\sigma\sqrt{\frac{E-m}{m}}\right] \right.$$

$$\left. \times (\mathbf{q}_4 - \mathbf{q}_2)\cdot\boldsymbol\sigma\left[\sqrt{\frac{E+m}{m}} - \hat{\mathbf{q}}_1\cdot\boldsymbol\sigma\sqrt{\frac{E-m}{m}}\right] \right)$$

$$+ \left[\sqrt{\frac{E+m}{m}} + \hat{\mathbf{q}}_3\cdot\boldsymbol\sigma\sqrt{\frac{E-m}{m}}\right]$$

$$\left. \times (\mathbf{q}_4 - \mathbf{q}_2)\cdot\boldsymbol\sigma\left[\sqrt{\frac{E+m}{m}} + \hat{\mathbf{q}}_1\cdot\boldsymbol\sigma\sqrt{\frac{E-m}{m}}\right]U_1 \right\}$$

$$= U_3^{-1}\left\{ \frac{A}{m}(\hat{\mathbf{q}}_1\cdot\boldsymbol{\sigma} - \hat{\mathbf{q}}_3\cdot\boldsymbol{\sigma}) + \frac{B}{2\mu m}[(E+m)(\mathbf{q}_4 - \mathbf{q}_2)\cdot\boldsymbol{\sigma}\right.$$

$$\left. + (E-m)\hat{\mathbf{q}}_e\cdot\boldsymbol{\sigma}(\mathbf{q}_4 - \mathbf{q}_2)\cdot\boldsymbol{\sigma}\hat{\mathbf{q}}_1\cdot\boldsymbol{\sigma}]\right\}U_1$$

$$= \frac{A}{m}(2\lambda q_1 - 2\lambda q_3)U_3^{-1}U_1 + \frac{B}{2\mu m}[(E+m) + 4\lambda\lambda(E-m)]$$

$$\times U_3^{-1}(\mathbf{q}_4 - \mathbf{q}_2)\cdot\boldsymbol{\sigma}U_1. \quad (12.45)$$

Now we may go to the center-of-mass frame (Fig. 12.4) where the rotation

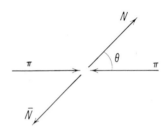

Figure 12.4 t-channel center-of-mass frame.

matrices are given by

$$U_3^{-1}U_1 = \exp\left(i\theta\frac{\sigma_2}{2}\right)\exp\left(-i(\pi+\theta)\frac{\sigma_2}{2}\right) = \exp\left(-i\pi\frac{\sigma_2}{2}\right)$$

$$= \begin{pmatrix} 0 & 1 \\ -1 & 0 \end{pmatrix}$$

and

$$U_3^{-1}(\mathbf{q}_4 - \mathbf{q}_2)\cdot\boldsymbol{\sigma}U_1 = -2\exp\left(i\theta\frac{\sigma_2}{2}\right)\mathbf{q}'\cdot\boldsymbol{\sigma}\exp\left(-i\theta\frac{\sigma_2}{2}\right)\exp\left(-i\pi\frac{\sigma_2}{2}\right)$$

$$= 2\begin{pmatrix} -\sin\theta & -\cos\theta \\ -\cos\theta & \sin\theta \end{pmatrix}.$$

[Note that $q':(0, 0 + 1)$]. Thus,

$$H_{\lambda,-\dot{\lambda}} = A\frac{q}{m}(2\lambda + 2\lambda)\begin{pmatrix} 0 & 1 \\ -1 & 0 \end{pmatrix}$$

$$+ B\frac{q'}{\mu m}[(E+m) + 4\lambda\lambda(E-m)]\begin{pmatrix} -\sin\theta & -\cos\theta \\ -\cos\theta & \sin\theta \end{pmatrix}. \quad (12.46)$$

Hence the two independent helicity amplitudes are

$$H_{\frac{1}{2},-\frac{1}{2}} = -B\frac{2Eq'}{\mu m}\sin\theta = -H_{-\frac{1}{2},\frac{1}{2}},$$

$$H_{\frac{1}{2},\frac{1}{2}} = A\frac{2q}{m} - B\frac{2q'}{\mu}\cos\theta = H_{-\frac{1}{2},-\frac{1}{2}}, \quad (12.47)$$

or, in terms of the h_1, h_2 amplitudes,

$$\left(\frac{2}{m} B = -\frac{\mu}{E} h_2; \frac{2}{m} A = h_1 + h_2 \frac{qq'}{E(E + m)}\right),$$

$$H_{\frac{1}{2}, -\frac{1}{2}} = h_2 q' \sin \theta,$$
$$H_{\frac{1}{2}, \frac{1}{2}} = h_1 q + h_2 q' \cos \theta. \tag{12.48}$$

The partial-wave expansion, Eq. (12.31), now has the form

$$H_{\lambda\lambda} = \frac{1}{2q} \sum_J (2J + 1) h_{\lambda\lambda}^J(s) d_{\lambda - \lambda, 0}^J, \tag{12.49}$$

where $(\lambda - \lambda)$ takes the values 0 and 1, hence J takes all positive integer values. Because of the relations

$$d_{0,0}^J = P_J,$$
$$d_{1,0}^J = d_{0,-1}^J = -d_{-1,0}^J = -\frac{\sin \theta}{\sqrt{J(J + 1)}} P_J', \tag{12.50}$$

we get

$$H_{\frac{1}{2}, \frac{1}{2}} = \frac{1}{2q} \sum_{J=0}^{\infty} (2J + 1) h_{\frac{1}{2}, \frac{1}{2}}^J P_J,$$
$$H_{\frac{1}{2}, -\frac{1}{2}} = -\frac{1}{2q} \sum_{J=0}^{\infty} (2J + 1) h_{\frac{1}{2}, -\frac{1}{2}}^J \frac{\sin \theta}{\sqrt{J(J + 1)}} P_J'. \tag{12.51}$$

(ii) Partial-Wave Amplitudes in t-Channel

The partial-wave amplitudes are given by

$$h_{\lambda\lambda}^J = \tfrac{1}{2} q \int_{-1}^{+1} dz \, H_{\lambda\lambda} d_{\lambda - \lambda, 0}^J, \tag{12.52}$$

and, using Eq. (12.48) in this equation, we obtain

$$h_{\frac{1}{2}, -\frac{1}{2}}^J = -\frac{qq'}{2} \int_{-1}^{+1} dz \, h_2 \sin \theta \frac{\sin \theta P_J'(\cos \theta)}{\sqrt{J(J + 1)}},$$
$$h_{\frac{1}{2}, \frac{1}{2}}^J = \frac{q}{2} \int_{-1}^{+1} dz \, (h_1 q + h_2 q' \cos \theta) P_J(\cos \theta),$$

or   (12.54)

$$h_{\frac{1}{2}, \frac{1}{2}}^J = q \int_{-1}^{+1} dz \left(\frac{q}{m} A - \frac{q'}{\mu} \cos \theta\right) P_J(\cos \theta),$$
$$h_{\frac{1}{2}, -\frac{1}{2}}^J = \frac{qq'}{m} \frac{E}{\mu} \int_{-1}^{+1} dz \, B \sin^2 \theta \frac{P_J'}{\sqrt{J(J + 1)}}.$$

Again we introduce partial-wave amplitudes A_J, B_J and use the relations

$$(1 - z^2) P_J' = (J + 1)(z P_J - P_{J+1}),$$
$$z P_J = \frac{J + 1}{2J + 1} P_{J+1} + \frac{J}{2J + 1} P_{J-1}.$$

to obtain

$$h^J_{\frac{1}{2}, -\frac{1}{2}} = \frac{qq'}{m} \frac{E}{\mu} \frac{2(J+1)}{\sqrt{J(J+1)}} \frac{1}{2} \int_{-1}^{+1} dz \, B(zP_J - P_{J+1}),$$

or

$$h^J_{\frac{1}{2}, -\frac{1}{2}} = -\frac{2qq'E}{m\mu} \frac{\sqrt{J(J+1)}}{2J+1} (B_{J+1} - B_{J-1})$$

and   (12.55)

$$h^J_{\frac{1}{2}, \frac{1}{2}} = q\left[\frac{q}{m} A_J - \frac{q'}{\mu} \frac{1}{(2J+1)} ((J+1)B_{J+1} + JB_{J-1})\right].$$

These are the equations corresponding to Eqs. (12.41) of the s-channel.

We also rewrite Eq. (12.51) in terms of the A and B amplitudes:

$$B = -\frac{\mu m}{2Eq' \sin \theta} H_{\frac{1}{2}, -\frac{1}{2}} = \frac{\mu m}{4Eqq'} \sum_J \frac{(2J+1)}{\sqrt{J(J+1)}} h^J_{\frac{1}{2}, -\frac{1}{2}} P'_J$$

and

$$A = \frac{m}{2q} H_{\frac{1}{2}, \frac{1}{2}} - \frac{m^2 \cos \theta}{2Eq \sin \theta} H_{\frac{1}{2}, -\frac{1}{2}}$$

$$= \frac{m}{4q^2} \sum_J (2J+1)h^J_{\frac{1}{2}, \frac{1}{2}} P_J + \frac{m^2}{4Eq^2} \sum_J \frac{2J+1}{\sqrt{J(J+1)}} h^J_{\frac{1}{2}, -\frac{1}{2}} zP'_J. \quad (12.56)$$

Finally we wish to expand $A(s,t,u)$ and $B(s,t,u)$ in terms of the partial-wave amplitudes A_J and B_J. Or, from

$$f_1 = \frac{E+m}{m}\left[A + \frac{W-m}{\mu} B\right] = \sum_J (f_{J-\frac{1}{2}, +}P'_{J+\frac{1}{2}} - f_{J+\frac{1}{2}, -}P'_{J-\frac{1}{2}}),$$

$$f_2 = \frac{E-m}{m}\left[-A + \frac{W+m}{\mu} B\right] = \sum_J (f_{J+\frac{1}{2}, -}P'_{J+\frac{1}{2}} - f_{J-\frac{1}{2}, +}P'_{J-\frac{1}{2}})$$

we find

$$A = \frac{m}{2Wq^2}\left[(E-m)(W+m) \sum_J (f_{J-\frac{1}{2}, +}P'_{J+\frac{1}{2}} - f_{J+\frac{1}{2}, -}P'_{J-\frac{1}{2}})\right.$$

$$\left. - (E+m)(w-m) \sum_J (f_{J+\frac{1}{2}, -}P'_{J+\frac{1}{2}} - f_{J-\frac{1}{2}, +}P'_{J-\frac{1}{2}})\right]$$

and   (12.56)

$$B = \frac{m\mu}{2Wq^2}\left[(E-m) \sum_J (f_{J-\frac{1}{2}, +}P'_{J+\frac{1}{2}} - P'_{J-\frac{1}{2}}f_{J+\frac{1}{2}})\right.$$

$$\left. + (E+m) \sum_J (f_{J+\frac{1}{2}, -}P'_{J+\frac{1}{2}} - f_{J-\frac{1}{2}, +}P'_{J-\frac{1}{2}})\right].$$

f. Crossing Symmetry

If we use the same basis $Y_i(k)$ in all channels, as we did up to now, changing only the *sign* of the momenta in going from one channel to another, then the same scalar amplitudes $A_i(s,t,u)$, with the same order of the arguments, describe all three channels in their respective physical regions. In practice, when one wishes to evaluate the effect of some intermediate states to other channels one takes a new basis, $\overline{Y}_i(k)$, e.g.; the basis is obtained by the interchange of two particles. In this case one has new amplitudes $\overline{A}(s,t,y)$ that must be related to the old amplitudes $A(s,t,u)$.

Combining spin and isospin we have in the s-channel, e.g.,

$$M = \sum_{i,j} A_j^{(i)}(s,t,u)\, Y_j \overline{Z}^i; \qquad \begin{array}{l} i = (+,-) \;\; \text{or} \;\; (\tfrac{1}{2},\tfrac{3}{2}), \\ j = 1, 2. \end{array} \tag{12.58}$$

The cross-channel amplitude is of the form

$$\overline{M} = \sum \overline{A}_j^{(i)}(s,t,u)\, \overline{Y}_j \overline{Z}^i, \tag{12.58'}$$

so that if $\overline{Y}$'s are expanded in terms of Y's, we get

$$\overline{A}_j^{(i)}(s,t,u) = \alpha^{ii'}\beta_{jj'}A_{j'}^{i'}(s,t,u). \tag{12.58''}$$

For the isospin we find

$$\alpha^{II'} = \begin{pmatrix} \dfrac{1}{\sqrt{6}} & -1 \\[2mm] \dfrac{1}{\sqrt{6}} & -\dfrac{1}{2} \end{pmatrix} \qquad (t \to s),$$

$$\alpha^{II'} = \frac{1}{3}\begin{pmatrix} -1 & 4 \\ 2 & 1 \end{pmatrix} \qquad (u \to s). \tag{12.59}$$

[*Note:* Under interchange of $s \leftrightarrow u$ (s and t): $R^+ \to R^+$, $R^- \to R^-$ by Eq. (12.2). Then using Eq. (12.3), we obtain the above matrices.]

$$\alpha^{II'} = \begin{pmatrix} \dfrac{1}{\sqrt{6}} & -1 \\[2mm] \dfrac{1}{\sqrt{6}} & -\dfrac{1}{2} \end{pmatrix} \qquad (t \to u).$$

The inverse crossing matrices are

$$\alpha_{t \leftrightarrow s} = \frac{1}{3}\begin{pmatrix} \sqrt{6} & 2\sqrt{6} \\ 2 & -2 \end{pmatrix}; \qquad \alpha_{u \leftrightarrow s} = \frac{1}{3}\begin{pmatrix} -1 & 2 \\ 2 & 1 \end{pmatrix};$$

$$\alpha_{t \leftrightarrow u} = \frac{1}{3}\begin{pmatrix} \sqrt{6} & 2\sqrt{6} \\ 2 & -2 \end{pmatrix}.$$

These equations tell us the contribution of a state of definite isospin I in one channel to the various isotopic spin states in the crossed channels.

Before discussing the spin case, let us first consider the interchange of s, t, u variables. Let $M(k_3k_4,k_1k_2)$ be the amplitude in the s-channel, $M(-k_1k_4;-k_3k_2)$ in the u-channel, and $M(-k_2k_4;k_1,-k_3)$ in the t-channel. Note that we have not only changed the signs of some of the momenta but also interchanged their positions so that we have new functions $\bar{M}$ and $\bar{\bar{M}}$ of the old arguments. These operations also interchange the variable s, t, u, as indicated below:

$s \leftrightarrow u$ *Symmetry*:

$$A_i(s,t,u)\, Y_i(k_3 k_4; k_1 k_2) = \bar{A}_i(s,t,u)\, \bar{Y}_i(k_3 k_4; k_1 k_2)$$
$$\equiv A_i(u,t,s)\, Y_i(k_3, -k_2; k_1, -k_4).$$

Spinor indices in this case are not changed and we find, from Eq. (12.5),

$$\begin{aligned} A(s,t,u) &= A(u,t,s) \equiv \bar{A}(s,t,u), \\ B(s,t,u) &= -B(u,t,s) \equiv \bar{B}(s,t,u). \end{aligned} \tag{12.60}$$

$s \leftrightarrow t$ *Symmetry*: The new basis may be chosen to be that obtained by the interchange $k_3 \leftrightarrow -k_2$,

$$A_i(s,t,u)\, Y_i(k_3 k_4; k_1 k_2) = A_i(t,s,u)\, Y_i(-k_2 k_4; k_1, -k_3).$$

We expand the new basis in terms of the old ones:

$$\frac{1}{m}(k_1 - k_2)\cdot\sigma = \beta_{11}\frac{1}{m}(k_1 + k_3)\cdot\sigma + \beta_{\frac{1}{2}}\left[n\cdot\sigma + \frac{k_3\cdot\sigma}{m}n\cdot\tilde{\sigma}\frac{k_1\cdot\sigma}{m}\right],$$

$$\frac{1}{\mu}(k_4 - k_3)\cdot\sigma - \frac{\beta\cdot\sigma}{m}\frac{1}{\mu}(k_4 - k_3)\cdot\tilde{\sigma}\frac{k_1\cdot\sigma}{m}$$
$$= \beta_{21}\frac{(k_1 + k_3)\cdot\sigma}{m} + \beta_{\frac{2}{2}}\left[n\cdot\sigma + \frac{k_3\cdot\sigma}{m}n\cdot\tilde{\sigma}\frac{k_1\cdot\sigma}{m}\right].$$

In the first equation we compare the coefficients of σ^μ on both sides and multiply both sides with k_1^μ and once with n^μ:[1]

$$(m^2 - k_1\cdot k_2) = \beta_{11}(m^2 + k_1\cdot k_3) + \beta_{\frac{1}{2}}\frac{m}{\mu}(k_1 + k_3)\cdot(k_2 + k_4),$$

$$(k_2 + k_4)\cdot(k_1 - k_2) = \beta_{11}(k_1 + k_3)\cdot(k_2 + k_4)$$
$$+ \beta_{\frac{1}{2}}(k_2 + k_4)^2(m^2 - k_1\cdot k_3),$$

or

$$(3m^2 + \mu^2 - s) = \beta_{11}(4m^2 - t) + \beta_{12}\frac{m}{\mu}(s - u),$$

$$2(m^2 - \mu^2 - u) = \beta_{11}4(s - u) + \beta_{\frac{1}{2}}\frac{1}{m\mu}(4\mu^2 - t)t,$$

$$\beta_{11} = \frac{1}{m\mu\Delta}\left[\tfrac{1}{2}(4\mu^2 - t)t(3m^2 + \mu^2 - s) - 2m^2(s - u)(m^2 - \mu^2 - u)\right],$$

$$\beta_{12} = \Delta[2(4m^2 - t)(m^2 - \mu^2 - u) - 4(s - u)(em^2 + \mu^2 - s)],$$

where

$$m\mu\Delta = \tfrac{1}{2}(4m^2 - t)(4m^2 - t)t - 4m^2(s - u)^2.$$

Similarly for the second equation.

[1] Note that

$$\frac{k_3\cdot\sigma}{m}n\cdot\tilde{\sigma}\frac{k_1\cdot\sigma}{m} = \frac{(n\cdot k_1)}{m^2}k_3\cdot\sigma - \frac{(k_1\cdot k_3)}{m^2}n\cdot\sigma + \frac{(n\cdot k_3)}{m^2}k_1\cdot\sigma + i\frac{[k_3 n k_1]}{m^2}\cdot\sigma.$$

We conclude that the exchange of s, t does not lead to a simple symmetry relation, but to a relation of the form

$$A(s,t,u) = \beta_{11}A(t,s,u) + \beta_{21}B(t,s,u),$$
$$B(s,t,u) = \beta_{12}A(t,s,u) + \beta_{22}B(t,s,u), \tag{12.61}$$

where β's are functions of s, t, and u, as given above.

Thus it is convenient to leave the order of s, t, u in the amplitudes A and B the same and distinguish the s- and the u-channels by their physical regions.

12.2   Unitarity and Analyticity

a. Kinematical Poles

We first note that the scalar amplitudes A and B defined by

$$M = A\frac{1}{m}(k_1 + k_3)\cdot\sigma + B\frac{1}{2}\left[n\cdot\sigma + \frac{k_3\cdot\sigma}{m}n\cdot\tilde{\sigma}\frac{k_1\cdot\sigma}{m}\right], \tag{12.62}$$
$$n = \frac{1}{\mu}(k_2 + k_4)$$

have no "*kinematical*" poles. As we have discussed in Chap. 4, these are the possible points where the basis function vanishes and where M is regular. E.g., when $k_1 = -k_3$ and/or $k_2 = -k_4$. The most direct way of proving this is to solve this equation for A and B in terms of M. We multiply both sides of Eq. (12.62) with $\tilde{\sigma}^{\nu}$ and take the trace of both sides [tr $(\sigma^{\mu}\tilde{\sigma}^{\nu}) = 2g^{\mu\nu}$], then multiply again both sides, once with k_1^{μ} and once with n^{μ}, and obtain the two equations

$$\frac{m}{2}k_1\cdot f = A(m^2 + k_1\cdot k_3) + B\frac{m}{2\mu}(k_2 + k_4)\cdot(k_1 + k_3),$$

$$\frac{m}{2}(k_2 + k_4)\cdot f = A(k_1 + k_3)\cdot(k_2 + k_4)$$

$$+ \tfrac{1}{2}B\frac{1}{m\mu}(k_2 + k_4)^2(m^2 - k_1\cdot k_3),$$

where

$$f^{\mu} = \text{tr}\,(M\tilde{\sigma}^{\mu}).$$

Or, in terms of the invariants,

$$mk_1\cdot f = A(4m^2 - t) + B\frac{m}{\mu}(s - u),$$

$$m(k_2 + k_4)\cdot f = A4(s - u) + B\frac{1}{2\mu m}(4\mu^2 - t)t.$$

Hence

$$A = \left\{\frac{1}{2\mu}[(4\mu^2 - t) + (s - u)^2]tk_1\cdot f - \frac{m^2}{\mu}(s - u)(k_2 + k_4)\cdot f\right\}\Big/\Delta,$$
$$B = \{m(4m^2 - t)(k_2 + k_4)\cdot f - 2m(s - u)k_1\cdot f\}/\Delta, \tag{12.63}$$

where

$$\Delta = \frac{1}{2\mu m}(4m^2 - t)[(4\mu^2 - t)t + (s - u)^2] - \frac{2m}{\mu}(s - u)^2$$

is the same determinant we had in the discussion of the $s \leftrightarrow t$ symmetry in the previous section. If we replace f by an arbitrary polynomial in k's, we see that when Δ vanishes, so do the numerators of A and B; thus these poles cancel.

b. Unitarity

s-Channel. We have already discussed in Chap. 8 that the nucleon pole contributes only to B-amplitude; A is free of the pole term, if the mass-differences between the nucleons is neglected.

(1) *s*-Channel Two-Body Unitarity. We shall calculate directly the unitarity of the f-amplitude. We start with the R-amplitudes:

$$R(k_f;k_i) + R^\dagger(k_i;k_f) = -\int_j \rho_j R(k_f;k_j)R^\dagger(k_i;k_j),$$

where the $\dagger$ is in the spin space ($R^+_{mn} = R^*_{nm}$). If we go back to Eq. (12.6') we see that in $R^\dagger(k_i;k_f)$ the factors $k_3 \cdot \bar{\sigma}$ and $k_1 \cdot \sigma$ are interchanged; the dagger gives back the original amplitudes so that in the center-of-mass frame we have

$$(f_1 + f_1^*) + (f_2 + f_2^*)\boldsymbol{\sigma}\cdot\hat{\mathbf{q}}'\boldsymbol{\sigma}\cdot\hat{\mathbf{q}} = -\rho \int d^3\hat{q}'$$
$$\times [f_1(s,\theta') + f_2(s,\theta')\boldsymbol{\sigma}\cdot\hat{\mathbf{q}}'\boldsymbol{\sigma}\cdot\hat{\mathbf{q}}][f_1^*(s,\theta'') + f_2^*(s,\theta'')\boldsymbol{\sigma}\cdot\hat{\mathbf{q}}''\boldsymbol{\sigma}\cdot\hat{\mathbf{q}}] \tag{12.64}$$

The last term on the right-hand side gives $f_2(s,\theta')f_2^*(s,\theta'')\boldsymbol{\sigma}\cdot\hat{\mathbf{q}}'\boldsymbol{\sigma}\cdot\hat{\mathbf{q}}$. The cross terms are

$$\int d^3\hat{q}'' f_1(s,\theta)f_2(s,\theta'')\boldsymbol{\sigma}\cdot\hat{\mathbf{q}}''\boldsymbol{\sigma}\cdot\hat{\mathbf{q}} + \int d^3\hat{q}'' f_1^*(s,\theta'')f_2(s,\theta')\boldsymbol{\sigma}\cdot\hat{\mathbf{q}}'\boldsymbol{\sigma}\cdot\hat{\mathbf{q}}''$$
$$= \lambda + \mu\boldsymbol{\sigma}\cdot\hat{\mathbf{q}}'\boldsymbol{\sigma}\cdot\hat{\mathbf{q}},$$

where the q-vectors are shown in Fig. 12.5. We have

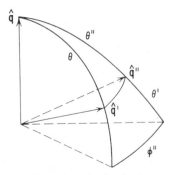

Figure 12.5 Labeling of angles in the intermediate state.

$$\boldsymbol{\sigma \cdot \hat{q}'' \sigma \cdot \hat{q}} = \begin{pmatrix} \cos \theta'' & -\sin \theta'' e^{i\varphi''} \\ \sin \theta'' e^{i\varphi''} & \cos \theta'' \end{pmatrix}$$

$$= \cos \theta'' + i \sin \theta'' (\sin \varphi'' \sigma_1 - \cos \varphi'' \sigma_2),$$

$$\boldsymbol{\sigma \cdot \hat{q}' \sigma \cdot \hat{q}''} = \begin{pmatrix} \cos \theta \cos \theta'' & \cos \theta \sin \theta'' e^{i\varphi''} \\ + \sin \theta \sin \theta'' e^{i\varphi''} & - \sin \theta \cos \theta'' \\ \sin \theta \cos \theta'' & \sin \theta \sin \theta'' e^{-i\varphi''} \\ - \sin \theta'' \cos \theta e^{i\varphi''} & + \cos \theta \cos \theta'' \end{pmatrix}$$

$$= \cos \theta \cos \theta'' + \sin \theta \sin \theta'' \cos \varphi + i \sin \theta \sin \theta'' \sin \varphi \sigma_3$$
$$- i \cos \theta \sin \theta'' \sin \varphi \sigma_1 + i (\cos \theta \sin \theta'' \cos \varphi - \sin \theta \cos \theta'') \sigma_2$$

$$\lambda + \mu \boldsymbol{\sigma \cdot \hat{q}' \sigma \cdot q} = \begin{pmatrix} \lambda + \mu \cos \theta & -\mu \sin \theta \\ \mu \sin \theta & \lambda + \mu \cos \theta \end{pmatrix}$$

$$= \lambda + \mu \cos \theta - i\mu \sin \theta \sigma_2.$$

Thus

$$\int d^3 \hat{q}'' [f_1(\theta') f_2^*(\theta'') \cos \theta'' + f_1^*(\theta'') f_2(\theta') (\underbrace{\cos \theta \cos \theta'' + \sin \theta \sin \theta'' \cos \varphi''}_{\cos \theta'})]$$

$$= \lambda + \mu \cos \theta,$$

$$\int d^3 \hat{q}'' [f_1(\theta') f_2^*(\theta'') \sin \theta'' \cos \varphi''$$
$$+ f_1^*(\theta'') f_2(\theta') (\sin \theta \cos \theta'' - \cos \theta \sin \theta'' \cos \varphi'')]$$
$$= \mu \sin \theta,$$

and

$$\int d^3 q'' [f_1(\theta') f_2^*(\theta'') \sin \theta'' \sin \varphi'' - f_1^*(\theta'') f_2(\theta') \cos \theta \sin \theta'' \sin \varphi''] = 0,$$

$$\int d^3 q'' f_1^*(\theta'') f_2(\theta') \sin \theta \sin \theta'' \sin \varphi = 0.$$

And, we obtain

$$\mu = \frac{1}{\sin \theta} \int [f_1 f_2^* \sin \theta'' \cos \varphi + f_1^* f_2 (\sin \theta \cos \theta'' - \cos \theta \sin \theta'' \cos \varphi)]$$

and

$$\lambda = \frac{1}{\sin \theta} \int [f_1 f_2^* (\cos \theta'' \sin \theta - \cos \theta \sin \theta'' \cos \varphi) + f_1^* f_2 \sin \theta'' \cos \varphi].$$

The elastic unitarity then takes the form

$$f_1 + f_1^* = \rho_2 \int d\hat{q} \left[f_1(\theta') f_1^*(\theta'') + f_1 f_2^* \frac{\cos \theta'' \sin \theta - \cos \theta \sin \theta'' \cos \varphi}{\sin \theta} \right.$$
$$\left. + f_1^* f_2 \frac{\sin \theta'' \cos \varphi}{\sin \theta} \right],$$

$$(12.65)$$

$$f_2 + f_2^* = -\rho_2 \int d\hat{q} \left[f_2 f_2^* + f_1 f_2^* \frac{\sin \theta'' \cos \varphi}{\sin \theta} \right.$$
$$\left. + f_1^* f_2 \frac{\sin \theta \cos \theta'' - \cos \theta \sin \theta'' \cos \varphi}{\sin \theta} \right].$$

We now introduce the following linear combinations

$$2\,Re(f_1 + zf_2) = -\rho_2 \int d\hat{q}\{[f_1(z') + z'f_2(z')][f_1(z'') + z''f_2(z'')]^*$$
$$+ (z - z'z'')f_2(z')f_2^*(z'')\},$$

$$2\,Re(zf_1 + f_2) = -\rho_2 \int d\hat{q}\{[z'f_1(z') + f_2(z')][z''f_1(z'') + f_2(z'')]^*$$
$$+ (z - z'z'')f_1(z')f_1^*(z'')\}. \quad (12.66)$$

The partial-wave amplitudes $f_{\ell,\pm}$ defined earlier obey uncoupled unitarity relations, as we may expect. We expand f_1, f_2 as follows:

$$f_1 = \sum_J (f_{J-\frac{1}{2},+}P'_{J+\frac{1}{2}} - f_{J+\frac{1}{2},-}P'_{J-\frac{1}{2}}),$$
$$f_2 = \sum_J (f_{J+\frac{1}{2},-}P'_{J+\frac{1}{2}} - f_{J-\frac{1}{2},+}P'_{J-\frac{1}{2}}).$$

Then,

$$f_1 + zf_2 = \sum_J (J + \tfrac{1}{2})(f_{J-\frac{1}{2},+}P_{J-\frac{1}{2}} + f_{J+\frac{1}{2},-}P_{J+\frac{1}{2}}),$$
$$zf_1 + f_2 = \sum_J (J + \tfrac{1}{2})(f_{J-\frac{1}{2},+}P_{J+\frac{1}{2}} + f_{J+\frac{1}{2},-}P_{J-\frac{1}{2}}). \quad (12.67)$$

With these formulas one can then obtain the unitarity of the partial-wave amplitudes (Exercise 2).

(2) t-Channel Two-Body Unitarity.   Referring to Fig. 12.6, the unitarity gives

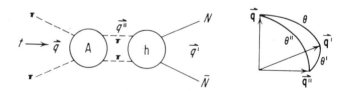

Figure 12.6 t-channel unitarity.

$$(h_1\boldsymbol{\sigma}\cdot\mathbf{q} + h_2\boldsymbol{\sigma}\cdot\mathbf{q}') + (h_1\boldsymbol{\sigma}\cdot\mathbf{q} + h_2\boldsymbol{\sigma}\cdot\mathbf{q}')^+$$
$$= -\int \rho_2\, d\hat{q}''[h_1(s,\theta')\boldsymbol{\sigma}\cdot\mathbf{q}'' + h_2(s,\sigma')\boldsymbol{\sigma}\cdot\mathbf{q}']A^*(s,\theta'')$$
$$= -\int \rho_2\, d\hat{q}''[h_2(s,\theta')A^*(s,\theta'')\boldsymbol{\sigma}\cdot\mathbf{q}' + h_1(s,\theta')A^*(s,\theta'')\boldsymbol{\sigma}\cdot\mathbf{q}'']. \quad (12.68)$$

Here $A(s,\theta)$ is the $\pi\pi \to \pi\pi$ amplitude, because

$$\boldsymbol{\sigma}\cdot\hat{\mathbf{q}}'' = \begin{pmatrix} \cos\theta'' & \sin\theta''\,e^{-i\varphi} \\ \sin\theta\,e^{i\varphi} & -\cos\theta'' \end{pmatrix} = \cos\theta''\sigma_3 + \sin\theta''\cos\varphi\sigma_1 + \sin\theta''\sin\varphi\sigma_2$$

$$\boldsymbol{\sigma}\cdot\hat{\mathbf{q}} = \sigma_3, \quad \boldsymbol{\sigma}\cdot\mathbf{q}' = \cos\theta\sigma_3 + \sin\theta\sigma_1,$$

we get

$$h_1 + h_1^* = -\rho_2 \int d\hat{q}'' \, h_1(z') A^*(z'') \frac{\cos \theta'' \sin \theta - \cos \theta \sin \theta'' \cos \varphi}{\sin \theta},$$

$$h_2 + h_2^* = -\rho_2 \int d\hat{q}'' \, h_1(z') A^*(z'') \frac{\sin \theta'' \cos \varphi}{\sin \theta} + h_2(z') A^*(z''),$$

so that finally

$$2Re(h_1 + zh_2) = -\rho_2 \int d\hat{q}'' [h_1(z') A^*(z'') z'' + z h_2(z') A^*(z'')],$$

$$2Re(zh_1 + h_2) = -\rho_2 \int d\hat{q}'' [h_1(z') A^*(z'') z' + h_2(z') A^*(z'')].$$

$$(12.69)$$

c. Analytic Properties of Partial-Wave Amplitudes

(1) s-Channel. On the basis of a double dispersion relation for $A^\pm(s,t,u)$ and $B^\pm(s,t,u)$ we can easily find, as in the π-π case, the analytic properties of partial-wave projections $A_\ell^\pm(s)$, $B_\ell^\pm(s)$. The only difference is in the pole terms and in unequal masses. For the A-amplitudes we get

$$A^\pm(s,t,u) = \frac{1}{\pi} \int_{4\mu^2}^\infty dt' \frac{A_2^\pm(s,t',u')}{t' - t} + \frac{1}{\pi} \int_{(m+\mu)^2}^\infty du' \frac{A_3(s,t',u')}{u' - u}, \quad s \text{ fixed}$$

$$A^\pm(s,\ell) = \frac{1}{\pi} \int_{4\mu^2}^\infty dt' \, A_2^\pm(s,t') \frac{1}{2q^2} \frac{1}{2} \int_{-4q^2}^0 dt \frac{P_\ell\left(1 + \dfrac{t}{2q^2}\right)}{t' - t}$$

$$+ \frac{1}{\pi} \int_{(m+\mu)^2}^\infty du' \, A_3^\pm(s,t',u') \left(-\frac{1}{2q^2}\right)$$

$$\times \int_{2m^2+2\mu^2+s+4q^2}^{2m^2+2\mu^2+s} \frac{du}{2} \frac{P_\ell\left(1 - \dfrac{u - 2m^2 - 2\mu^2}{2q^2}\right)}{u' - u},$$

$$A^\pm(s,\ell) = \frac{1}{\pi} \int_{4\mu^2}^\infty dt' \, A_2^\pm(s,t',u') \frac{1}{2q^2} Q_\ell\left(1 + \frac{t'}{2q^2}\right)$$

$$+ \frac{1}{\pi} \int_{(m+\mu)^2}^\infty du' \, A_3^\pm(s,t',u') \left(\frac{-1}{2q^2}\right) Q_\ell\left(1 - \frac{u' - 2m^2 - 2\mu^2 + s}{2q^2}\right),$$

$$(12.70)$$

where

$$q^2 = \frac{1}{4s} [(\sqrt{s} + m)^2 - \mu^2][(\sqrt{s} - m)^2 - \mu^2]$$

$$= \frac{(s + m^2 - \mu^2)^2 - 4m^2 s}{4s},$$

and

$$A_2^\pm(s,t) = \frac{1}{\pi} \int_{(m+\mu)^2}^\infty ds' \frac{\rho_{st}(s',t)}{s' - s} + \frac{1}{\pi} \int_{(m+\mu)^2}^\infty du' \frac{\rho_{ui}(s,u')}{u' - u},$$

$$A_3^\pm(s,t) = \frac{1}{\pi} \int_{(m+\mu)^2}^\infty ds' \frac{\rho_{su}(s',u)}{s' - s} + \frac{1}{\pi} \int dt' \frac{\rho_{tu}(t',u)}{u' - u}.$$

The boundaries of the spectral functions shown in Fig. 12.7 are given by the equations

ρ_{st}:

I: $(t - 4\mu^2)[s - (m + 2\mu)^2][s - (m - 2\mu)^2]$
$$- 16\mu^4(s + 3m^2 - 3\mu^2) = 0.$$

II: $(t - 16\mu^2)[s - (m + \mu)^2][s - (m - \mu)^2] - 64\mu^4 s = 0.$

(ρ_{tu}: interchange s and u).

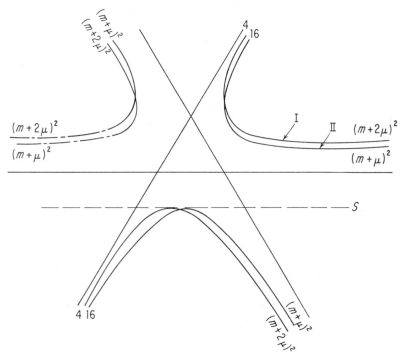

Figure 12.7 Spectral regions.

ρ_{su}:

$$[u - (m + 2\mu)^2][u - (m - 2\mu)^2][s - (m + \mu)^2][s - (m - \mu)^2]$$
$$- 16 su m^2\mu^2 + 16\mu^2(m^2 - \mu^2)^2(s + u - m^2 - 2\mu^2) = 0.$$

The B-amplitudes have, in addition, pole terms whose contributions to the partial-wave amplitudes are obtained as follows:

$$B^{\pm} = \frac{g^{\pm}}{s - m^2} + \frac{\bar{g}^{\pm}}{u - m^2},$$

$$B^{\pm}(s,\ell) = \frac{g^{\pm}}{s - m^2} \frac{1}{2} \int_{-1}^{+1} dz\, P_\ell(z)$$
$$+ \bar{g}^{\pm} \frac{1}{2} \int_{-1}^{+1} dz\, \frac{P_\ell(z)}{2m^2 + 2\mu^2 - s + 2q^2 - 2q^2 z - m^2}, \quad (12.71)$$

with additional integral terms as in *A*-amplitude. Thus

$$B^{\pm}s_1\ell = \frac{g^{\pm}}{s - m^2}\,\delta_{\ell 0} + \bar{g}^{\pm}\,\frac{1}{2q^2}\,Q_\ell\!\left(1 + \frac{m^2 + 2\mu^2 - s}{2q^2}\right) + \cdots.$$

The first term gives a fixed *s*-wave pole only; from the second term we get a cut between

$$s = m^2 + 2\mu^2 \quad \text{and} \quad s_0 = \frac{(m^2 - \mu^2)^2}{m^2}$$

[s_0 is the solution of $m^2 + 2\mu - s_0 = -4q^2(s_0)$].

In the integral terms we have the following cuts coming from Q_ℓ:

1st term: Cut from $4q^2 = -4\mu^2$ to $4q^2 = -\infty$.

2nd term: From

$$Q_\ell\!\left(1 - \frac{u' - 2m^2 - 2\mu^2 + s}{2q^2}\right)$$

we get a cut from $s = (m - \mu)^2$ to $-\infty$ (two parts: one from $s = 0$ to $-\infty$ other from 0 to $(m - \mu)^2$).

Spectral cuts: A_2 from $(m + \mu)^2$ to $+\infty$, and from s_L to $-\infty$. A_3 also from $(m + \mu)^2$ to ∞ and from s_L to $-\infty$ (Fig. 12.8).

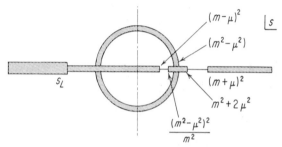

Figure 12.8 Cuts of the partial-wave amplitudes: *s*-plane.

The partial-wave amplitudes corresponding to transitions of definite *J* and $\ell = J \pm \frac{1}{2}$ have, in addition, the $\sqrt{s}$ singularities.

In the $W = \sqrt{s}$ plane we get the following cuts shown in Fig. 12.9.

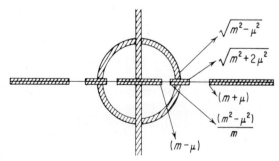

Figure 12.9 Cuts of the partial-wave amplitudes: *w*-plane.

(2) Partial-Wave Amplitudes in t-Channel. In a similar manner as in the s-channel we have the relations

$$A^{\pm}(s,t,u) = \frac{1}{\pi}\int_{(m+\mu)^2}^{\infty} ds' \frac{A_1^{\pm}(s',t,u')}{s' - s} + \frac{1}{\pi}\int_{(m+\mu)^2}^{\infty} du' \frac{A_3^{\pm}(s',t,u')}{u' - u},$$

$$A^{\pm}(t,\ell) = \frac{1}{\pi}\int_{(m+\mu)^2}^{\infty} ds' \, A_1^{\pm}(s',t,u') \frac{1}{2}\int_{-1}^{+1} dz_t \frac{P_{\ell}(z_t)}{s' - (-q_t^2 - q_t'^2 + 2qq'z)}$$

$$+ \frac{1}{\pi}\int_{(m+\mu)^2}^{\infty} du' \, A_3^{\pm}(s',t,u') \frac{1}{2}\int_{-1}^{+1} dz_t \frac{P_{\ell}(z_t)}{u' - (-q_t^2 - q_t'^2 - 2qq'z)},$$

where now

$$q_t^2 = \frac{t}{4} - m^2; \quad q_t'^2 = \frac{t}{4} - \mu^2,$$

$$A^{\pm}(t,\ell) = \frac{1}{\pi}\int_{(m+\mu)^2}^{\infty} ds' \, A_1^{\pm}(s',t,u') \frac{1}{2qq'} Q_{\ell}\left(\frac{s' + q^2 + q'^2}{2qq'}\right)$$

$$+ \frac{1}{\pi}\int_{(m+\mu)^2}^{\infty} du' \, A_3^{\pm}(s',t,u')\left(-\frac{1}{2qq'}\right)Q_{\ell}\left(-\frac{u' + q^2 + q'^2}{2qq'}\right). \quad (12.72)$$

$$\underbrace{\qquad\qquad}_{-(-1)^{\ell} Q_{\ell}(z)}$$

Because

$$A^{\pm}(s,t,u) = \pm A^{\pm}(u,t,s),$$

we find

$$A_1^{\pm}(u',t,s') = \pm A_3^{\pm}(s',t,u').$$

Hence in the t-channel we have simply

$$A^{\pm}(t,\ell) = \frac{1}{\pi}\int_{(m+\mu)^2}^{\infty} ds' \, A_1^{\pm}(s',t,u') \frac{1}{2qq'} Q_{\ell}\left(\frac{s' + q^2 + q'^2}{2qq'}\right)[1 + (\pm 1)(-1)^{\ell}]$$

$$= \frac{1}{\pi}\frac{\Gamma^2(\ell + 1)}{\Gamma(2\ell + 2)} (4qq')^{\ell}(1 \pm (-1)^{\ell})\int_{(m+\mu)^2}^{\infty} \frac{ds'}{[s' + (q - q')^2]^{\ell + 1}}$$

$$\times F\left(\ell + 1, \ell + 1; 2\ell + 2; \frac{-4qq'}{s' + (q - q')^2}\right). \quad (12.72')$$

Consequently $A_{\ell}^{+} = 0$ for ℓ odd and $A^{-} = 0$ for ℓ even.

For B-amplitudes we find

$$B_{(s,t,u)}^{\pm} = \frac{g^{\pm}}{s - m^2} + \frac{\bar{g}^{\pm}}{u - m^2} + \frac{1}{\pi}\int_{(m+\mu)^2}^{\infty} ds' \frac{B_1^{\pm}(s',t)}{s' - s}$$

$$+ \frac{1}{\pi}\int_{(m+\mu)^2}^{\infty} du' \frac{B_3^{\pm}(s',t)}{u' - t}$$

$$B^{\pm}(t,\ell) = g^{\pm}\frac{1}{2}\int_{-1}^{+1} dz_t \frac{P_{\ell}(z_t)}{-q^2 - q'^2 + 2qq'z - m^2}$$

$$+ \bar{g}^{\pm}\frac{1}{2}\int_{-1}^{+1} dz_t \frac{P_{\ell}(z)}{-q^2 - q'^2 - 2qq'z} + \text{integral terms.}$$

$$B^{\pm}(t,\ell) = g^{\pm}\left(-\frac{1}{2qq'}\right)Q_{\ell}\left(\frac{q^2 + q'^2 + m^2}{2qq'}\right)$$

$$+ \bar{g}^{\pm}\left(\frac{1}{2qq'}\right)Q_{\ell}\left(-\frac{q^2 + q'^2 + m^2}{2qq'}\right) + \cdots.$$

Now

$$B_{\bar{1}}^{\pm}(u',t,s') = \mp B_3^{(\pm)}(s',t,u'),$$

so that finally

$$B^{\pm}(t,\ell) = \frac{-1}{2qq'}\, Q_\ell\!\left(\frac{q^2 + q'^2 + m^2}{2qq'}\right)[g^{\pm} + (-1)^\ell \bar{g}^{\pm}]$$

$$+ \frac{1}{\pi}\int_{(m+\mu)^2}^{\infty} ds'\, B_{\bar{1}}^{\pm}(s',t,u')\,\frac{1}{2qq'}\, Q_\ell\!\left(\frac{s' + q^2 + q'^2}{2qq'}\right)[1 \mp (-1)^\ell]$$

$$= \frac{\Gamma^2(\ell + 1)}{\Gamma(2\ell + 2)}\,(4qq')^\ell$$

$$\times \left\{\frac{1}{\pi}(1 \mp (-1)^\ell)\int \frac{ds'}{[s' + (q - q')^2]^{\ell+1}}\right.$$

$$\times F\!\left[\ell + 1, \ell + 1, \ell;\, \frac{-4qq'}{s' + (q - q')^2}\right] - \frac{[g^{\pm} + (-1)^\ell \bar{g}^{\pm}]}{[m^2 + (q - q')^2]^{\ell+1}}$$

$$\times \left.F\!\left[\ell + 1, \ell + 1, 2\ell + 2;\, \frac{-4qq'}{m^2 + (q - q')^2}\right]\right\}. \quad (12.73)$$

Now $g^{\pm} = \mp \bar{g}^{\pm}$, and hence

$$B_\ell^- = 0 \quad \text{for} \quad \ell \text{ even,}$$
$$B_\ell^+ = 0 \quad \text{for} \quad \ell \text{ odd.}$$

The cut of

$$F\!\left(a, b, c;\, \frac{-4qq'}{s' + (q - q')^2}\right)$$

is from

$$t = \frac{4m^2\mu^2 - (s' - m^2 - \mu^2)^2}{s} \quad \text{to} \quad t = -\infty;$$

for $s' = (m + \mu)^2$, the lowest limit of integration, we get a cut from $t = 0$ to $t = -\infty$. The pole term at $s' = m^2$, gives a cut starting from

$$t = \frac{4m^2\mu^2 - \mu^4}{m^2} = 4\mu^2 - \frac{\mu^4}{m^2}.$$

The singularities so obtained are shown in Fig. 12.10.

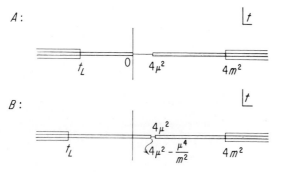

Figure 12.10   *t*-channel partial-wave cuts.

d. Analytic Continuation in Angular Momentum s-Channel

(1) s-Channel. We have defined partial-wave amplitudes

$$f_{J-\frac{1}{2},+}; \qquad f_{J+\frac{1}{2},-},$$

satisfying separately the elastic unitarity condition.

We now make (formally first) a Watson-Sommerfeld transformation of the partial-wave expansions of $f_{1,2}$ in the J-plane:[2]

$$f_1(s,z) = \frac{1}{2i} \int_C \frac{dJ}{\sin \pi(J - \frac{1}{2})} [f_{J-\frac{1}{2}}(s)P'_{J+\frac{1}{2}}(-z) + f_{J+\frac{1}{2}}(s)P'_{J-\frac{1}{2}}(-z)].$$

$$f_2(s,z) = \frac{1}{2i} \int_C \frac{dJ}{\sin \pi(J - \frac{1}{2})} [f_{J+\frac{1}{2}}(s)P'_{J+\frac{1}{2}}(-z) + f_{J-\frac{1}{2}}(s)P'_{J-\frac{1}{2}}(-z)].$$

(12.74)

We continue $f_{J\pm\frac{1}{2}}$ via the double-dispersion relations:

$$\tfrac{1}{2}f_{J-\frac{1}{2}}_{+} = \frac{E + m}{m}\left(A_{J-\frac{1}{2}}_{+} + \frac{W - m}{\mu} B_{J-\frac{1}{2}}_{+}\right)$$

$$+ \frac{E - m}{m}\left(-A_{J+\frac{1}{2}}_{-} + \frac{W + m}{\mu} B_{J+\frac{1}{2}}_{-}\right)$$

where

$$A_{J-\frac{1}{2}}(s) = \frac{1}{\pi}\int_{4\mu^2}^{\infty} dt'\, A_2(s,t',u') \frac{1}{2q^2} Q_{J-\frac{1}{2}}\left(1 + \frac{t'}{2q^2}\right)$$

$$+ \frac{1}{\pi}\int_{(m+\mu)^2}^{\infty} du'\, A_3(s,t',u') \frac{-1}{2q^2} Q_{J-\frac{1}{2}}\left(1 - \frac{u' - 2m^2 - 2\mu^2 + s}{2q^2}\right).$$

Let

$$1 - \frac{u' - 2m^2 - 2\mu^2 + s}{2q^2} = -1 - \frac{x}{2q^2}$$

or

$$x = u' - 2m^2 - 2\mu^2 + s - \frac{(s + m^2 - \mu^2)^2 - 4m^2 s}{s},$$

$$= u' - \frac{(m^2 - \mu^2)^2}{s};$$

then the lower limit of the second integral is $u' = (m + \mu)^2$, or

$$x_0 = (m + \mu)^2 - (m^2 - \mu^2)^2/s.$$

Then

$$A_{J-\frac{1}{2}}(s) = \frac{1}{2\pi q^2}\int_{\min(x_0, 4\mu^2)} dx$$

$$\times \left[A_2(s,x,u') + (-1)^{J-\frac{1}{2}} A_3\left(s, t', x + \frac{(m^2 - \mu^2)^2}{s}\right)\right]$$

$$\times Q_{J-\frac{1}{2}}\left(1 + \frac{x}{2q^2}\right). \quad (12.75)$$

[2] Note

$$P'_\ell(-z) = (-1)^{\ell+1}P'_\ell(z).$$

Note that
$$A_2 = 0 \quad \text{for } t < 4\mu^2,$$
$$A_3 = 0 \quad \text{for } u < (m + \mu)^2,$$

and t' above is

$$t' = -x - \frac{[s - (m^2 + \mu^2)]^2 - 4m^2\mu^2}{s}.$$

We can then introduce two functions

$$A_{J-\frac{1}{2}}^{(J-\frac{1}{2} \text{ even})} = \frac{1}{2\pi q^2} \int dx [A_2 + A_3] Q_{J-\frac{1}{2}},$$

$$A_{J-\frac{1}{2}}^{(J-\frac{1}{2} \text{ odd})} = \frac{1}{2\pi q^2} \int dx [A_2 - A_3] Q_{J-\frac{1}{2}}. \tag{12.75'}$$

Similarly for $A_{J+\frac{1}{2}}$ and $B_{J\pm\frac{1}{2}}$.

Note that the pole term $g^2/(s - m^2)$ in B giving a $\delta_{\ell 0}$ in partial waves cannot be continued analytically in ℓ. We may subtract this term and continue the remainder. Or, we may get this pole dynamically when continued to $\ell = 0$ from high angular momenta downward.

This gives the following set of four amplitudes:

$$f_{\substack{J-\frac{1}{2} \\ J+\frac{1}{2}}}^{\text{even}}, \qquad f_{\substack{J-\frac{1}{2} \\ J+\frac{1}{2}}}^{\text{odd}}.$$

Because these amplitudes individually satisfy unitarity, we put the independent Regge poles in them, and obtain:

$$f_{\frac{1}{2}}(s,z) = \frac{1}{2i} \int_C \frac{dJ}{\sin \pi(J - \frac{1}{2})} \{f_{J-\frac{1}{2}}^{(t)}(s) P'_{J+\frac{1}{2}}(-z) + f_{J-\frac{1}{2}}^{(u)}(s)(-1)^{J-\frac{1}{2}} P'_{J+\frac{1}{2}}$$
$$\times (-f_{J+\frac{1}{2}}^{(t)}(s) P'_{J-\frac{1}{2}}(-z) + f_{J+\frac{1}{2}}^{(u)}(s)(-1)^{J-\frac{1}{2}} P'_{J-\frac{1}{2}}(-z)\}. \tag{12.76}$$

Now the usual conditions are valid for the feasibility of Watson-Sommerfeld transformation, and one can derive similar conclusions.

In particular, the Regge pole term is of the following form (putting independent poles in f^{even} and f^{odd} means that $f_{J-\frac{1}{2}}^{(t)}$ and $f_{J-\frac{1}{2}}^{(u)}$ have the same poles with equal and opposite residues):

Pole at $J = \alpha$ in $f_{J-\frac{1}{2}}$:

$$f_1(s,z) = \frac{\beta_{J-\frac{1}{2}}}{\sin \pi(\alpha - \frac{1}{2})} [P'_{\alpha+\frac{1}{2}}(-z) \mp P'_{\alpha+\frac{1}{2}}(z)],$$
$$-\quad \text{for } (J - \tfrac{1}{2}) \text{ even}$$
$$+\quad \text{for } (J - \tfrac{1}{2}) \text{ odd}$$

$$f_2(s,z) = \frac{\beta_{J-\frac{1}{2}}}{\sin \pi(\alpha - \frac{1}{2})} [P'_{\alpha-\frac{1}{2}}(-z) \pm P'_{\alpha-\frac{1}{2}}(z)].$$

Pole at $J = \alpha$ in $f_{J+\frac{1}{2}}$:

$$f_1(s,z) = \frac{\beta_{J+\frac{1}{2}}}{\sin \pi(\alpha - \frac{1}{2})} [P'_{\alpha-\frac{1}{2}}(-z) \pm P'_{\alpha-\frac{1}{2}}(z)],$$

$$f_2(s,z) = \frac{\beta_{J+\frac{1}{2}}}{\sin \pi(\alpha - \frac{1}{2})} [P'_{\alpha+\frac{1}{2}}(-z) \mp P'_{\alpha+\frac{1}{2}}(z)],$$

$$R = (f_1 + f_2 \sigma \cdot \hat{q}' \sigma \cdot \hat{q}).$$

Thus for each isotopic spin state we may have poles in $f_{J-\frac{1}{2}}$ or $f_{J+\frac{1}{2}}$, each with two possible signatures and altogether giving eight trajectories.

(A) $I = \frac{1}{2}$:

Nucleon

$$N: \quad \ell = 1 \text{ (in the } \pi N \text{ system)}, \quad J = \frac{1}{2}.$$

That is,

$$\text{Pole in } f_{J+\frac{1}{2}}^{(I=\frac{1}{2})}; \quad \text{at } \alpha(m^2) = \frac{1}{2}.$$

$$J - \frac{1}{2} = 0 \text{ even, upper sign, } + \text{ signature.}$$

Next member: $J = \frac{5}{2}$ $\therefore \ell = 3$, F-wave resonance;

$$[f_{J+\frac{1}{2}}^{I=\frac{1}{2}} \text{ could have a } - \text{ sign trajectory; } D^{3/2}, G^{7/2}, \ldots].$$

Similarly, the amplitude $f_{J-\frac{1}{2}}^{I=\frac{1}{2}}$ has poles

$$S_{\frac{1}{2}}, D_{\frac{3}{2}}, \ldots \quad \text{at } + \text{ signature trajectory,}$$
$$P_{\frac{3}{2}}, F_{\frac{7}{2}}, \ldots \quad \text{at } - \text{ signature trajectory.}$$

(B) $I = \frac{3}{2}$:

$$f_{J+\frac{1}{2}}^{I=\frac{3}{2}}: \quad P_{\frac{1}{2}}, F_{\frac{7}{2}}, \ldots \quad + \text{ signature,}$$
$$D_{\frac{3}{2}}, G_{\frac{9}{2}}, \ldots \quad - \text{ signature.}$$
$$f_{J-\frac{1}{2}}^{I=\frac{3}{2}}: \quad S_{\frac{1}{2}}, D_{\frac{5}{2}}, \ldots \quad + \text{ signature,}$$
$$P_{\frac{3}{2}}, F_{\frac{7}{2}}, \ldots \quad - \text{ signature.}$$

Table 12–1
Observed Pion-Nucleon Resonances

AMPLITUDE	POLES			SIGNATURE	PARITY
$f_{J+\frac{1}{2}}^{I=\frac{1}{2}}$	P_{11}————————F_{15}———— (938) (1688)			+	+
	D_{13}———————— G_{17}—— (1512) (2190)			−	−
$f_{J-\frac{1}{2}}^{I=\frac{1}{2}}$	P_{13}———————— F_{17}———— (1489)			−	+
	S_{11}————D_{15}———— (1690) (1690)			+	−
$f_{J-\frac{1}{2}}^{I=\frac{3}{2}}$	P_{33}———— F_{37}————$H_{3,11}$—— (1236) (1920) (2420)			−	+
	S_{31}————D_{35}—— (1690)			+	−
$f_{J+\frac{1}{2}}^{I=\frac{3}{2}}$	D_{35}———————— G_{39}——— (1650) (2360)			−	−
	P_{31}————————F_{35}————			+	+

Table 12–1 and Fig. 12.11 show the observed trajectories in the pion-nucleon system. Thus it seems, experimentally, that all but one trajectory are realized at the present time.

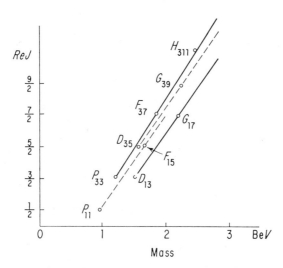

Figure 12.11 πN-resonance trajectories.

(2) t-Channel: $\pi\pi \to N\bar{N}$. The partial-wave amplitudes in t-channel are given by

$$A_J(t) = \frac{1}{2} \int_{-1}^{+1} dz_t \, A(s,t)P_J(z_t), \tag{12.77}$$

or, from a fixed t-dispersion relation as we had before, by

$$A_J^{\pm}(t) = \frac{1}{\pi} \int_{(m+\mu)^2}^{\infty} ds' \, A_1(s',t,u') \frac{1}{2qq'} \, Q_J\!\left(\frac{s' + q^2 + q'^2}{2qq'}\right)[1 \pm (-1)^J], \tag{12.77'}$$

$$q^2 = \frac{t}{4} - m^2; \quad q'^2 = \frac{t}{4} - \mu^2;$$

$B_J(t)$ is similar, except for a pole contribution.

The helicity amplitudes h^J are expressed in terms of A_J, B_{J-1}, B_{J+1} by Eq. (12.55). Thus we obtain formal expressions for

$$h_{\frac{1}{2},-\frac{1}{2}}^J \quad \text{and} \quad h_{\frac{1}{2},\frac{1}{2}}^J$$

for purposes of analytic continuation. We recall that

$$\begin{aligned} B_J^+ &= 0, \quad A_J^- = 0 \qquad \text{for } J \text{ even,} \\ B_J^- &= 0, \quad A_J^+ = 0 \qquad \text{for } J \text{ odd.} \end{aligned}$$

Hence for $I = 0$ ($+$amplitude),

$$h^J \neq 0 \quad \text{only for } J \text{ even,}$$

and for $I = 1$,

$$h^J \neq 0 \quad \text{only for } J \text{ odd.}$$

Here in contrast to the πN system the signature of the trajectory is determined by the Pauli principle (Fig. 12.12). For the initial state of the two-pion system,

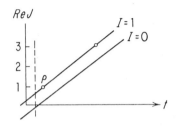

Figure 12.12 $\pi\pi$-system trajectories.

$\ell = J$; and in the final state,

$$N\bar{N} \quad \text{has} \quad \ell' = J; J + 1, J, J - 1.$$

However, there are no $J \to J = 1$ transitions. Hence the combinations

$$h^J_{\frac{1}{2},\frac{1}{2}} \pm h^J_{\frac{1}{2},-\frac{1}{2}}$$

have definite ℓ-values.

We can make the Watson-Sommerfeld transformation on the helicity amplitudes, e.g.,

$$H_{\frac{1}{2},\frac{1}{2}} = \frac{1}{2q} \sum_J (2J + 1)h^J_{\frac{1}{2}\frac{1}{2}}P_J$$

$$\to \frac{1}{2q}\left[\int dJ \frac{(2J + 1)}{\sin \pi J} h^J_{\frac{1}{2}\frac{1}{2}}P_J(-z) + \sum_n \frac{\beta_n P_{\alpha_n}(-z)}{\sin \pi \alpha_n}\right],$$

$$H_{\frac{1}{2},-\frac{1}{2}} = -\frac{1}{2q}\left[\int \frac{(2J + 1)h^J_{\frac{1}{2},-\frac{1}{2}}}{\sin \pi J} \frac{-\sin \theta}{\sqrt{J(J + 1)}} P'_J(-z) + \sum_n \frac{\beta'_n P_{\alpha'_n}}{\sin \pi \alpha'_n}\right]. \quad (12.78)$$

12.3   Applications

a. πN-Forward-Scattering Amplitude

The forward scattering amplitude is expected to be dominated by poles in the t-channel, $\pi\pi \to N\bar{N}$. We then have

$$R = f_1 + f_2\boldsymbol{\sigma}\cdot\hat{\mathbf{q}}'\boldsymbol{\sigma}\cdot\hat{\mathbf{q}}$$
$$= f_1 + f_2 \cos \theta + if_2(\hat{\mathbf{q}}' \times \hat{\mathbf{q}})\cdot\boldsymbol{\sigma}.$$

From optical theorem,

$$Im R(t = 0) = Im(f_1 + f_2)|_{t=0} = \lambda \sigma_{tot}$$

$$\frac{d\sigma}{d\Omega} = \frac{m^2\mu^2}{s} |f_1 + f_2 \boldsymbol{\sigma} \cdot \hat{\mathbf{q}}' \boldsymbol{\sigma} \cdot \hat{\mathbf{q}}|^2$$

$$= \frac{m^2\mu^2}{s} \{|f_1|^2 + |f_2|^2(\cos^2\theta + \sin^2\theta) + 2\cos\theta\, Re f_1^* f_2\}$$

$$= \frac{m^2\mu^2}{s} \left\{|f_1 + f_2|^2 + \frac{t}{q^2} Re f_1^* f_2\right\}.$$

We can express f_1 and f_2 in terms of $A(s,t,u)$ and $B(s,t,u)$. If now $H_{\frac{1}{2}, \pm\frac{1}{2}}$ are approximated by a pole term in t-channel, we can express by Eq. (12.50) the same A and B asymptotically by this pole and insert these formulas into $d\sigma/d\Omega$ and σ_{tot} (Exercise 3).

b. *πN-Backward-Scattering Amplitude*

The amplitude is expected to be dominated by the N and N^* poles in the u-channel:

$$\frac{d\sigma}{d\Omega} = \frac{m^2\mu^2}{s} \left[|f_1 + f_2|^2 + \frac{t}{q^2} Re f_1^* f_2\right]\Bigg|_{u \approx 0}.$$

Now we use $s \leftrightarrow u$ symmetry, e.g., and express $f_1(u,z_u)$, $f_2(u,z_u)$ by pole terms:

$$f_1^{(I=\frac{1}{2})}(u,z_u) = \frac{\beta_{J+\frac{1}{2}}^{(I=\frac{1}{2})}}{\sin\pi(\alpha - \frac{1}{2})} [P'_{\alpha-\frac{1}{2}}(-z_u) + P'_{\alpha-\frac{1}{2}}(z_u)],$$

$$f_2^{(I=\frac{1}{2})}(u,z_u) = \frac{\beta_{J+\frac{1}{2}}^{(I=\frac{1}{2})}}{\sin\pi(\alpha - \frac{1}{2})} [P'_{\alpha+\frac{1}{2}}(-z_u) - P'_{\alpha+\frac{1}{2}}(z_u)],$$

and insert these into $d\sigma/d\Omega$.

c. *Dispersion Relations and Subtractions*

A pole contribution from t-channel gives, in the amplitude, a term behaving like $s^{\alpha(t)}$, which is bounded by $s^{\alpha_{max}}$. If $\alpha_{max} \geqslant 0$ the dispersion integrals do not converge. However, if we separate pole terms with $\alpha \geqslant 0$, the remainder should give a convergent unsubtracted dispersion relation.

Suppose we substract the Pomeranchuk pole and have no other pole between $\alpha = 0$ and 1. Then letting

$$A(s,t) = A'(s,t) + \frac{\beta(t)}{\sin\pi\alpha(t)} \left[P_{\alpha(t)}\left(-1 - \frac{2s}{t-4}\right) \pm P_{\alpha(t)}\left(+1 + \frac{2s}{t-4}\right)\right],$$

we can write

$$A'(s,t) = \frac{1}{\pi}\int ds' \frac{Im A'(s',t)}{s' - s},$$

$$Im A' = Im A - Im\left\{\frac{\beta(t)}{\sin\pi\alpha(t)} \left[P_{\alpha(t)}\left(-1 - \frac{2s}{t-4}\right) \pm P_{\alpha(t)}\left(1 + \frac{2s}{t-4}\right)\right]\right\}.$$

At $t = 0$, in particular,

$$ImA(s, t = 0) = s\sigma_{tot}(s),$$

$$Im[A_{pole}] = -\frac{1}{2}\beta(0)s = s\sigma_{tot}(\infty).$$

Hence

$$A'(s, t = 0) = \frac{1}{\pi}\int ds' \frac{s'[\sigma_{tot}(s') - \sigma_{tot}(\infty)]}{s' - s},$$

$$A(s,0) = \frac{1}{\pi}\int ds' \frac{s'[\sigma(s') - \sigma(\infty)]}{s' - s} - \frac{-i\beta(0)s}{2}.$$

This formula can be checked, e.g., by calculating the scattering length at low energies. The calculation indicates[3] that there must be one other pole or another singularity between $\alpha^{(0)} = 0$ and 1.

12.4   Effective-Range Formula

a. Spinless Case

We start from the partial-wave amplitudes, with cuts as obtained in Sec. 11.2 and the N/D equations:

$$N_\ell(s) = A_\ell(s_0) + \frac{s - s_0}{\pi}\int_{-\infty}^{s_L = 0} ds' \frac{\text{disc. } A_\ell(s')D_\ell(s')}{(s' - s)(s' - s_0)},$$

$$D_\ell(s) = 1 - \frac{s - s_0}{\pi}\int_{s_R}^{\infty} ds' \sqrt{\frac{s' - 4}{s'}} R(s',\ell) \frac{N(s',\ell)}{(s' - s)(s' - s_0)}.$$

Let us now approximate the left-hand cut by an "average" pole at $s = -s_1$. This should be sufficient at very low energies; we also consider a particular ℓ. Then

$$\text{disc. } A(s',\ell) = -\pi\Gamma_\ell\delta(s + s_1).$$

Let D be normalized such that

$$D(s_1) = 1.$$

Then

$$N(s,\ell) = A_\ell(s_0) - \frac{s - s_0}{\pi}\pi\Gamma_\ell \frac{1}{(s_1 + s)(s_1 + s_0)}.$$

Actually for a single pole no subtraction is necessary and we can write

$$N(s,\ell) = \pi\Gamma_\ell \frac{1}{s_1 + s}$$

and obtain

$$D_\ell(s) = 1 - \frac{s - s_0}{\pi}\int_4^{\infty} ds' \sqrt{\frac{s' - 4}{s'}} R \frac{\pi\Gamma_\ell}{(s_1 + s')(s' - s)(s' - s_0)}.$$

[3] K. Igi, *Phys. Rev.*, **130**, 820 (1963).

Choosing $s_0 = -s_1$ and the inelasticity parameter R to be approximately the unity, we have

$$D_\ell(s) = 1 - \frac{s + s_1}{\pi} \int_4^\infty ds' \sqrt{\frac{s' - 4}{s'}} \frac{\pi \Gamma_\ell}{(s' + s_1)^2 (s' - s)}.$$

The integral can be performed, and for s_1 and $s \ll 1$ we get

$$D(s) \cong 1 - \frac{\Gamma}{m} \frac{s + s_1}{\sqrt{s_1 - 4}\,[\sqrt{s_1 - 4} - \sqrt{s - 4}]^2}.$$

In the physical region, $s > 4$, the amplitude has the form

$$A_\ell = \frac{N}{D} = \frac{1}{\dfrac{q}{m} \cot \delta - i \dfrac{q}{m}},$$

from unitarity, and

$$Re \frac{D}{N} = \cot \delta \frac{q}{m} = \frac{1}{N} Re D$$

$$= \left[\frac{\nu_1}{\Gamma} - \frac{\sqrt{\nu_1}}{2m}\right] + \nu \left[\frac{1}{\Gamma} + \frac{1}{2m\sqrt{\nu_1}}\right] = \frac{1}{a} + \frac{1}{2}\Gamma\nu,$$

which is the usual effective-range formula. In particular, for s-wave,

$\Gamma < 0$ corresponds to a repulsive force and
$\Gamma > 0$ to an attractive force.

For positive and sufficiently large Γ we obtain a bound state at

$$-\nu = \alpha^2 = \nu_1 \left[\frac{\Gamma - 2m\sqrt{(s - 4)/4}}{\Gamma + 2m\sqrt{(s_1 - 4)/4}}\right]^2.$$

EXAMPLE—*n-p scattering (spin neglected).* Effective-range formula is very accurate in the energy range 0–10 Bev both for singlet and triplet with $\nu_1 \cong 1\ (s_1 = 8)$.[4]

b. π-N Case

If one replaces the short cut $(m^2 - \mu^2)^2/m^2 < s < (m^2 + 2\mu^2)$ (see Fig. 12.13) by a pole with residue g^2 and all other singularities by a distant pole

Figure 12.13

[4] H. P. Noyes and D. Wong, *Phys. Rev. Letters*, **3**, 191 (1959).

(Fig. 12.13) one obtains for the $\frac{3}{2} - \frac{3}{2}$ state the Chew-Low effective-range formula

$$\tfrac{4}{3}f^2 \frac{q^3}{W - m} \cot \delta \cong \frac{W_R - W}{W_R - m};$$

W_R is the energy of the resonance, and

$$f^2 = \frac{\mu^2}{4m^2} g^2 \cong 0.08.$$

The width of the resonance comes out to be correct, but not the position.[5] (See also Sec. 12.5.)

c. Effective-Range Formula for $I = \frac{1}{2}, J = \frac{1}{2}$ Partial-Wave Amplitude

The correct cut in the partial-wave amplitude is replaced by an equivalent cut along the real axis so as to give the same physical amplitude on the real axis (Fig. 12.14).

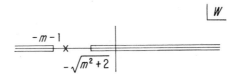

Figure 12.14

We again write the amplitude in the form of a quotient:

$$g = \frac{N(W)}{D(W)},$$

where $D(W)$ has cuts only in the left-hand physical region in $W = \sqrt{s}$ plane. From unitarity we have

$$g(W) = \frac{W^2}{(W + m)^2 - 1} \frac{\eta_\ell(W)e^{2i\delta_\ell(W)} - 1}{2iq(W)}$$

$$= \frac{-W^2}{(W + m)^2 - 1} \frac{\eta_{11}(-W)e^{i\delta_{11}(-W)} - 1}{2iq(-W)}$$

where

$$q(W) = \frac{[(W + m)^2 - 1]^{\frac{1}{2}}[(W - m)^2 - 1]^{\frac{1}{2}}}{2W}.$$

For δ_{11}-phase shift we take only the nucleon pole into account which is very close to the physical region $-m - 1 > \omega > -\infty$. Hence

$$D(W) = 1 + \frac{W + m + 1}{\pi} \int_{-\infty}^{-m-1} dW' \frac{Im D(W')}{(W' - W)(W' + m + 1)},$$

$$Im D(W) = -\frac{q(-W)[(W + m)^2 - 1]}{W^2} Re N(W); \quad W < -M - 1.$$

[5] S. Frautschi and D. Walecka, *Phys. Rev.*, **120**, 1486 (1960).

On the other hand, the numerator $N(W)$ is real in the elastic region $-M - 1 > W > -W_{\text{inel}}$ and is given by

$$N(W) = \frac{1}{\pi} \int_{-\sqrt{m^2+2}}^{\infty} dW' \frac{\mathrm{Img}(W')D(W')}{W' - W} + \frac{1}{\pi} \int_{-\infty}^{-W_{\text{inel}}} dW' \frac{\mathrm{Im}[gD]}{W' - W}.$$

If one neglects the first term and replaces the second term by two poles at fixed positions, $\sum_{i=1}^{2} \alpha_i/(W_i - W)$, then $D(W)$ can be explicitly integrated.[6] The two parameters α_1, α_2 are then determined by requiring that

$$D(-M) = 0,$$

and that the residue of the pole is $\gamma = -[N(-M)]/[D(-M)]$. This last equation gives

$$\gamma = \frac{-1}{D'(m)} \sum_{1}^{2} \frac{\alpha_i}{W_i + m} \simeq \tfrac{8}{3}f^2 M^2.$$

With $f^2 = 0.08$, one obtains $\alpha_1 = 68.5$, $\alpha_2 = 3.83$.
Experimental comparison with

$$Re \frac{D}{N} = \frac{(W + m)^2 - 1}{-W^2} q(-W) \cot \delta_{11}(-W)$$

is shown in Fig. 12.15.

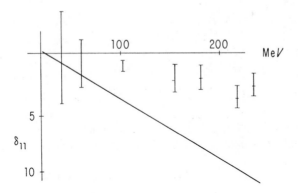

Figure 12.15 $I = \tfrac{1}{2}$ phase shifts.

12.5 "Reciprocal Bootstrap" Calculation of N and N_{33}^*

This is essentially the same idea as we discussed in the case of the ρ-meson, except that now different particles are involved in different channels. The t-channel ($\pi\pi$-$N\bar{N}$) can accommodate the ρ-meson but perhaps its contribution to the low-energy πN-channel would be small. In the u-channel we

[6] L. A. P. Balàzs, *Phys. Rev.*, **128**, 1935 (1962).

have the 3-3 resonance N^* which may be thought to provide the main force for the binding of π and N in the $I = \frac{1}{2}, J = \frac{1}{2}$ channel to form the nucleon, and vice versa. The essence of Chew-Low theory for the 3-3 resonance in static approximation is that in first approximation N^* is a pion-nucleon system held together primarily by the exchange of a nucleon.[7]

First, qualitatively, we can calculate the effect of N and N^* (introduced as a particle) on the four p-wave amplitudes: $f_{J-\frac{1}{2}}$ $(J = \frac{3}{2})$ and $f_{J+\frac{1}{2}}$ $(J = \frac{1}{2})$. The residues are given by

$I =$	$\dfrac{1}{2}$	$\dfrac{1}{2}$	$\dfrac{3}{2}$	$\dfrac{3}{2}$	
Amplitude	$f_{J+\frac{1}{2}}$	$f_{J-\frac{1}{2}}$	$f_{J+\frac{1}{2}}$	$f_{J-\frac{1}{2}}$	
	$\dfrac{1}{9}$	$-\dfrac{2}{9}$	$-\dfrac{2}{9}$	$\dfrac{4}{9}$	$\times \gamma_{11}$

showing that the force is most attractive in the $\frac{3}{2} - \frac{3}{2}$ state. On the other hand, the residues in these same four states, because of exchange of N^* with residue γ_{33}, are, respectively,

$$\frac{16}{9} \qquad \frac{4}{9} \qquad \frac{4}{9} \qquad \frac{1}{9} \times \gamma_{33},$$

i.e., most attractive in the $\frac{1}{2}, \frac{1}{2}$ state. This is the basis of the reciprocal bootstrap calculation.[8]

Let us now use the N/D-method, as in Sec. 12.4. We write

$$f_{33} = \frac{N_{33}}{D_{33}}$$

with

$$N_{33}(\omega) = \frac{1}{\pi} \int d\omega' \frac{\text{disc. } [D_{33}f_{33}]}{\omega' - \omega}, \qquad \omega = W - m.$$

The integral is over unphysical and inelastic cuts. For $0 \leqslant \omega \leqslant 2$ the pole at $\omega = 0$ should dominate, and the last integral reduces to

$$N_{33}(\omega) = \frac{4}{3} \frac{\gamma_{11}}{\omega}, \qquad \gamma_{11} = 3f^2 = 0.24.$$

In a more detailed calculation one may approximate the left-hand cut by two additional poles.[9] Then

$$D_{33}(\omega) = 1 - \frac{\omega}{\pi} \int_1^\infty d\omega' \frac{\rho(\omega')N_{33}(\omega')}{\omega'(\omega' - \omega)},$$

$$= 1 + P\frac{\omega}{\pi} \int_1^\infty i\rho(\omega)N_{33}(\omega)\theta(\omega - 1).$$

[7] G. F. Chew and F. Low, *Phys. Rev.*, **101**, 1570 (1956).
[8] G. F. Chew, *Phys. Rev. Letters*, **9**, 233 (1962).
[9] B. Udgaonkar and V. Singh, *Phys. Rev.*, **130**, 1177 (1963).

We replace the integral by an empirical constant a and require that

$$Re\,D(\omega_{33}) = 1 - \omega_{33}a = 0.$$

Hence

$$D = 1 - \frac{\omega}{\omega_{33}} - i\rho(\omega)N_{33}(\omega)\theta(\omega - 1),$$

which gives

$$\gamma_{33} = \omega_{33}N_{33}(\omega_{33}) = \tfrac{4}{9}\gamma_{11} = 0.11$$

and the effective-range formula

$$q\cot\delta = Re\,\frac{D}{N} = \frac{1 - \dfrac{\omega}{\omega_R}}{\dfrac{4}{3}\dfrac{\gamma_{11}}{\omega}},$$

both in agreement with experiment.

Reciprocally to evaluate the $f_{11} = N_{11}/D_{11}$ amplitudes we replace N_{11} by the N^* and by the u-channel N pole as well as by ρ-cuts:

$$N_{11}(\omega) = \frac{\tfrac{16}{9}\gamma_{33}D_{11}(-\omega_{33})}{\omega_{33} + m} + \frac{\tfrac{1}{9}\gamma_{11}D_{11}(0)}{\omega} + \frac{1}{\pi}\int_{\rho\,\text{cuts}} d\omega'\,\frac{C_{11}^{\rho}(\omega')D_{11}(\omega')}{\omega' - \omega}.$$

The ρ-meson contribution can be evaluated, e.g., from the nucleon form-factor calculations.

Ignoring the integral, as a rough approximation, we normalize

$$D_{11}(-\omega_{33}) = 1$$

and adjust $D_{11}(0) = 0$. Then

$$D_{11}(\omega) = -\frac{\omega}{\omega_{33}} \qquad \text{for} \quad |\omega| \lesssim 2,$$

so that the residue of $f_{11} = N_{11}D_{11}^{-1}$ at $\omega = 0$ is

$$-\gamma_{11} = \frac{N_{11}(0)}{D_{11}'(0)} = -\frac{16}{9}\gamma_{33} - \frac{1}{9}\gamma_{11}$$

or

$$\gamma_{11} = 2\gamma_{33},$$

again in agreement with experiment.

If we include the contribution of N in the dispersion relation for N_{33}, we can write the *reciprocal bootstrap conditions* in the form

$$\begin{pmatrix}\gamma_{11} \\ \gamma_{33}\end{pmatrix} = \begin{pmatrix}\dfrac{1}{9} & \dfrac{16}{9} \\ \dfrac{4}{9} & \dfrac{1}{9}\end{pmatrix}\begin{pmatrix}\gamma_{11} \\ \gamma_{33}\end{pmatrix},$$

or in matrix notation,

$$\gamma = A\gamma.$$

It is an eigenvalue equation and a solution exists because A has one eigenvalue $+1$. This consistency equation is the basis of the generalization of the bootstrap condition from SU_2 to higher symmetry groups,[10] such as SU_3 and SU_6.

Problems and Further Developments

1. Obtain the partial-wave amplitudes $f_{J\pm\frac{1}{2}}$ given in Eq. (12.40) by an alternate method using Eq. (12.44′).
2. Derive from Eq. (12.66) the unitarity for the $f_{J\pm\frac{1}{2}}$ amplitudes.
3. Assuming that the forward-scattering πN-amplitude is dominated by a pole term in the t-channel, obtain a formula for σ_{tot} and $d\sigma/d\Omega$ ($t = 0$).
4. Find the contribution of the N and N^* (1236) poles in the u-channel to the πN backward-scattering cross section.
5. Show that for π-N interactions, charge independence plus CP-invariance implies P- and C-invariance separately.
6. Derive the helicity amplitudes for the so-called V-A spinorial amplitude given in Eq. (10.19), i.e.,

$$M = A(s,t,u)\sigma^\mu \otimes \sigma_\mu.$$

7. Find the poles of the amplitudes in the q-plane in an effective range approximation.
8. Express Eq. (12.44′) in terms of the $3j$–symbols.

[10] I. Gerstein and K. T. Mahanthappa, *Nuovo Cimento*, **32**, 239 (1964). E. Abers, L. A. P. Balázs and Y. Hara, *Phys. Rev.*, **136**, B1328 (1964).

CHAPTER 13

Electromagnetic Interactions

13.1 Survey of Electromagnetic Processes

We shall consider in this chapter the most general form of the interaction of charged particles with photons. From the beginning, however, the framework is general enough to account in principle for the effect of all other particles, by considering sufficient terms in the unitarity condition. The scope of the electromagnetic effects can be roughly classified as follows:

(1) Electromagnetic interactions of leptons: Scattering processes, $ee \rightarrow ee$, $e\gamma \rightarrow e\gamma$, $\gamma\gamma \rightarrow \gamma\gamma$ with all the crossed channels; inelastic reactions $ee \rightarrow ee\gamma, \ldots$, etc.; anomalous magnetic moments of e and μ.

(2) Electromagnetic interactions in the presence of or via the weak interactions: $\mu \rightarrow e\gamma$, $\mu \rightarrow e\nu\bar{\nu}$, $\nu\gamma \rightarrow \nu\gamma, \ldots$.

(3) Electromagnetic interactions of strongly interacting particles: Scattering and decay processes $eN \rightarrow eN$, $\pi^0 \rightarrow 2\gamma$, $\Sigma^0 \rightarrow \Lambda + \gamma, \ldots$; electromagnetic form factors; electromagnetic mass differences.

We shall discuss some typical examples, but begin with the important point: The description of the spin 1 particle and the photon (in its irreducible form).

13.2 Description of Spin-1 Particles and Photons

For completeness we review briefly here the formalism for spin 1 particles. Consider a process with one outgoing spin 1 particle, the other $(n - 1)$ particles being of spin 0, for the time being. The equation for the spinorial amplitude takes the form

$$M(K) = \mathscr{D}^{01}(A)M(\Lambda^{-1}K). \tag{13.1}$$

If we define an irreducible spinorial object[1] transforming as

$$\mathscr{D}^{01}(A)\varepsilon_\mu(\Lambda^{-1}k) = \Lambda_\mu{}^\nu(k), \tag{13.2}$$

---

[1] There are other types of polarization vectors used in the literature; we shall keep the precise definition, Eq. (13.2), via the irreducible representation $\mathscr{D}^{01}(A)$ of the homogeneous Lorentz group.

where k is the momentum of the spin 1 particle, we can write the most general solution of Eq. (13.1) in the form

$$M(K) = \sum_{i=1}^{4} A_i v_i^\mu \varepsilon_\mu(k), \quad n \geqslant 4, \tag{13.3}$$

where, as before, v_i are the four-linearly independent fourvectors and A_i scalar functions. (The case $n = 3$ will be treated in Sec. 13.3.) The four amplitudes in Eq. (13.3) reduce however automatically to three, as they must because spin 1 particles have three directions of polarization. To see this we derive the explicit form of $\varepsilon_\mu(k)$ from Eq. (13.2). Let us decompose $\mathscr{D}^{01}$ into the product of two $\mathscr{D}^{0\frac{1}{2}}(A) = A$:

$$\mathscr{D}^{01}(A)_m^n = [\tfrac{1}{2}\tfrac{1}{2}1]_m^{\alpha\beta}\{\tfrac{1}{2}\tfrac{1}{2}1\}_{\gamma\delta}^n A_\alpha^\gamma A_\beta^\delta, \tag{13.4}$$

where the brackets are the Clebsch-Gordan coefficients with the upper and lower indices as shown. Inserting Eq. (13.4) into Eq. (13.2) and using the orthogonality of the Clebsch-Gordan coefficients, we obtain

$$A_\alpha^\gamma \{\tfrac{1}{2}\tfrac{1}{2}1\}_{\gamma\delta}^n \varepsilon_n^\mu(\Lambda^{-1}k)A_\beta^\delta = \Lambda_\nu^\mu\{\tfrac{1}{2}\tfrac{1}{2}1\}_{\alpha\beta}^m \varepsilon_m^\nu(k).$$

This equation shows that the product $\{\tfrac{1}{2}\tfrac{1}{2}1\}_{\alpha\beta}^n \varepsilon_n^\mu(k)$ transforms exactly like $\sigma_{\alpha\beta}^\mu(k)$. These Pauli spinors with two undotted indices can be obtained from the usual Pauli matrices $\sigma_{\alpha\dot\beta}^\mu$ (see Chap. 4) by the use of the metric spinors $G_{\dot\beta}^\beta(k)$ changing a dotted index into an undotted one:

$$\sigma_{\alpha\beta}^\mu(k) = G_{\dot\beta}^\beta(k)\sigma_{\alpha\dot\beta}^\mu = \sigma_{\alpha\dot\beta}^\mu G^{T\dot\beta}{}_\beta(k)$$

$$= \sigma^\mu \frac{k\cdot\bar\sigma}{m} C, \tag{13.5}$$

where C is the metric spinor, $C = \begin{pmatrix} 0 & -1 \\ 1 & 0 \end{pmatrix}$, and, in the second line, we have inserted the explicit form of G. Thus, apart from a scalar function which can be incorporated into the scalar amplitudes, ε_μ is given, with a normalization factor $1/\sqrt{2}$, by

$$\varepsilon_n^\mu(k) = \frac{1}{\sqrt{2}} [\tfrac{1}{2}\tfrac{1}{2}1]_n^{\alpha\beta}\left(\sigma^\mu \frac{k\cdot\bar\sigma}{m} C\right)_{\alpha\beta}. \tag{13.6}$$

From this form it follows immediately that

$$\varepsilon^\mu(k)k_\mu = 0, \tag{13.7}$$

because $k\cdot\sigma k\cdot\bar\sigma = m^2$, and trace $\{[\tfrac{1}{2}\tfrac{1}{2}1]C\} = 0$, so that the four amplitudes in Eq. (13.3) are indeed reduced to one.

A more convenient formalism which has Eq. (13.7) built in is to introduce the three k-independent irreducible matrices

$$\tau_1^{\mu\nu}, \quad \tau_0^{\mu\nu}, \quad \tau_{-1}^{\mu\nu}, \tag{13.8}$$

which are antisymmetric:

$$g_{\mu\nu}\tau_n^{\mu\nu} = 0, \tag{13.9}$$

and satisfy

$$\mathscr{D}^{01}\tau^{\mu\nu} = \Lambda_{\mu'}^{\mu}\Lambda_{\nu'}^{\nu}\tau^{\mu'\nu'}. \tag{13.10}$$

The amplitudes M, Eq. (13.3), have then the form

$$M = \sum A_i t_{\mu\nu}^i(k)\tau^{\mu\nu}, \tag{13.11}$$

where the tensors $t_{\mu\nu}^i$ constructed out of momenta are also antisymmetric.

If $k^2 > 0$, there are indeed three independent spacelike vectors $\varepsilon_n^{\mu}(k)$, $n = 1, 0, -1$, uniquely determined up to three-dimensional rotations, which are orthogonal to k_{μ}. If now, $k^2 = 0$, there are only two linearly independent spacelike vectors orthogonal to k_{μ}. Furthermore, ε_{μ} are now not uniquely determined, for ε_{μ} can be replaced by $\varepsilon_{\mu} + \lambda k_{\mu}$, λ arbitrary, without violating the condition $\varepsilon \cdot k = 0$. Because all such polarization vectors $(\varepsilon + \lambda k)$ are physically equivalent, they should not be distinguishable, and we require the amplitudes to be invariant under the substitution

$$\varepsilon \to \varepsilon + \lambda k. \tag{13.12}$$

This is one way of formulating *gauge invariance* in S-matrix theory; it shows the limiting process for a spin 1 particle when mass is made zero. Of course, one can also use directly the representation $e^{i\varphi(k,A)}$, $[(m = 0, S = 1)]$, instead of $\mathscr{D}^{01}$.[2] By "gauge invariance" we shall mean in the following always that we are using the zero-mass representation of the Lorentz group with one direction of polarization.

13.3   Vertex Amplitudes Involving Photons

In this section we consider amplitudes of the type

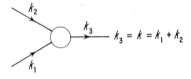

Figure 13.1   Vertex amplitude.

with, in general, complex momenta on the mass shell. We shall denote their spins by $\langle S_1\ S_2\ S_3 \rangle$. There are only two linearly independent momenta in the problem which we choose conveniently as $(k_1 + k_2)$ and $(k_1 - k_2)$.

A. $\langle 0\ 0\ 1 \rangle$: There is a single amplitude

$$M = A(k_1 - k_2) \cdot \varepsilon \tag{13.13}$$

[2] D. Zwanziger, in *Proceedings of the Symposium on the Lorentz Group* (Boulder, Colo.: U. of Colorado Press, 1965).

valid for all values of masses of the three particles. (Thus parity is necessarily conserved.) If now the spin 1 particle has zero mass, we get, from Eq. (13.12),

$$A(k_1 - k_2) \cdot (k_1 + k_2) = 0;$$

hence[3]

$$A = 0, \quad \text{if } k_1^2 \neq k_2^2. \tag{13.14}$$

A may or may not be zero if $k_1^2 = k_2^2$. We observe here the remarkable fact that the above vertex amplitude with one photon is a nonanalytic function of the masses of the other two—the nonanalyticity (or the discrete nature of the amplitude) being related to the charge degree of freedom. The energetically possible reactions like $K \to \pi + \gamma$, $\eta \to \pi + \gamma, \ldots$, are forbidden.

B. $\langle \frac{1}{2} \frac{1}{2} 1 \rangle$: From particles 1 and 2 we can form the following five tensorial forms with transformation property and parity indicated:

$$S \quad \left(\frac{k_1}{m_1} + \frac{k_2}{m_2} \right) \cdot \sigma, \qquad\qquad \eta_P = +$$

$$P \quad \left(\frac{k_1}{m_1} - \frac{k_2}{m_2} \right) \cdot \sigma, \qquad\qquad -$$

$$V \quad \left(\sigma^\mu + \frac{k_2 \cdot \sigma}{m_2} \tilde{\sigma}^\mu \frac{k_1 \cdot \sigma}{m_1} \right), \qquad\qquad + \tag{13.15}$$

$$A \quad \left(\sigma^\mu - \frac{k_2 \cdot \sigma}{m_2} \tilde{\sigma}^\mu \frac{k_1 \cdot \sigma}{m_1} \right), \qquad\qquad -$$

$$T \quad \frac{k_2 \cdot \sigma}{m_2} (\tilde{\sigma}^\mu \sigma^\nu - \tilde{\sigma}^\nu \sigma^\mu) + (\sigma^\mu \tilde{\sigma}^\nu - \sigma^\nu \tilde{\sigma}^\mu) \frac{k_1 \cdot \sigma}{m_1}. \qquad +$$

Thus we have for the vertex amplitudes, under parity conservation,

$$M = A_1 \left(\frac{k_1}{m_1} + \frac{k_2}{m_2} \right) \cdot \sigma (k_1 - k_2) \cdot \varepsilon + A_2 \left(\sigma^\mu + \frac{k_2}{m_2} \cdot \sigma \tilde{\sigma}^\mu \frac{k_1}{m_1} \cdot \sigma \right) \varepsilon_\mu$$

$$+ A_3 \left[\frac{k_2 \cdot \sigma}{m_2} (\tilde{\sigma}^\mu \sigma^\nu - \tilde{\sigma}^\nu \sigma^\mu) + (\sigma^\mu \tilde{\sigma}^\nu - \sigma^\nu \tilde{\sigma}^\mu) \frac{k_1 \cdot \sigma}{m_1} \right] (k_1 - k_2)_\mu \varepsilon_\nu \tag{13.16}$$

$$= A_1 Y_1 + A_2 Y_2 + A_3 Y_3.$$

The last term can be written as $Y_3 = a Y_1 + b Y_2 + \Delta m Y_3'$, where $\Delta m = m_1 - m_2$, so that the term Y_3' is not analytic in the masses.

Let now the spin 1 particle be a photon. The amplitude $A_2 Y_2$ is already gauge-invariant, the amplitude A_1 must vanish, as before, unless $k_1^2 = k_2^2$;

---

[3] Equation (13.14) is valid for an arbitrary choice of Eq. (13.13): $M = A v^\mu(K) \varepsilon_\mu$.

i.e., it is also nonanalytic in the masses. We rewrite Eq. (13.16), using the identity,[4]

$$\left[(n \cdot \sigma \varepsilon \cdot \tilde{\sigma} - \varepsilon \cdot \sigma n \cdot \tilde{\sigma}) \frac{k_1 \cdot \sigma}{m_1} + \frac{k_2 \cdot \sigma}{m_2} (n \cdot \tilde{\sigma} \varepsilon \cdot \sigma - \varepsilon \cdot \tilde{\sigma} n \cdot \sigma) \right]$$

$$= 4 \left(\varepsilon \cdot \sigma + \frac{k_2 \cdot \sigma}{m_2} \varepsilon \cdot \tilde{\sigma} \frac{k_1 \cdot \sigma}{m_1} \right) - 2 \left(\frac{k_1}{m_1} + \frac{k_2}{m_2} \right) \cdot \sigma \left(\frac{k_1}{m_1} + \frac{k_2}{m_2} \right) \cdot \varepsilon \quad (13.17)$$

$$\left(n = \frac{k_2}{m_2} - \frac{k_1}{m_1} \right)$$

in the form corresponding to the usual electric and magnetic couplings:

$$M = e \left(\varepsilon \cdot \sigma + \frac{k_2 \cdot \sigma}{m_2} \varepsilon \cdot \tilde{\sigma} \frac{k_1 \cdot \sigma}{m_1} \right)$$

$$+ \mu \left[(n \cdot \sigma \varepsilon \cdot \tilde{\sigma} - \varepsilon \cdot \sigma n \cdot \tilde{\sigma}) \frac{k_1 \cdot \sigma}{m_1} + \frac{k_2 \cdot \sigma}{m_2} (n \cdot \tilde{\sigma} \varepsilon \cdot \sigma - \varepsilon \cdot \tilde{\sigma} n \cdot \sigma) \right]$$

$$+ A_3 \, \Delta m \, Y_3', \quad (13.18)$$

with

$$e = 2A_1 + A_2, \quad \mu = -\tfrac{1}{2} A_1.$$

The μ-term is nonanalytic in the masses, so that the only term analytic in the masses is the electric coupling

$$y_e = e \left(\varepsilon \cdot \sigma + \frac{k_2 \cdot \sigma}{m_2} \varepsilon \cdot \tilde{\sigma} \frac{k_1 \cdot \sigma}{m_1} \right). \quad (13.21)$$

This may be the formulation of *minimal electromagnetic coupling* in the *S*-matrix theory.

If masses are unequal we have anyway a single amplitude. Thus reactions like $\mu \to e + \gamma$, $\Lambda \to n + \gamma$, $\Sigma^0 \to \Lambda + \gamma$, $\Sigma^+ \to p + \gamma$ are described by the single amplitude, Eq. (13.21), and conserve parity.

C. $\langle 1 \ 1 \ 0 \rangle$: The independent tensors formed out of the momenta of the spin 1 particles, k_1 and k_2, are

$$k_i^\mu k_j^\nu \quad (i, j = 1, 2), \qquad \varepsilon^{\mu\nu\lambda\rho} k_{1\lambda} k_{2\rho}. \quad (13.22)$$

---

[4] Note that the plus combinations give

$$\left[(n \cdot \sigma \varepsilon \cdot \tilde{\sigma} + \varepsilon \cdot \sigma n \cdot \tilde{\sigma}) \frac{k_1 \cdot \sigma}{m_1} + \frac{k_2 \cdot \sigma}{m_2} (n \cdot \tilde{\sigma} \varepsilon \cdot \sigma + \varepsilon \cdot \tilde{\sigma} n \cdot \sigma) \right] = 2 \left(\frac{k_1}{m_1} + \frac{k_2}{m_2} \right) \cdot \sigma n \cdot \varepsilon.$$

In these and other calculations we make use of the relations

$$\sigma^\mu \tilde{\sigma}^\nu + \sigma^\nu \tilde{\sigma}^\mu = 2g^{\mu\nu},$$

$$\sigma^\mu \tilde{\sigma}^\lambda \sigma^\nu = i\varepsilon^{\rho\mu\lambda\nu} \sigma_\rho + \sigma^\mu g^{\lambda\nu} - \sigma^\lambda g^{\mu\nu} + \sigma^\nu g^{\lambda\mu}; \quad (13.19)$$

hence

$$a \cdot \sigma b \cdot \tilde{\sigma} c \cdot \sigma = i[a \ b \ c] + (b \cdot c)a \cdot \sigma - (a \cdot c)b \cdot \sigma + (a \cdot b)c \cdot \sigma,$$

$$b \cdot \sigma a \cdot \tilde{\sigma} c \cdot \sigma = 2(a \cdot b)c \cdot \sigma - a \cdot \sigma b \cdot \tilde{\sigma} c \cdot \sigma. \quad (13.20)$$

Hence the spinorial amplitude is given by

$$M = A_1 k_1 \cdot \varepsilon_2 k_2 \cdot \varepsilon_1 + A_2 \varepsilon_1 \cdot \varepsilon_2 + A_3 \varepsilon_{\mu\nu\lambda\rho} k_1^\lambda k_2^\rho \varepsilon_1^\mu \varepsilon_2^\nu. \tag{13.24}$$

The last term is gauge-invariant and has opposite parity relative to the first two terms. The masslessness condition, Eq. (13.12), then gives, if one or both of the spin 1 particles is a photon (e.g., $\rho \to \pi\gamma$, $\omega \to \pi\gamma$; $\pi^0 \to 2\gamma$, $\eta \to 2\gamma$),

$$A_2 = -(k_1 \cdot k_2) A_1.$$

Thus

$$M = A_1 [k_1 \cdot \varepsilon_2 k_2 \cdot \varepsilon_1 - (k_1 \cdot k_2) \varepsilon_1 \cdot \varepsilon_2]. \tag{13.25}$$

If parity is not conserved we have to add the third term in Eq. (13.24). Note that under parity $\varepsilon_\mu(k)$, given by Eq. (13.6). transforms into

$$\varepsilon_n^{\mu(P)}(k) = \frac{1}{\sqrt{2}} [\tfrac{1}{2} \tfrac{1}{2} 1]_n^{\alpha\beta} (\bar\sigma^\mu k \cdot \sigma C)_{\alpha\beta}.$$

D. $\langle 1\ 1\ 1 \rangle$: We now have

$$M = \sum_i A_i t_{\mu\nu\lambda}^i \varepsilon_1^\mu \varepsilon_2^\nu \varepsilon_3^\lambda. \tag{13.26}$$

The independent tensors $t_{\mu\nu\lambda}^i$ formed out of k_1 and k_2 are

$$k_i^\mu k_j^\nu k_\ell^\lambda \quad (i, j, \ell = 1, 2); \quad g^{\mu\nu} k_i^\lambda, \quad g^{\mu\lambda} k_i^\nu, \quad g^{\nu\lambda} k_i^\mu; \quad \varepsilon_{\mu\nu\lambda\rho} k_i^\rho. \tag{13.27}$$

Under parity conservation we then obtain the four amplitudes (*Note:* $k_1 \cdot \varepsilon_3 = -k_2 \cdot \varepsilon_3$):

$$M = A_1 k_1 \cdot \varepsilon_2 k_2 \cdot \varepsilon_1 k_1 \cdot \varepsilon_3 + A_2 \varepsilon_1 \cdot \varepsilon_2 k_1 \cdot \varepsilon_3$$
$$+ A_3 \varepsilon_1 \cdot \varepsilon_3 k_1 \cdot \varepsilon_2 + A_4 \varepsilon_2 \cdot \varepsilon_3 k_2 \cdot \varepsilon_1. \tag{13.28}$$

If two of the particles are massless, the condition, Eq. (13.12), on particles 1 and 2 gives

$$A_1 (k_1 \cdot k_2) + A_2 + A_3 = A_4. \tag{13.25}$$

The remaining three amplitudes may be further reduced if Bose statistics are used for the two photons. The terms A_1 and A_2 in Eq. (13.28) are antisymmetric under the interchange $(k_1 \varepsilon_1) \leftrightarrow (k_2 \varepsilon_2)$. The decay of spin 1 particles into two photons has been first considered by Landau and Yang.[5]

13.4 Soft Photons and Cluster Decomposition of the *S*-Matrix

The *S*-matrix is defined between the asymptotic free-particle states which belong to direct products of unitary irreducible representations of the inhomogeneous Lorentz group. In the case of short-range interactions, such states of irreducible representations are indeed realized in experiments. For long-range interactions one does not have really irreducible representations in the initial and final states, because charged particles are accompanied

[5] L. Landau, *Doklady*, **60**, 207 (1948); C. N. Yang, *Phys. Rev.*, **77**, 242 (1950).

always by photons. Thus in the case of scattering of charged particles we have to use in the initial and final states products of reducible representations of massive and massless particles (soft photons). This leads us to consider, from the beginning, larger S-matrix elements. In the example of Fig. 13.2 we assume,

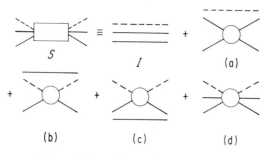

Figure 13.2   Cluster decomposition.

for simplicity, a single soft photon and separate from the S-matrix the disconnected parts.

In Fig. 13.2, a straight line indicates an energy-momentum δ-function factor in the corresponding amplitude. The part (d) represents the connected part of the amplitude. Thus, all the terms (a), (b), (c), and (d) must be separately evaluated. In the next section we explicitly carry an approximation method in which every amplitude occurring in the unitarity equation is approximated by its "pole" terms in all channels. We assume thereby that e^2 is small and collect all terms in Fig. 13.2 that are of the same order in e^2. We do this to show the connection with the renormalized perturbation theory.

In the lowest order we get a contribution from (a), Fig. 13.2, and we shall write the unitarity for the connected part of (a) in the next section. The connected parts of (b) and (c) may at first be neglected because of the very small momenta of the soft photons. Hence the lowest-order term is essentially the pole terms of (a). The higher-order terms of (a) must now be combined with the terms of the same order in (b), (c), and (d). It is interesting that unitarity condition for (a) alone, in the higher orders, would give divergent results (Sec. 13.7) and that the cluster expansion of Fig. 13.2 is essential to obtain finite results. This so-called infrared problem occurs, of course, almost in the same form in field theory.

If the initial charged particles are well prepared and if one considers scattering from neutral targets, then soft photons only in the final states need to be considered—namely, those in the range of experimental detection of charged particles: energy range ΔE and solid-angle range $\Delta \Omega$.[6]

[6] For a recent discussion of infrared corrections see, e.g., D. R. Yennie, S. C. Frautschi and H. Suura, *Ann. Phys.*, **13**, 379 (1961).

13.5　Successive Pole Approximation

In this section we discuss how unitarity and analyticity are used to evaluate the scattering amplitude. If we write the S-matrix as

$$S = I + R = I + i(2\pi)^4 \delta(P_f - P_i)G,$$

then the unitarity condition is given by

$$G_{fi} - G_{fi}^\dagger = i \sum_j G_{fj} G_{ji}^\dagger (2\pi)^4 \delta(P_f - P_i). \tag{13.29}$$

The sum over states will be taken to be

$$\sum_{\text{states of } j} = \sum_{\text{spins}} \int \frac{dk_j}{(2\pi)^4} 4\pi \delta(k_j^2 - m_j^2)\theta(k_j^0).$$

As we have explained in Sec. 8.1, this equation will be used as an analytic equation even below threshold where we pick up the analytically continued processes. We shall show that in quantum electrodynamics it is a very good approximation to consider only the one-particle states in Eq. (13.22) and their iterations. At least this is sufficient to reproduce the results of renormalized perturbation theory. It is, of course, also possible to treat the two- and higher-particle states differently from the perturbation theory.

We shall introduce the analyticity assumptions—i.e., the nature of singularities in the complex planes of the variables, to every order of unitarity as we go along.

It is best to illustrate the procedure in terms of an example; it can easily be applied to any other case.

Example: Compton Scattering of a Fermion[7].　Let k_1 and k_3 be the momenta of the fermions f and f', and (k_2, ε_2), (k_4, ε_4) the momenta and the polarization vectors of the photons. There are, in general, four related antiparticle processes: s-channel[8]: $f\gamma \to f'\gamma$ t-channel: $ff' \to \gamma\gamma$: u-channel: $f\gamma \to f\gamma$, and the decay channel $f' \to f + \gamma + \gamma$. (Note that a reaction like $\mu \to e + \gamma + \gamma$ is not forbidden by Lorentz invariance, but by an additional quantum number, the μ-ness quantum number.)

There are 36 amplitudes to begin with, starting with massive vector particles, but this number reduces to six under Eqs. (13.7) and (13.12), plus the parity and time-reversal invariance. One could write down these amplitudes. It is however most convenient to choose the basis functions Y_i in such a way that the unitarity condition is diagonalized, at least for one-particle states in all channels. We therefore let the unitarity condition choose the basis functions. The physical regions of the three scattering channels in the

[7] We follow here essentially A. O. Barut and R. Blade, *Nuovo Cimento*, **39**, 331 (1965).

[8] We use the standard variables $s = (k_1 + k_2)^2$, $t = (k_1 - k_3)^2$, $u = (k_1 - k_4)^2$, with $s + t + u = \sum m_i^2$.

variables s, t, u (for equal masses of the fermions) and, diagrammatically, the three unitarity conditions are shown in Figs. 13.3 and 13.4:

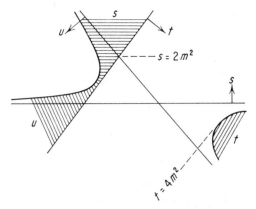

Figure 13.3   Compton scattering: physical regions.

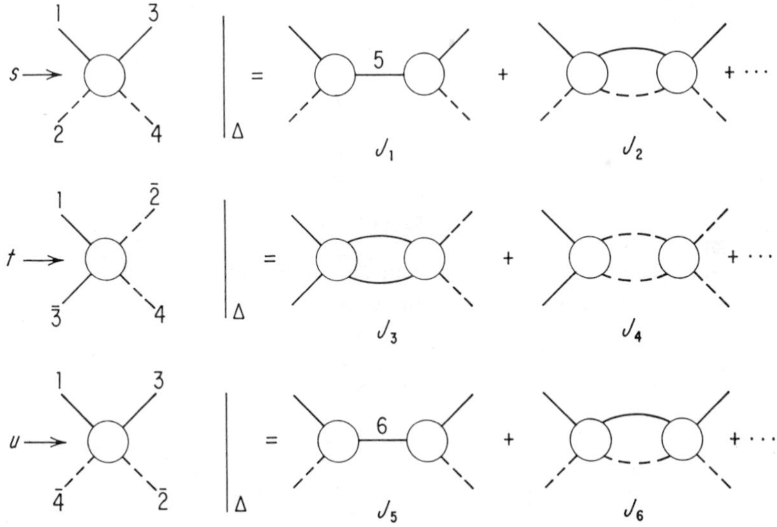

Figure 13.4   Compton scattering: unitarity in three crossed channels.

Because we are primarily interested in reproducing the field theory results here we shall use on the right-hand side of the unitarity equation the minimal coupling, Eq. (13.21). Even without a fundamental principle of minimal coupling we would be justified to take the e-term alone on the right-hand side of unitarity. This is because the unitarity is a nonlinear equation, and because $\mu \ll e$, we would get terms like $e\mu$ and μ^2, which are lower order than e^2. (See also next Sec. 13.6.)

The contribution of J_1, with Eq. (13.21), is given by

$$\sum_j A_j Y_j - \left(\sum_j A_j Y_j\right)^{\dagger}$$

$$= i \sum_{\text{spins}} \rho_1 y_e^{\dagger} \mathcal{D}^{01} \left(\frac{k_5 \cdot \tilde{\sigma}}{m_5}\right) y_e$$

$$= i\rho_1 |e|^2 \left[\left(\varepsilon_4 \cdot \sigma + \frac{k_3 \cdot \sigma}{m_3} \varepsilon \cdot \tilde{\sigma} \frac{k_5 \cdot \sigma}{m_5}\right) \frac{k_5 \cdot \tilde{\sigma}}{m_5}\right.$$

$$\left. \times \left(\varepsilon_2 \cdot \sigma + \frac{k_5 \cdot \sigma}{m_5} \varepsilon_2 \cdot \tilde{\sigma} \frac{k_1 \cdot \sigma}{m_1}\right)\right],$$

where we can put symmetrically

$$k_5 = \tfrac{1}{2}(k_1 + k_2 + k_3 + k_4).$$

We now choose the basis Y_1 to be just the term in the square bracket in Eq. (13.29). This term has positive parity[9] and satisfies

$$Y_1^{\dagger} = Y_1. \tag{13.30}$$

Consequently the term J_1 contributes only to the amplitude A_1, so defined, and we have immediately

$$A_1 - A_1^* = i\rho_1 |e|^2 = i4\pi |e|^2 \delta(s - m_5^2),$$

$$A_j - A_j^* = 0, \quad j \neq 1, \tag{13.31}$$

where we have used the one-particle phase-space factor

$$\rho_1 = 4\pi \delta(s - m^2). \tag{13.32}$$

In exactly the same way, the term J_5, in the unitarity equation of the u-channel, leads to a second basis function:

$$Y_2 = \left[\varepsilon_2 \cdot \sigma k_6 \cdot \tilde{\sigma} \varepsilon_4 \cdot \sigma + \frac{k_3 \cdot \sigma}{m_3} \varepsilon_2 \cdot \tilde{\sigma} \frac{k_6 \cdot \sigma}{m_6} \varepsilon_4 \cdot \tilde{\sigma} \frac{k_1 \cdot \sigma}{m_1}\right.$$

$$\left. + \varepsilon_2 \cdot \sigma \varepsilon_4 \cdot \tilde{\sigma} \frac{k_1 \cdot \sigma_1}{m_1} + \frac{k_3 \cdot \sigma}{m_3} k_2 \cdot \tilde{\sigma} \varepsilon_4 \cdot \sigma\right], \tag{13.33}$$

$$k_6 = \tfrac{1}{2}(k_1 - k_4 + k_3 - k_2),$$

$$Y_2^{\dagger} = Y_2;$$

i.e., Y_2 is obtained from Y_1 by the interchange $\varepsilon_2 \leftrightarrow \varepsilon_4$ and $k_2 \leftrightarrow -k_2$, $k_4 \leftrightarrow -k_4$. [The arguments of ε_2 and ε_4 in Eq. (13.33) are $(-k)$.] Thus, J_5 contributes only to the amplitude A_2 so defined:

$$A_2 - A_2^* = i4\pi |e|^2 \delta(u - m_6^2),$$

$$A_j - A_j^* = 0, \quad j \neq 2. \tag{13.34}$$

---

[9] Note that because unitarity is a nonlinear equation we must use all positive parity terms throughout.

In the t-channel, as well as for the higher-order terms in s- and u-channels, we have again two-particle amplitudes on the right-hand side. We have to write a unitarity condition for these amplitudes as well. It is clear that if these amplitudes themselves are approximated by their one-particle contributions, the results will be of higher order in $|e|^2$. Thus to order $|e|^2$ the terms (13.31) and (13.34) are the only terms.

Now we consider Eqs. (13.31) and (13.34) as analytic equations with only singularities indicated by the right-hand side. It is true that many-particle intermediate states in the unitarity give branch points and other singularities. But the discontinuities of these singularities are of higher order in $|e|^2$ than the one-particle states so that to this order we can neglect these higher singularities. Thus the approximate appropriate analyticity assumptions to order $|e|^2$ can be expressed by the dispersion relations

$$A_i = \frac{1}{\pi} \int_{-\infty}^{+\infty} \frac{Im A_i(s_i') \, ds_i'}{(s_i' - s_i)},$$

$$i = 1, 2, \quad s_1 = s, \quad s_2 = u. \tag{13.35}$$

No subtractions are necessary to this order because $Im A$ is just a δ-function, and we obtain

$$A_i = -\frac{2e^2}{s_i - m_i^2}, \quad i = 1, 2. \tag{13.36}$$

Hence the full amplitude to this order is given by

$$M = -2e^2 \left[\frac{Y_1}{s - m_s^2} + \frac{Y_2}{u - m_u^2} \right]. \tag{13.37}$$

We can now easily pass from this spinorial amplitude to the actual R- or G-amplitudes by Eq. (2.50). Denoting the corresponding basis functions by R_1 and R_2 we have finally

$$G = -2e^2 \left[\frac{R_1}{s - m_s^2} + \frac{R_2}{u - m_u^2} \right],$$

where $\tag{13.38}$

$$R_i = \sqrt{\frac{k_3 \cdot \bar{\sigma}}{m_3}} \, Y_i \sqrt{\frac{k_1 \cdot \bar{\sigma}}{m_1}}, \quad i = 1, 2,$$

with Y_1 and Y_2 given by Eqs. (13.29) and (13.33). Note that in the t-channel G is invariant under the interchange of the two photons: $k_2 \leftrightarrow k_4$; $\varepsilon_2 \leftrightarrow \varepsilon_4$.

The remaining trace calculations are easier to do in the above two-component form rather than in four-component form. But because these calculations already exist in four-component form it is sufficient to give the four-component form of Eq. (13.38). By means of App. 1 we find

$$R_1 = \bar{u}_3(k_3) \varepsilon_4 \cdot \gamma (k_1 \cdot \gamma + k_2 \cdot \gamma + m) \varepsilon_2 \cdot \gamma u_1(k_1),$$

$$R_2 = \bar{u}_3(k_3) \varepsilon_2 \cdot \gamma (k_1 \cdot \gamma - k_4 \cdot \gamma + m) \varepsilon_4 \cdot \gamma u_1(k_1). \tag{13.39}$$

With these, Eq. (13.38) is precisely the field theoretical result.[10] By crossing symmetry, Eq. (13.38) holds for all three channels in their respective physical regions.

Remark: Clearly the spin summation in the unitarity contains only physical polarization states, because the particles are on the mass shell. In particular, for the one-photon intermediate state in $e - e$ scattering, e.g. (Fig. 13.5),

Figure 13.5 Møller scattering: pole contribution.

the two vertex amplitudes are already gauge invariant, then in the unitarity of the M-functions we use the relation

$$\varepsilon_\mu \mathscr{D}^{01}(k \cdot \tilde{\sigma}) \varepsilon_\nu = g_{\mu\nu}. \tag{13.40}$$

Although $\mathscr{D}^{01}$ appears in the spin sum of the intermediate state, only the physical states of the photon contribute. We give here, for further reference, the first-order result for $e - e$ scattering, which can be derived in a similar way[7]:

$$G_{ee \to ee} = -2e^2 \left[\frac{\bar{u}_4 \gamma^\mu u_2 \otimes \bar{u}_3 \gamma_\mu u_1}{t} - \frac{\bar{u}_3 \gamma^\mu u_2 \otimes \bar{u}_4 \gamma_\mu u_1}{u} \right]. \tag{13.41}$$

The relative sign between the two terms is such that G is antisymmetric under the exchange of two identical fermions in s-channel: $G(1 \leftrightarrow 2) = G(3 \leftrightarrow 4) = -G$.

Before we consider higher order scattering terms J_2, J_3, J_4, J_6 in Fig. 13.4 we shall discuss the anomalous magnetic moment of the leptons.

13.6 Anomalous Magnetic Moment of the Leptons

The vertex amplitude, with all the particles on the mass shell, cannot of

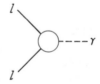

Figure 13.6 Electromagnetic vertex.

[10] See, for example, J. M. Jauch and F. Rohrlich, *The Theory of Electrons and Photons* (Reading, Mass.: Addison-Wesley, 1953), p. 229.

course be realized with real momenta, and there are no variables to write dispersion relations. The magnetic moment of the lepton ℓ is measured by the interaction with an external field or by a scattering experiment. We can represent this complicated interaction (e.g., the external field) by introducing a fictitious spin 0 particle α carrying energy momentum,

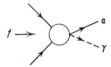

Figure 13.7   Electromagnetic vertex with energy-momentum loss.

Because we are interested in the limiting case, Fig. 13.6, it is a sufficient approximation to couple the sum of the momenta of α and the photon to leptons. This is equivalent to giving the photon a mass.

We therefore need only forward-scattering dispersion relations in t (for $s = 0$) in Fig. 13.7. Both forward-scattering dispersion relation and the dispersion relation for the vertex amplitude in the mass of one of the particles are proved to all order of perturbation theory, whereas dispersion relations in both variables s, t (Mandelstam representation) are at present not proved. We need in our approximations only the forward-scattering dispersion relations.[11]

In Fig. 13.7 we have then one variable t and we can write unitarity and dispersion relations (forward scattering). The unitarity in all three channels is shown in Fig. 13.8.

Now we approximate the two-body amplitudes in L_1, L_2, and L_3 by their pole terms in *all* channels (Fig. 13.9).

In the interesting case of t-channel we find[7]

$$M_3 = -\int \rho_2 \, d\Omega \left[\varepsilon_2 \cdot \sigma + \frac{k_5 \cdot \sigma}{m_5} \, \varepsilon_2 \cdot \tilde{\sigma} \, \frac{k_6 \cdot \sigma}{m_6} \right] \frac{k_6 \cdot \tilde{\sigma}}{m_6} \otimes \frac{k_5 \cdot \tilde{\sigma}}{m_5}$$

$$\times \frac{-2e^2}{m_2^2} \left[\left(\sigma^\mu + \frac{k_6 \cdot \sigma}{m_6} \, \tilde{\sigma}^\mu \, \frac{k_5 \cdot \sigma}{m_5} \right) \otimes \left(\sigma_\mu + \frac{k_3 \cdot \sigma}{m_3} \, \tilde{\sigma}_\mu \, \frac{k_1 \cdot \sigma}{m_1} \right) \right]$$

$$\times (2\pi)^4 \delta(P_{56} - P_{13})$$

$$= 2h(t) \left[\varepsilon_2 \cdot \sigma + \frac{k_3 \cdot \sigma}{m_3} \, \varepsilon_2 \cdot \tilde{\sigma} \, \frac{k_1 \cdot \sigma}{m_1} \right], \tag{13.42}$$

where ρ_2 is the two-body phase space,

$$\rho_2 = \frac{1}{4\pi^2} \frac{1}{2t} \left[(t - (m_5 + m_6)^2)(t - (m_5 - m_6)^2) \right]^{\frac{1}{2}} \tag{13.43}$$

---

[11] In fact if one starts from the dispersion relation for a scattering process (for all s and t) one can derive a dispersion relation for the form factor only if one neglects the crossed channels (see H. P. Stapp, *Phys. Rev.*, **139**, B257 (1965), Part VI).

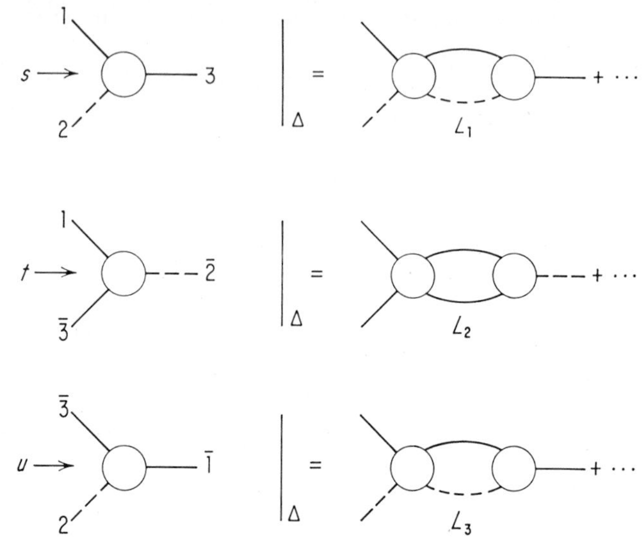

Figure 13.8 Electromagnetic vertex: unitarity in three crossed channels.

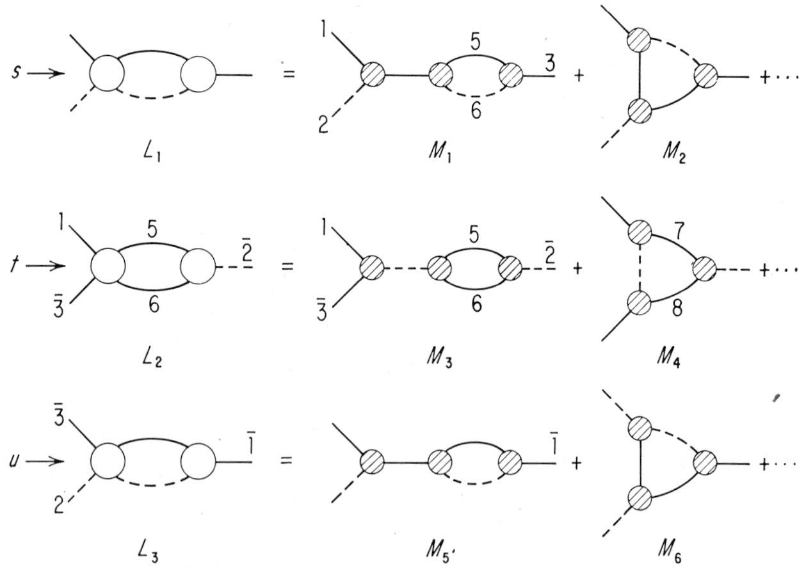

Figure 13.9 Further expansion of unitarity diagrams.

and we have used t-channel Born approximation to Møller scattering given in Eq. (13.41) and the relation (13.40). Similarly,

$$M_4 = -\int \rho_2 \, d\Omega \, e\left(\varepsilon_2 \cdot \sigma + \frac{k_7 \cdot \sigma}{m_7} \varepsilon_2 \cdot \tilde{\sigma} \frac{k_8 \cdot \sigma}{m_8}\right) \frac{k_8 \cdot \tilde{\sigma}}{m_8} \otimes \frac{k_7 \cdot \tilde{\sigma}}{m_7}$$

$$\times \frac{2e^2}{(k_7 - k_8)^2} \left(\sigma^\mu + \frac{k_3 \cdot \sigma}{m_3} \tilde{\sigma}^\mu \frac{k_7 \cdot \sigma}{m_7}\right) \otimes \left(\sigma_\mu + \frac{k_8 \cdot \sigma}{m_8} \tilde{\sigma}_\mu \frac{k_1 \cdot \sigma}{m_1}\right)$$

$$\times (2\pi)^4 \delta(P_{78} - P_{15})$$

$$= 2f_1(t)\left[\varepsilon_2 \cdot \sigma + \frac{k_3 \cdot \sigma}{m_3} \varepsilon_2 \cdot \tilde{\sigma} \frac{k_1 \cdot \sigma}{m_1}\right]$$

$$+ 2f_2(t)\left[\left(\frac{k_1}{m_1} + \frac{k_3}{m_3}\right) \cdot \sigma(k_1 + k_3) \cdot \varepsilon\right]. \quad (13.44)$$

Integrals of this type have been already evaluated by Källen[12] and we find

$$h(t) = \text{const.} \sqrt{1 - \frac{4m^2}{t}} \left(1 + \frac{2m^2}{t}\right) \theta(t - 4m^2) \xrightarrow[|t| \to \infty]{} \text{const.}$$

$$f_1(t) = \text{const.} \left[\frac{3}{2}\left(1 - \frac{4m^2}{t}\right) - \left(1 - \frac{2m^2}{t}\right)\right]$$

$$\times \ln\left(1 + \frac{t - 4m^2}{\lambda}\right) \frac{\theta(t - 4m^2)}{\sqrt{1 - \frac{4m^2}{t}}} \xrightarrow[|t| \to \infty]{} \ln|t|$$

$$f_2(t) = \frac{e^2}{4\pi} \left[\frac{m^2}{t} \frac{\theta(t - 4m^2)}{\sqrt{1 - \frac{4m^2}{t}}}\right] \xrightarrow[|t| \to \infty]{} 0. \quad (13.45)$$

It is seen from Eq. (13.44) that only $f_2(t)$ generates a magnetic moment term, if we start with a minimal coupling in the right-hand side of Fig. 13.9. And it is the asymptotic behavior

$$f_2(t) \xrightarrow[|t| \to \infty]{} 0$$

that allows us to calculate μ; whereas due to the logarithmic and constant asymptotic behavior of $h(t)$ and $f_1(t)$ we cannot calculate the electric coupling constant e, as we shall see. In the integration of $f_1(t)$ we have taken the lower limit of integration to be λ to avoid infrared divergences; $f_2(t)$ is free of infrared terms.

Now we write dispersion relations for the amplitude $G(t)$ and because of the asymptotic behavior of $h(t)$ and $f_1(t)$ we must use one subtraction in these terms, whereas $f_2(t)$ term does not need any subtraction:

$$G(t) = \left\{\frac{t}{\pi} \int_{-\infty}^{\infty} \frac{dt'}{t'(t' - t)} [h(t') + f_1(t') + 2f_2(t')] + [h(0) + f_1(0) + 2f_2(0)]\right\}$$

$$\times y_e(K) + \frac{1}{\pi} \int_{-\infty}^{\infty} \frac{dt'}{t' - t} f_2(t') y_\mu(K), \quad (13.46)$$

[12] G. A. O. Källen, in *Elementary Particle Physics and Field Theory*, K. W. Ford, editor, (W. A. Benjamin, New York, 1961), and references therein.

where the spinor functions $y_e(K)$ and $y_\mu(K)$ are those given in Eq. (13.18). For $t = 0$, Eqs. (13.46) and (13.18) must coincide; hence, with $\Delta m = 0$,

$$h(0) + f_1(0) + 2f_2(0) = e \qquad (13.47)$$

and

$$\frac{1}{\pi} \int_{-\infty}^{\infty} \frac{dt'}{t'} f_2(t') = \mu(2m\pi) \qquad (13.48)$$

or

$$\mu = \frac{2}{\pi} \int_{4m^2}^{\infty} \frac{e^3 m}{16\pi} \frac{dt'}{\sqrt{t'(t' - 4m^2)}} = \frac{e^3}{16\pi^2 m}, \qquad (13.49)$$

which is the known lowest-order value of the anomalous magnetic moment.

13.7   Higher-Order Terms and Relation to Feynman Graphs

To evaluate the second-order corrections J_2, J_3, and J_6 to Compton scattering shown in Fig. 13.4, we approximate the amplitudes in these terms by their lowest-order terms in all channels. We have thus the situation shown in Fig. 13.10.

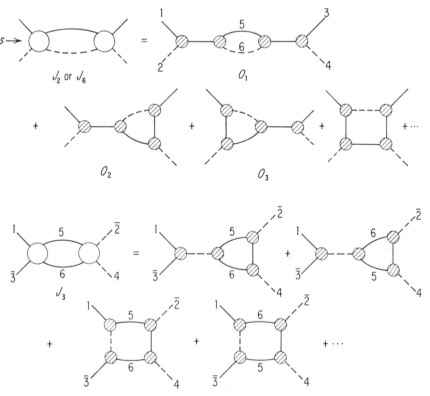

Figure 13.10   Higher order unitarity diagrams to Compton scattering.

For comparison, the Feynman diagrams corresponding to 0_1-0_4 are shown in Fig. 13.11.

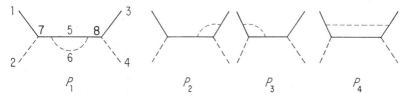

Figure 13.11 Feynman diagrams corresponding to Fig. 13.10.

The relation of the perturbation terms to the unitarity diagrams is the following. In Fig. 13.10 we calculate the contribution of terms $0_1, \ldots,$ to the imaginary part of the amplitude. In Fig. 13.10, we calculate the contribution of $P_1, \ldots,$ to the full amplitude. It will be shown that the imaginary part of the Feynman diagram, say for P_1, is equal to the contribution of 0_1, and so on. The contribution of P_1 is infinite by the renormalization terms and can be "renormalized" by evaluating its imaginary part and recovering its real part through the dispersion integral, which is precisely the prescription of the S-matrix theory from the beginning. The contribution of 0_1 (Fig. 13.10) is given by (in four-component form, for comparison)

$$0_1 = i \sum_{\substack{\text{spins} \\ 5,6}} \int \frac{d^4k_5}{(2\pi)^4} \frac{d^4k_6}{(2\pi)^4} (4\pi)^2 \delta(k_5^2 - m_5^2) \theta(k_5^0) \delta(k_6^2) \theta(k_6^0)$$

$$\times \left[-2e^2 \bar{u}_3 \varepsilon_4 \frac{(P_{12} + m)}{s - m^2} \varepsilon_6 u_5 \right] \left[-2e^2 \bar{u}_5 \varepsilon_6 \frac{(P_{12} + m)}{s - m^2} \varepsilon_2 u_1 \right]$$

$$\times (2\pi)^4 \delta(P_{56} - P_{12}). \tag{13.50}$$

The corresponding Feynman amplitude (Fig. 13.11) is

$$P_1 = i(\text{const.}) \sum \int \frac{dk_5}{k_5^2 - m^2 - i\varepsilon_5} \frac{dk_6}{k_6^2 - i\varepsilon_6} \frac{dk_7}{k_7^2 - m^2 - i\varepsilon_7} \frac{dk_8}{k_8^2 - m^2 - i\varepsilon_8}$$

$$\times G(8 \to 31) \delta(k_{34} - k_8) G(56 \to 8) \delta(k_8 - k_{56}) G(7 \to 56)$$

$$\times \delta(k_{56} - k_7) G(12 \to 7) \delta(k_7 - k_{12}). \tag{13.51}$$

We can take the imaginary part of Eq. (13.51) by the rule

$$\frac{1}{k_j^2 - m_j^2 - i\varepsilon_j} = P \frac{1}{k_j^2 - m_j^2} + i\pi \delta(k_j^2 - m_j^2). \tag{13.52}$$

It is seen then that the integrals involving the principal parts vanish; the cross terms also vanish for any $s = k_{12} \geqslant m^2 + \lambda^2$. The resulting imaginary part is equivalent to 0_1, except for $\delta(k_{34} - k_{12})$ [which is due to the fact that P_1 is actually $G\delta(k_{34} - k_{12})$] and for $\theta(k_5^0)\theta(k_6^0)$ in 0_1. These θ-functions serve to eliminate the poles in the unphysical sheets of the s-plane.

In general there are more Feynman diagrams than unitarity diagrams. Those Feynman diagrams that have no corresponding unitarity diagrams contribute only to renormalization constants, which are of course absent in *S*-matrix theory.

13.8   On the Derivation of Charge Conservation

As we have seen, the condition of masslessness considerably restricts the form of the amplitude. As a further application we consider a process involving n spinless particles and a photon of momentum k. The spinorial amplitude can be written as

$$M = \sum_i A_i(s, t, \ldots) k_i^\mu \varepsilon_\mu. \tag{13.53}$$

The gauge condition implies

$$\sum_i A_i(s, t, \ldots) k_i^\mu k_\mu = 0. \tag{13.54}$$

Let us draw all particles as ingoing; the conservation of momenta,

$$k + \sum k_j = 0,$$

gives

$$\sum_{j=1}^n k_j^\mu k_\mu = 0. \tag{13.55}$$

If we introduce new form factors $E_i(s, t, \ldots)$ defined by

$$E_i = A_i(s, t, \ldots)(k_i \cdot k), \tag{13.56}$$

then Eq. (13.54) gives immediately

$$\sum_{i=1}^n E_i(s, t, \ldots) = 0. \tag{13.57}$$

Thus the form factors E_i so introduced satisfy a conservation law. If we go to crossed channels by changing some k_j into $-k_j$, then it follows from Eqs. (13.54) through (13.56) that E_j must change signs as well; i.e., these form factors behave like additive quantum numbers; they have opposite signs for antiparticles. The amplitude now has the form

$$M = \sum_{i=1}^n E_i(s, t, \ldots) \frac{k_i \cdot \varepsilon}{k_i \cdot k}. \tag{13.58}$$

Because there is only *one* unknown transition amplitude under the proper Lorentz group, Eq. (13.58) is of the form

$$M = E(s, t, \ldots) \sum_{i=1}^n \eta_j \frac{k_i \cdot \varepsilon}{k_i \cdot k} \tag{13.59}$$

with constants η_i such that

$$\sum_{j=1}^{n} \eta_j = 0. \tag{13.60}$$

Clearly there are many ways of introducing form factors. The form factors E_i have been so introduced that they go in the limit $k \to 0$ (soft photon) to the charge coupling constant e_i. For if we approximate for $k \to 0$ the amplitude we are considering as a sum of pole terms (Fig. 13.12), we have

$$M \simeq \sum_i e_i \frac{k_i \cdot \varepsilon}{(k + k_i)^2 - m_i^2} = \sum_i e_i \frac{k_i \cdot \varepsilon}{2k \cdot k_i}, \tag{13.61}$$

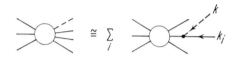

Figure 13.12 Soft photon emission.

which is the same as Eqs. (13.58) or (13.59) for constant form factors. Thus the approximation indicated in Fig. 13.12 implies charge conservation.[13]

Problems and Further Developments

1. Calculate the electron-proton scattering cross section with one photon approximation in the unitarity in the t-channel, including the two form factors for the $pp\gamma$-vertex (Rosenbluth formula).
2. Same problem with electron form factors as well.
3. Calculate lowest-order meson contributions to nucleon form factors.
4. Evaluate Y_3 in Eq. (13.16).
5. Calculate the anomalous magnetic moment of the electron if minimal electromagnetic coupling does not hold.
6. Show that minimal electromagnetic coupling plus PC-invariance implies P- and C-invariance separately.
7. Calculate the decay process: $\mu \to e + \gamma$, $\Sigma \to \Lambda + \gamma$.
8. Show that in the process $\eta \to \pi^0 + e^+ + e^-$, there is no contribution of one photon state to the unitarity in the e^+e^--channel.

[13] The derivation based on the pole approximation of Fig. 13.12 was first given by S. Weinberg, *Phys. Rev. Letters*, **9**, 357 (1964). For the derivation of the conservation of form factors, Eq. (3.57), see A. O. Barut, *Phys. Rev. Letters*, **10**, 356 (1964).

CHAPTER 14

On Gravitational Interactions

We discuss in this chapter some consequences of the interaction of a massless particle of spin 2 (and higher). We deviate from the general relativity insofar as the particles interacting via the graviton are assumed to have definite spin and mass, i.e., are defined again by the unitary representations of the Lorentz group.

14.1 Spin-2 Irreducible Polarization Tensor

A spin-2 massless particle of momentum k is described by the symmetric *polarization tensor*

$$\rho_m^{\mu\nu}(k) = [112]_m^{\alpha\beta}\varepsilon_\alpha^\mu(k)\varepsilon_\beta^\nu(k), \tag{14.1}$$

which then transforms according to

$$\mathscr{D}^{02}\rho^{\mu\nu}(\Lambda^{-1}k) = \Lambda_\sigma^\mu\Lambda_\lambda^\nu\rho^{\sigma\lambda}(k). \tag{14.2}$$

The ε^μ's have been given in Eq. (13.6). We have now the restrictions

$$\rho^{\mu\nu}(k)k_\mu = \rho^{\mu\nu}(k)k_\nu = 0 \tag{14.3}$$

and

$$\rho_\mu^\mu(k) = 0. \tag{14.4}$$

The condition of masslessness is expressed again by the invariance of the spinorial amplitudes under the replacement $\varepsilon \to \varepsilon + \lambda k$, for all λ, or by

$$\rho^{\mu\nu} \to \rho^{\mu\nu} + \lambda[112]_m^{\alpha\beta}k^\mu\varepsilon^\nu + \lambda[112]\varepsilon^\nu k^\mu + \lambda^2[112]k^\mu k^\nu, \quad \lambda \text{ arbitrary.} \tag{14.5}$$

14.2 Vertex Amplitudes

Consider first the vertex $\langle 0\ 0\ 2\rangle$ of two spin-0 particles of momenta k_1 and k_2 with $k = k_1 + k_2$. We have for this case the single amplitude

$$M = f(k_1 - k_2)^\mu(k_1 - k_2)^\nu\rho_{\mu\nu}. \tag{14.6}$$

282

Gauge invariance, Eq. (14.5), implies

$$f\{2\lambda(k_1 - k_2)\cdot(k_1 + k_2)[112](k_1 - k_2)\cdot\varepsilon + \lambda^2(k_1^2 - k_2^2)^2[112]\} = 0.$$

Hence

$$f = 0, \quad \text{unless } k_1^2 = k_2^2. \tag{14.7}$$

Thus a spinless particle cannot decay with one graviton emission as in the case of photon.

Next we consider the vertex $\langle\frac{1}{2}\frac{1}{2}2\rangle$. Using the "currents" of definite parity, Eq. (13.15), we have

$$M = A_1\left(\frac{k_1}{m_1} + \frac{k_2}{m_2}\right)\cdot\sigma(k_1 - k_2)^\mu(k_1 - k_2)^\nu\rho_{\mu\nu}$$

$$+ A_2\left(\frac{k_1}{m_1} - \frac{k_2}{m_2}\right)\cdot\sigma(k_1 - k_2)^\mu(k_1 - k_2)^\nu\rho_{\mu\nu}$$

$$+ A_3\left(\sigma^\mu + \frac{k_2\cdot\sigma}{m_2}\tilde{\sigma}^\mu\frac{k_1\cdot\sigma}{m_1}\right)(k_1 - k_2)^\nu\rho_{\mu\nu}$$

$$+ A_4\left(\sigma^\mu - \frac{k_2\cdot\sigma}{m_2}\tilde{\sigma}^\mu\frac{k_1\cdot\sigma}{m_1}\right)(k_1 - k_2)^\nu\rho_{\mu\nu}$$

$$+ A_5\left[\frac{k_2\cdot\sigma}{m_2}(\tilde{\sigma}^\mu\sigma^\nu - \tilde{\sigma}^\nu\sigma^\mu) + (\sigma^\mu\tilde{\sigma}^\nu - \sigma^\nu\tilde{\sigma}^\mu)\frac{k_1\cdot\sigma}{m_1}\right]\rho_{\mu\nu}$$

$$+ A_6\left[\frac{k_2\cdot\sigma}{m_2}(\tilde{\sigma}^\mu\sigma^\nu - \tilde{\sigma}^\nu\sigma^\mu) - (\sigma^\mu\tilde{\sigma}^\nu - \sigma^\nu\tilde{\sigma}^\mu)\frac{k_1\cdot\sigma}{m_1}\right]\rho_{\mu\nu}. \tag{14.8}$$

The three form factors A_1, A_3, A_5 have positive parity, the other three negative parity. It has been pointed out recently [1] that the experimental results so far cannot tell us whether P, C, or T are conserved in gravitational interactions.

14.3 Scattering Amplitudes

We now consider the scattering of two spinless particles via the exchange of a graviton in pole approximation of the unitarity condition. In t-channel the extended unitarity gives the following single-particle contribution:

$$f^2\delta(t)\rho_{\mu\nu}\mathscr{D}^{02}(k\cdot\tilde{\sigma})\rho_{\lambda\sigma}(k_1 - k_3)^\mu(k_1 - k_3)^\nu(k_2 - k_4)^\lambda(k_2 - k_4)^\sigma. \tag{14.9}$$

It follows from Eqs. (14.1) and (13.40) that

$$\rho_{\mu\nu}\mathscr{D}^{02}\rho_{\lambda\sigma} = g_{\mu\lambda}g_{\nu\sigma}.$$

Hence Eq. (4.9) becomes

$$f^2\delta(t)[(k_1 - k_3)\cdot(k_2 - k_4)]^2,$$

[1] J. Leitner and S. Okubo, *Phys. Rev.*, **136**, B1542 (1964); K. Hiida and Y. Yamaguchi, *Suppl. Prog. Theor. Physics*, Commemorative issue for Meson Theory of Yukawa (1965), p. 261.

and, with the same analyticity assumption as in Eq. (13.35), we find

$$R = f^2 \left\{ \frac{[(k_1 - k_3) \cdot (k_2 - k_4)]^2}{t} + \frac{[(k_1 + k_4) \cdot (k_2 + k_3)]^2}{u} \right\}. \quad (14.10)$$

14.4   Universality

Finally we consider the analog considerations leading to the conservation of charge (Sec. 13.8). For a process involving n spinless particles and a graviton of momentum k, we write

$$M = \sum A_i(s, t, \ldots) k_i^\mu k_i^\nu \rho_{\mu\nu}(k). \quad (14.11)$$

The gauge condition (14.5) gives

$$\sum_i A_i(s, t, \ldots)(k_i \cdot k)(k_i \cdot \varepsilon) = 0$$

and

$$\sum_i A_i(s, t, \ldots)(k_i \cdot k)^2 = 0.$$

If we now define new form factors $F_i(s, t, \ldots)$ by

$$F_i(s, t, \ldots) = A_i(s, t, \ldots)(k_i \cdot k) \quad (14.12)$$

we obtain

$$M = \sum F_i(s, t, \ldots) \frac{k_i^\mu k_i^\nu \rho_{\mu\nu}}{k_i \cdot k} \quad (14.13)$$

with

$$\sum_i F_i(k_i \cdot \varepsilon) = 0, \quad \text{and} \quad \sum F_i(k_i \cdot k) = 0. \quad (14.14)$$

These equations must be satisfied together with the momentum conservation equations

$$\sum_i (k_i \cdot k) = 0$$

and

$$\sum_i (k_i \cdot \varepsilon) = 0. \quad (14.15)$$

The solution of these equations is

$$F_i(s, t, \ldots) = F(s, t, \ldots), \quad \text{for all } i. \quad (14.16)$$

On the other hand, Eq. (14.13) is a sum of pole terms as in Fig. 13.12. Thus, if the approximation of Fig. 13.12 holds in the limit $k \to 0$ the single form factor F goes over to the coupling constant f, which is then universal.

In general, if we have a spin j, mass zero particle, the condition (14.14) modifies into

$$\sum F_i(k_i \cdot k)^{j-1} = 0, \quad (14.17)$$

which cannot be satisfied for $j \geqslant 3$, *if* there is a universal coupling constant.

APPENDIX 1

Empirical Properties of Particles and Resonances

We have the following groups of "stable" particles:

Photon: γ

Leptons: $\nu_e, \nu_\mu, \bar{\nu}_e, \bar{\nu}_\mu, e^\pm, \mu^\pm$

Mesons: $\pi^\pm, \pi^0, K^\pm, K^0, \bar{K}^0, \eta$

Baryons: $N(p,n), \bar{N}(\bar{p},\bar{n}), \Lambda_0, \bar{\Lambda}_0, \Sigma^{\pm,0}, \bar{\Sigma}, \Xi^{-,0}, \bar{\Xi}^{-,0}, \Omega^-\bar{\Omega}$

Here $\gamma, \nu_{e,\mu}, e^\pm, p$ are absolutely stable, the rest decay via weak interactions or electromagnetic interactions like

$$\pi^0 \to 2\gamma(2\cdot10^{-16} \text{ sec}), \quad \Sigma^0 \to \Lambda + \gamma(\sim10^{-19} \text{ sec}).$$

In addition we have a whole series of "resonances" decaying via strong interactions ($\sim10^{-23}$ sec). Quantum numbers masses, decay modes, and widths of these particles are given in the following tables. For higher multiplet schemes for the classification of these particles see Sec. 10.4. [See also A. H. Rosenfeld et al., *Rev. Mod. Phys.*, 1967.]

285

Appendix Table 1-1
"Stable" Particles

Particle		$I(J^{PG})C$	Mass, Mev	Mean Life, sec	Decay Modes
Photon	γ	$1^- C^-$	0		Stable
Leptons	$\nu_e \nu_\mu$	$\frac{1}{2}$	$0 \left(\begin{array}{l} <0.2 \text{ Mev} \\ <2.5 \text{ Mev} \end{array}\right)$		Stable
	$e^\pm$	$\frac{1}{2}$	0.511006 ± 0.000002		Stable
	$\mu^\pm$	$\frac{1}{2}$	105.659 ± 0.002	2.200×10^{-6}	$e^+ + \nu + \bar{\nu}$ / $e^- + \nu + \bar{\nu}$
	$\pi^\pm$	$1(0^{--})C^+$	139.580 ± 0.015	2.55×10^{-8}	$\mu^\pm + \nu_2; (e^\pm + \nu_1)$
	π^0		134.974 ± 0.015	$1.78 \times 10^{-16} \pm 0.26$	$2\gamma, e^+e^-\gamma, (e^+e^-, 2e^+2e^-)$
Mesons	$K^\pm$	$\frac{1}{2}(0^-)$	493.78 ± 0.17	$1.224 \times 10^{-8} \pm 0.008$	$\mu + \nu, 2\pi, 3\pi, e\nu, \mu(e)\pi^0\nu$
	K^0	$\frac{1}{2}(0^-)$	497.7 ± 0.3	$K^0: 50\% K_1, 50\% K_2$	
	K_1 K_2		$\Delta m = -0.91 \frac{1}{\tau_1}$	$K_1: 0.881 \times 10^{-10}$ / $K_2: 5.77 \times 10^{-8}$	$\pi^+\pi^-, \pi^0\pi^0$ / $3\pi, \mu\pi\nu, e\pi\nu$
	η	$0(0^{-+})C^+$	548.8 ± 0.5	$\Gamma < 10$ Bev	$\gamma\gamma, 3\pi^0, \pi^0 2\gamma, \pi^+\pi^-\pi^0$
	$\eta'(X_0)$	$0(0^{-+})C^+$	958.6 ± 1.6	$\Gamma < 4$ Bev	$\eta 2\pi(76\%), \pi^+\pi^-\gamma(24\%)$

Appendix Table 1-1 (Continued)
"Stable" Particles

Particle	$I(J^{PG})C$	Mass, Mev	Mean Life, sec	Decay Modes
p	$\frac{1}{2}(\frac{1}{2}^+)$	938.256 ± 0.005	—	Stable
n	$\frac{1}{2}(\frac{1}{2}^+)$	939.550 ± 0.005	1.01×10^3	$p + e^- + \bar{\nu}$
Λ	$0(\frac{1}{2}^+)$	1115.44 ± 0.12	2.53×10^{-10}	$p\pi^-,\ n\pi^0$
Σ^+	$1(\frac{1}{2}^+)$	1189.39 ± 0.14	0.794×10^{-10}	$p\pi^0,\ n\pi^+$
Σ^-	$1(\frac{1}{2}^+)$	1197.20 ± 0.14	1.58×10^{-10}	$n\pi^-$
Σ^0	$1(\frac{1}{2}^+)$	1192.3 ± 0.2	$<1.0 \times 10^{-14}$	$\Lambda^0 + \gamma$
Ξ^-	$\frac{1}{2}(\frac{1}{2}?)$	1320.8 ± 0.2	1.75×10^{-10}	$\Lambda^0\pi^-$
Ξ^0	$\frac{1}{2}(\frac{1}{2}?)$	1314.3 ± 1.0	3.05×10^{-10}	$\Lambda^0\pi^0$
Ω^-	$0(\frac{3}{2}?)$	1675 ± 3.0	1.3×10^{-10}	$\Xi\pi,\ \Lambda\bar{K}$

Baryons

Nuclei and Hyperfragments, etc.				
d	$0(1\ \ )$	1875.46		Stable

Appendix Table 1–2
Meson Resonances (August 1966)

	Particle	$I(J^{PG})C$	Mass, Mev	Width, Mev	Decay Modes
Vector mesons	ρ	$1(1^{-+})C-$	765 ± 3	124 ± 4	2π(100%); very small 4π, πγ
	K^*	$\frac{1}{2}(1^-)$	891.4 ± 0.8	49 ± 2	Kπ(100%)
	ω	$0(1^{--})C-$	782.8 ± 0.5	12 ± 1.7	$\pi^+\pi^-\pi^0$(88%), neutrals (10%)
	ϕ	$0(1^{--})C-$	1019.5 ± 0.3	3.3 ± 0.6	$K_1 K_2$(30%), K^+K^-(30%), πρ, πππ(32%)
Axial vector mesons	D	$0(1^{++})C+$	1286 ± 6	40 ± 10	$K\bar{K}\pi$
	A_1	$1(1^{+-})C+$?	1072 ± 8	125	ρπ(100%)
	K^*	$\frac{1}{2}(1^+)$?	1215 ± 15	60 ± 10	$K\rho, K^*\pi$
	E	$0(1^+)$?	1420 ± 10	60 ± 10	$K^*\bar{K}, K\bar{K}\pi$ (possible spin 0)
	B	$1(1^+)$?	1220		πω
	H	$0(1^+)$?	1000		πρ
Spin 2+ mesons	f	$0(2^{++})C+$	1253 ± 20	118 ± 16	ππ, 4π(<4%), $\bar{K}K$(<4%)
	f'	$0(2^{++})C+$	1500	80	$K_1K_2, K\bar{K}^*$
	A_2	$1(2^{+-})C+$	1324 ± 9	90 ± 10	ρπ, $\bar{K}K$, ηπ
	K^*	$\frac{1}{2}(2^+)$	1405 ± 8	95 ± 11	Kπ
Possible 0+ mesons	S^0	$0(0^+)$?	720		
	$K\bar{K}$	$1(0^+)$?	1003		
	$\mathscr{H}$	$\frac{1}{2}(0^+)$?	725	<12	Kπ
	S^*	$0(0^+)$?	1068		K_1K_1
Possible other and higher spin mesons	R		1691 ± 30		
	S		1929 ± 14		
	T		2195 ± 15		
	U		2382 ± 24		

Appendix Table 1–3
Baryon Resonances (August 1966)

	Particle	$I(J^P)$	Mass, Mev	Width, Mev	Decay Modes
Spin $\frac{1}{2}^+$	$N^*_{\frac{1}{2}}$	$\frac{1}{2}(\frac{1}{2}^+)$	1400	200	πN
Spin $\frac{3}{2}^+$	$N^*_{\frac{3}{2}}$	$\frac{3}{2}(\frac{3}{2}^+)$	1236 ± 0.4	120 ± 1.5	$\pi N(100\%)$
	Y^*_1	$1(\frac{3}{2}^+)$	1382.7 ± 0.5	44 ± 2	$\Lambda\pi(90\%), \Sigma\pi(10\%)$
	Ξ^*	$\frac{1}{2}(\frac{3}{2}^+)$	1529.7 ± 0.9	7.5 ± 1.7	$\Xi\pi(100\%)$
	Ω^-	$0(\frac{3}{2}^+)$	1675 ± 3	(1.3×10^{-10})	$\Xi\pi, \Lambda\bar{K}$
Spin $\frac{1}{2}^-$	$N^*_{\frac{1}{2}}$	$\frac{1}{2}(\frac{1}{2}^-)$	1570	130	πN
	$N^*_{\frac{1}{2}}$	$\frac{1}{2}(\frac{1}{2}^-)$	1700	240	πN
	Y^*_0	$0(\frac{1}{2}^-)$	1405	35 ± 5	$\Sigma\pi(100\%) \cdot [K_{\bar{p}}$ bound state]
	$N^*_{\frac{3}{2}}$	$\frac{3}{2}(\frac{1}{2}^-)$	1670	180	πN
Spin $\frac{3}{2}^-$	$N^*_{\frac{1}{2}}$	$\frac{1}{2}(\frac{3}{2}^-)$	1518 ± 10	120	$\pi N(75\%), N\pi\pi$
	Y^*_0	$0(\frac{3}{2}^-)$	1518.9 ± 1.5	16 ± 2	$\Sigma\pi(55\%), \bar{K}N(29), \Lambda\pi\pi(16)$
	Y^*_1	$1(\frac{3}{2}^-?)$	1660 ± 10	44 ± 5	$\bar{K}N, \Sigma\pi, \Lambda\pi, \Sigma\pi\pi, \Lambda\pi\pi$
	Ξ^*	$\frac{1}{2}(\frac{3}{2}^-)$	1816 ± 3	16 ± 1	$\Xi^*\pi(25\%), \Lambda\bar{K}(65\%)$
Spin $\frac{5}{2}^+$	$N^*_{\frac{1}{2}}$	$\frac{1}{2}(\frac{5}{2}^+)$	1688	100	$\pi N(85\%), \pi\pi N, \eta N, \Lambda K$
	Y^*_0	$0(\frac{5}{2}^+)$	1815 ± 5	50	$\bar{K}N(75\%), \Lambda\pi\pi(15), \Sigma\pi, \Lambda\eta$
	Ξ^*	$\frac{1}{2}(\frac{5}{2}^+)$	1933 ± 16	140 ± 15	$\Xi\pi$
	$\cdots$	$\cdots$			
Spin $\frac{7}{2}^+$	$N^*_{\frac{3}{2}}$	$\frac{3}{2}(\frac{7}{2}^+)$	1924	~ 200	πN
	Y^*_1	$1(\frac{7}{2}^+)$	2050	~ 160	$\bar{K}n, \Lambda\pi$

Appendix Table 1-3 (Continued)
Baryon Resonances (January 1966)

PARTICLE	$I(J^P)$	MASS, Mev	WIDTH, Mev	DECAY MODES
SPIN $\frac{5}{2}^-$				
$\left\{ N^*_{\frac{1}{2}} \right.$	$\frac{1}{2}(\frac{5}{2}^-)$	1688	100	$\pi N,\ \Lambda K$
$\left. Y^*_1 \right.$	$1(\frac{5}{2}^-)$	1762 ± 17	75 ± 7	$\bar{K}N(60\%),\ \Lambda\pi(16\%),\ Y^*\pi$
$\vdots$		$\vdots$		
SPIN $\frac{7}{2}^-$				
$N^*_{\frac{1}{2}}$	$\frac{1}{2}(\frac{7}{2}^-)$?	2190	~ 200	$\pi N,\ \eta N$
$\vdots$		$\vdots$		
SPIN $\frac{9}{2}^-$				
$N^*_{\frac{3}{2}}$	$\frac{3}{2}(\frac{9}{2}^-)$?	2360	~ 200	πN
$\vdots$		$\vdots$		
SPIN $\frac{9}{2}^+$				
$N^*_{\frac{1}{2}}$	$\frac{1}{2}(\frac{9}{2}^+)$?	2645 ± 10	~ 200	$\pi N,\ \eta N$
$\vdots$		$\vdots$		
SPIN $\frac{11}{2}^+$				
$N^*_{\frac{3}{2}}$	$\frac{3}{2}(\frac{11}{2}^+)$?	2420	260	$\pi N,\ 2K$
$\vdots$		$\vdots$		
SPIN $\frac{11}{2}^-$				
$N^*_{\frac{1}{2}}$	$\frac{1}{2}(\frac{11}{2}^-)$?	2650	300	$\pi N,\ \Lambda K$
SPIN $\frac{15}{2}^+$				
$N^*_{\frac{3}{2}}$	$\frac{3}{2}(\frac{15}{2}^+)$?	2850	300	πN

APPENDIX 2

The Inhomogeneous Lorentz Group
(Poincaré Group)

The *Poincaré group* consists of homogeneous Lorentz transformations Λ plus translations. The transformations Λ defined in momentum space by $k' = \Lambda k$ form a subgroup, the *full homogeneous Lorentz group*, the translations form another subgroup. We shall write an element of L in the form $L = (a,\Lambda)$, or in matrix form $\begin{pmatrix} 1 & 0 \\ a & A \end{pmatrix}$. For the product of two elements of L, (a_1,Λ_1), and (a_2,Λ_2) we obtain the group property

$$(a_2,\Lambda_2)(a_1,\Lambda_1) = (a_2 + \Lambda_2 a_1,\ \Lambda_2\Lambda_1), \tag{A2.1}$$

or, in matrix form,

$$\begin{pmatrix} 1 & 0 \\ a_2 & \Lambda_2 \end{pmatrix}\begin{pmatrix} 1 & 0 \\ a_1 & \Lambda_1 \end{pmatrix} = \begin{pmatrix} 1 & 0 \\ a_2 + \Lambda_2 a_1 & \Lambda_2\Lambda_1 \end{pmatrix}. \tag{A2.2}$$

The unit element is $(0,I)$, hence the element inverse to (a,Λ) is $(-\Lambda^{-1}a,\Lambda^{-1})$.

The homogeneous Lorentz transformations leave an indefinite form $k^{0^2} - \mathbf{k}^2$ invariant; they are defined by the equation

$$\Lambda^T G \Lambda = G, \tag{A2.3}$$

where G is the diagonal matrix with elements $(1,-1,-1,-1)$. It follows immediately that either

Λ_+: det $\Lambda = +1$: *proper* homogeneous Lorentz transformations,

or Λ_-: det $\Lambda = -1$: *improper* homogeneous Lorentz transformations. Furthermore, we divide the elements of Λ according to

$\Lambda^\uparrow$: $\Lambda_0^0 \geqslant 1$: *orthochronous* homogeneous Lorentz transformation,

$\Lambda^\downarrow$: $\Lambda_0^0 \leqslant -1$: *antichronous* homogeneous Lorentz transformation. (Note that $|\Lambda_0^0| > +1$.)

The proper transformations Λ_+ form a subgroup, the impropers do not. Similarly, the set $\Lambda^\uparrow$ forms a subgroup, the set $\Lambda^\downarrow$ does not. The intersection of Λ_+ and $\Lambda^\uparrow$, $\Lambda_+^\uparrow$ forms also a subgroup, the *restricted Lorentz group*.

We have thus the four pieces of the real Lorentz group $\Lambda^\uparrow_+$, $\Lambda^\downarrow_+$, $\Lambda^\uparrow_-$, $\Lambda^\downarrow_-$ which are disconnected; i.e., one cannot pass from one piece to another by varying continuously the parameters of the elements.

The Lorentz transformation to a moving frame with relative velocity w, e.g.,

$$\Lambda_w = \begin{bmatrix} \gamma & -\beta\gamma & 0 & 0 \\ -\beta\gamma & \gamma & 0 & 0 \\ 0 & 0 & 1 & 0 \\ 0 & 0 & 0 & 1 \end{bmatrix}, \quad \beta = \frac{w}{c}, \quad \gamma = \frac{1}{\sqrt{1-\beta^2}}, \qquad (A2.4)$$

belongs to the piece $\Lambda^\uparrow_+$, the space reflections to $\Lambda^\uparrow_-$, time reflections to $\Lambda^\downarrow_-$, space-time reflections to $\Lambda^\downarrow_+$.

It follows from Eq. (A2.3) that Λ and Λ^{T-1} are equivalent representations: $\Lambda = G\Lambda^{T-1}G$. We write, by convention, the vectors transforming with Λ with upper indices, those transforming with Λ^{T-1} with lower indices: $k'^\mu = \Lambda^\mu{}_\nu k^\nu$ and $k'_\mu = (\Lambda^{T-1})^\nu_\mu k_\nu \equiv \Lambda_\mu{}^\nu k_\nu$. This is in agreement with $\Lambda = G\Lambda^{T-1}G$ or, in matrix form,

$$\Lambda^\mu{}_\nu = g^{\mu\sigma}\Lambda_\sigma{}^\rho g_{\rho\nu}.$$

Because Λ is real the representation, Λ^* and $\Lambda^{\dagger-1}$ coincide with Λ and Λ^{T-1}, respectively.

Complex Lorentz Group of the First and Second Kind

This is the group of *complex* matrices satisfying exactly the same equation (A2.3) as before. They transform a complex fourvector k^μ in such a way that the complex norm $k^{02} - \mathbf{k}^2$ is invariant. This group contains the real homogeneous group as a subgroup. The two pieces $\Lambda^\uparrow_+$ and $\Lambda^\downarrow_+$ of the real Lorentz group are now connected through the elements of the complex group. For example, the complex matrices

$$\begin{bmatrix} \cos\phi & i\sin\phi & 0 & 0 \\ i\sin\phi & \cos\phi & 0 & 0 \\ 0 & 0 & \cos\phi & \sin\phi \\ 0 & 0 & -\sin\phi & \cos\phi \end{bmatrix}, \quad 0 \leqslant \phi \leqslant \pi \qquad (A2.6)$$

contain I as well as $-I$ by varying the parameters. Similarly, $\Lambda^\uparrow_-$ and $\Lambda^\downarrow_-$ are connected. The 12-parameter complex group has thus only two pieces with det $= +1$ and det $= -1$.

A second generalization of the real Lorentz group is the *complex Lorentz group of the second kind*, which leaves the real norm $|k^0|^2 - |\mathbf{k}|^2$ invariant. These matrices satisfy the equation

$$\Lambda^+ G\Lambda = G; \quad \det \Lambda = e^{i\varphi}, \quad \varphi \text{ real}, \qquad (A2.7)$$

and form a 16-parameter group, which now connects all four pieces of the real Lorentz group. For example, the matrix

$$\begin{bmatrix} e^{i\varphi_1} & 0 & 0 & 0 \\ 0 & e^{i(\varphi_3 - \varphi_1)} & 0 & 0 \\ 0 & 0 & \cos\phi_3 & \sin\phi_3 \\ 0 & 0 & -\sin\phi_3 & \cos\phi_3 \end{bmatrix} \tag{A2.8}$$

connects I, P, PT, and T.

For further details see A.O. Barut, *Electrodynamics and Classical Theory of Fields and Particles* (The Macmillan Company, New York, 1964) pp. 3–43.

APPENDIX 3

Representations of the Restricted Lorentz Group and the Rotation Group by 2×2 Unimodular and Unitary-Unimodular Groups

The restricted Lorentz group $\Lambda_+^\uparrow$ is homomorphic to two-dimensional unimodular group $SL(2,C)$, the group of 2×2 complex matrices A with $\det A = +1$. The correspondence is actually one to two: $\Lambda \to \pm A$; $SL(2,C)$ is a faithful but two-valued representation of $\Lambda_+^\uparrow$. To prove these statements we consider any 2×2 hermitian matrix X, which can be written as

$$X = k^\mu \sigma_\mu, \qquad \text{tr } X = 2k^0, \tag{A3.1}$$

where σ_μ are the Pauli matrices, k^μ a fourvector. Consider also the transformation

$$X = AXA^\dagger \equiv k'^\mu \sigma_\mu; \quad \det A = +1, \tag{A3.2}$$

where the last step follows from the fact that X' is also hermitian. Now because $\det X' = \det X$, we find

$$k^{0'2} - \mathbf{k}'^2 = k^{02} - \mathbf{k}^2;$$

in other words, the transformation (2) induces a Lorentz transformation on the space of fourvectors k^μ. Let $k'^\mu = L^\mu_\nu k^\nu$, then

$$L^\mu_\nu k^\nu \sigma_\mu = A \sigma_\mu k^\mu A^\dagger,$$

for all k, or

$$L^\mu_\nu \sigma_\mu = A \sigma_\nu A^\dagger,$$

or multiplying both sides with $\bar{\sigma}^\mu$ and taking the trace[1] we finally obtain,

$$L(A)^\mu_\nu = \tfrac{1}{2} \text{tr } [\bar{\sigma}^\mu A \sigma_\nu A^\dagger]. \tag{A3.3}$$

[1] Note that $\sigma^\mu = (\sigma_0, -\boldsymbol{\sigma})$; we shall also use, when convenient, the notation

$$\bar{\sigma}_\mu = (\sigma_0, -\boldsymbol{\sigma}); \qquad \bar{\sigma}^\mu = (\sigma_0, \boldsymbol{\sigma}).$$

We have the useful relations $\text{tr } (\sigma_\mu \bar{\sigma}_\nu) = 2g_{\mu\nu}$, and

$$(\sigma^\mu)_{\alpha\beta}(\sigma_\mu)_{\gamma\delta} = 2\delta_{\alpha\delta}\delta_{\beta\gamma}.$$

294

The trace of the matrix X in (A3.1) transforms therefore like the zero component of a fourvector.

To see the group property, consider two transformations of the type (2): $X'' = A_2 X' A_2^\dagger$ and $X' = A_1 X A_1^\dagger$. Hence

$$X'' = (A_2 A_1) X (A_2 A_1)^\dagger$$

and

$$(L_2 L_1)_\nu^\mu = \tfrac{1}{2} \operatorname{tr} [\tilde{\sigma}^\mu A_2 A_1 \sigma_\nu A_1^\dagger A_2^\dagger].$$

It follows from Eq. (A3.3) that for improper Lorentz transformations no corresponding A exists; e.g., $k = (1000)$ and a time reflection leads to the equation $AA^\dagger = -I$, which is a contradiction; similarly for other reflections. One can also directly prove from Eq. (A3.3) that det $L = +1$.

We now consider the group R_3 along the same lines. Consider the hermitian and traceless matrix

$$X = \mathbf{k} \cdot \mathbf{\sigma}, \quad X^\dagger = X, \quad \operatorname{tr} X = 0, \tag{A3.4}$$

and the transformation

$$X' = UXU^\dagger, \quad \det U = +1. \tag{A3.5}$$

In order that X is also traceless, i.e., $X' = \mathbf{k}' \cdot \mathbf{\sigma}$, U must be unitary:

$$U^\dagger = U^{-1}, \tag{A3.6}$$

for $\operatorname{tr} (UXU^\dagger) = \operatorname{tr} (U^\dagger UX) = \operatorname{tr} X \to U^\dagger U = 1$.

We note that trace of a matrix is invariant under similarity transformations and the unitary and unimodular matrices U form a subgroup of the group of unimodular matrices A discussed before. As before, we get from det $X' =$ det X the condition $\mathbf{k}^2 = \mathbf{k}'^2$; hence the transformation (5) induces an orthogonal transformation in the $\mathbf{k}$-space:

$$\mathbf{k}' = R\mathbf{k}.$$

The trace of the matrix X transforms now like a scalar (it is actually zero). From Eq. (A3.5) we obtain

$$\sigma_i R_j^i k^j = U\sigma_j k^j U^\dagger,$$

or

$$\sigma_i R_j^i = U\sigma_j U^\dagger,$$

or, finally,

$$R_{ij} = \tfrac{1}{2} \operatorname{tr} (\sigma_i U\sigma_j U^\dagger), \tag{A3.7}$$

which is the analog of Eq. (A3.3). We can again prove that det $R = +1$, R is real, and $R(U_1) \cdot R(U_2) = R(U_1 U_2)$.

The inverse of Eq. (A3.7) is given by

$$\pm U = \frac{1}{N} (1 + R^{ij}\sigma_i \sigma_j);$$

$$N^2 = 4(1 + \operatorname{tr} R). \tag{A3.8}$$

The inverse of Eq. (A3.3) is a little more complicated:

$$\pm A = \frac{1}{N'} L^{\mu\nu} \tilde{\sigma}_\mu \sigma_\nu, \tag{A3.9}$$

$$N'^2 = L_{\mu\nu} L_{\gamma\delta} \sigma^\mu \tilde{\sigma}^\nu \sigma^\delta \tilde{\sigma}^\gamma.$$

Two-Component Spinors. Having obtained a two-dimensional representation of R_3 and $\Lambda_+^\uparrow$ we now introduce "vectors" in this two-dimensional representation space transforming according to R_3 or $\Lambda_+^\uparrow$, respectively—namely, the two-component spinors:

$$\xi'_\alpha = U_\alpha^\beta \xi_\beta \qquad \text{for} \quad R_3, \tag{A3.10}$$

and

$$\xi'_\alpha = A_\alpha^\beta \xi_\beta \qquad \text{for} \quad \Lambda_+^\uparrow. \tag{A3.11}$$

We know that together with A or U, also A^*, A^{T-1}, and $A^{\dagger-1}$ (or U^*, U^{T-1}, $U^{\dagger-1}$) are also representations. For R_3 there are actually two: U and U^*. But these two representations are equivalent:

$$C^{-1} U C = U^*, \tag{A3.12}$$

where [2]

$$C = \begin{pmatrix} 0 & -1 \\ 1 & 0 \end{pmatrix} = -C^{-1} = -C^T = -C^\dagger. \tag{A3.13}$$

Thus under three-dimensional rotations there is only one kind of spinor. The spinor transforming according to U^* will be written with upper indices (or equivalently a lower dotted index):

$$\xi'^\alpha = U^{*\alpha}{}_\beta \xi^\beta. \tag{A3.15}$$

It follows immediately from Eqs. (A3.10), (A3.12), and (A3.15) that the raising and lowering *metric spinors* are $C^{-1\alpha\beta}$ and $C_{\alpha\beta}$:

$$\xi^\alpha = C^{-1\alpha\beta} \xi_\beta; \quad \xi_\alpha = C_{\alpha\beta} \xi^\beta. \tag{A3.16}$$

Because U is unitary, the form

$$\xi^\alpha \eta_\alpha = \xi_\alpha C^{-1\alpha\beta} \eta_\beta = \xi_2 \eta_1 - \xi_1 \eta_2 = \xi_1^* \eta_1 + \xi_2^* \eta_2$$

is an invariant; in particular,

$$\xi^\alpha \xi_\alpha = 0.$$

For the restricted Lorentz group $\Lambda_+^\uparrow$, however, the four matrices A, A^{T-1}, A^*, and $A^{\dagger-1}$ are different. From Eq. (A3.14) we see that A and A^{T-1} and A^* and $A^{\dagger-1}$ are equivalent:

$$A = C^{-1} A^{T-1} C, \quad \text{and} \quad A^* = C^{-1} A^{\dagger-1} C. \tag{A3.17}$$

---

[2] For any 2×2 matrix M we have the identity

$$C^{-1} M^T C = M^{-1} \det M. \tag{A3.14}$$

Equation (A3.12) is a special case of this.

The two representations A and A^*, however, are not equivalent; there is no fixed matrix connecting the two. We must therefore introduce two kinds of spinors, which we denote by undotted and dotted indices:

$$\xi'_\alpha = A_\alpha{}^\beta \xi_\beta,$$
$$\xi'_{\dot\alpha} = A^*_{\dot\alpha}{}^{\dot\beta} \xi_{\dot\beta}.$$

(A3.18)

The spinors corresponding to A^{T-1} and $A^{\dagger-1}$ have upper undotted and upper dotted indices, respectively. The raising and lowering metric spinors are again $C^{-1\alpha\beta} = C^{-1\dot\alpha\dot\beta}$ and $C_{\alpha\beta} = C_{\dot\alpha\dot\beta}$.

Finally let us obtain the rotations and restricted Lorentz transformations corresponding to U, U^* and A, A^*, ... We find from Eqs. (A3.7) and (A3.3):

$$R_{ij}(U^*) = \tfrac{1}{2} \operatorname{tr} [\sigma_i C^{-1} U C \sigma_j C^{-1} U^\dagger C] = \tfrac{1}{2} \operatorname{tr} [\sigma_i^T U \sigma_j^T U^\dagger]$$
$$= \tfrac{1}{2} \operatorname{tr} [(U^*\sigma_j U^T \sigma_i)^T] = \tfrac{1}{2} \operatorname{tr} [\sigma_i U^* \sigma_j U^T].$$

On the other hand,

$$R(U^*) = R(C^{-1})R(U)R(C) = R^{-1}(C)R(U)R(C)$$

or

$$R_{ij}(U^*) = (-1)^{i+j} R_{ij}(U)$$

because

$$R_{ij}(C^{-1}) = R_{ij}(C) = -\tfrac{1}{2} \operatorname{tr} (\sigma_i \sigma_j^T) = (-1)^i \delta_{ij}, \quad \text{etc.}$$

Similarly, the Lorentz transformation $\Lambda(A^{T-1})$ and $\Lambda(A)$ are related by

$$\Lambda(A) = \Lambda(C^{-1})\Lambda(A^{T-1})\Lambda(C).$$

Because[3]

$$\Lambda(C)^\mu_\nu = \Lambda(C^{-1})^\mu_\nu = \tfrac{1}{2} \operatorname{tr} (\tilde\sigma^\mu \tilde\sigma^T_\nu) = g^\mu_\nu \quad \text{or} \quad \Lambda(C) = G$$

we get back

$$\Lambda^T G \Lambda = G.$$

Furthermore,[3]

$$\Lambda(A^*)^\mu_\nu = \tfrac{1}{2} \operatorname{tr} (\tilde\sigma^\mu A^* \sigma_\nu A^T)$$
$$= \tfrac{1}{2} \operatorname{tr} (\tilde\sigma^{\mu T} A \sigma^T_\nu A^\dagger)$$
$$= \tfrac{1}{2} \operatorname{tr} (\sigma^\mu A^{T-1} \tilde\sigma_\nu (A^{T-1})^\dagger)$$
$$= \tfrac{1}{2} \operatorname{tr} (\sigma^{\mu T} A^{\dagger-1} \tilde\sigma^T_\nu A^{-1}),$$

etc.

Higher-Order Spinors. Higher-order spinors can be built up from the two-component spinors in the same way as the higher-order tensors. Thus we can define quantities

$$\xi_{\alpha\beta}, \; \xi^\beta_\alpha, \; \xi^{\alpha\beta}; \; \xi_{\alpha\dot\alpha}, \; \xi^{\dot\alpha}_\alpha, \; \xi^{\alpha\dot\alpha}; \; \xi_{\dot\alpha\beta}, \; \xi^\beta_{\dot\alpha}, \dots,$$

[3] Note that

$$\tilde\sigma^{\mu T} = C \sigma^\mu C^{-1}; \qquad \sigma^T_\mu = C \tilde\sigma_\mu C^{-1}.$$

(A3.19)

transforming according to the representations $A \otimes A$, $A \otimes A^*$, $A^* \otimes A^*$, and the corresponding equivalent transformations, respectively.[4] The process of taking the direct product of representations can be continued to spinors of arbitrary rank.

Irreducible Representations. A representation D is *irreducible* if it is not equivalent to a representation which leaves any subspace of the representation space invariant—i.e., one which has, in matrix form, a triangular form. It is *fully reducible* if it separates into a block form. *Every reducible representation of a compact group is fully reducible* (Theorem of Maschke).

The 2×2 representation of the noncompact Lorentz group $\begin{pmatrix} a & 0 \\ c & 1/a \end{pmatrix}$, e.g., is reducible but not fully reducible; it cannot be diagonalized

A very useful and important property of irreducible representations is expressed by *Schur's lemma* which can also be used as a criterion to test that a given representation is irreducible:

Schur's Lemma (1908)

(a) *Let $D(L)$ and $\Delta(L)$ be two irreducible representations on two vector spaces R_n and L_m. If there exist a (rectangular) matrix P such that $y = Px$ from R_n and S_m implies also $PD(L)x = \Delta(L)y$, i.e.,*

$$PD(L) = \Delta(L)P,$$

then either $P = 0$ or nonsingular; in the latter case $n = m$ and $D(L)$ and $\Delta(L)$ are equivalent.

(b) *If a matrix P commutes with all the matrices of an irreducible representation $D(L)$ then P is a multiple of identity.*

Proof of (a). Let x be a vector in R_n: $x \in R_n$. All images Px form a subspace M in S_m. Because $\Delta(L)Px = PD(L)x \in M$, this subspace is invariant under $\Delta(L)$. But $\Delta(L)$ is irreducible, hence either $M = 0$ (i.e., $P = 0$) or $P = S_m$, in which case $n \geqslant m$. On the other hand all vectors x with $Px = 0$ form a subspace N or R_n which is invariant under $D(L)$, for $PD(L)x - \Delta(L)Px = \Delta(L)0 = 0$. But $D(L)$ is also irreducible; hence either $R = 0$ (then $m \geqslant n$), or $R = R_n$ (then $P = 0$). Q.E.D.

Proof of (b). Let us identify in Part (a) the two representations D and Δ, then either $P = 0$ or P nonsingular. Now if P commutes with all $D(L)$ so does $P - \lambda I$. Hence either $P = \lambda I$ or det $(P - \lambda I) \neq 0$ for all λ. But there exist a λ for which det $(P - \lambda I) = 0$, by the fundamental theorem of algebraic equations; hence $P = \lambda I$.

---

[4] Because

$$[D_1(L_1) \otimes D_2(L_1)][D_1(L_2) \otimes D_2(L_2)] = [D_1(L_1)D_1(L_2)] \otimes [D_2(L_1)D_2(L_2)],$$

the Kroenecker product $D_1 \otimes D_2$ of two representations is again a representation.

All $n \times n$ complex matrices, all hermitian matrices, all traceless and hermitian matrices, all unitary matrices, all unitary and unimodular matrices are examples of irreducible systems. (It is sufficient to show that any two vectors in the space can be connected by a matrix in the system.)

As an application of Schur's lemma we have already quoted the result that the only matrices transforming hermitian and traceless matrices again into hermitian and traceless ones are the multiples of unitary matrices:

If $(BHB^{-1})^{\dagger} = BHB^{-1}$ with $H^{\dagger} = H$ and tr $H = 0$, then $HA^{\dagger}A = A^{\dagger}AH$ for all H, or $A^{\dagger}A = \lambda I$; $A^{\dagger}A \geqslant 0 \Rightarrow \lambda > 0 \Rightarrow U = A/\sqrt{\lambda}$ is unitary.

As another application we shall need the theorem that "every irreducible representation of an Abelian (commutative) group is one-dimensional." Every $D(L)$ commutes with all, hence must be a multiple of I. The identity matrix is irreducible only for $n = 1$.

The Kroenecker product of two representation, like $A \otimes A, \ldots$, is in general reducible. As in tensor calculus, the spinors reduce into their symmetric, antisymmetric, and traceless parts.

The irreducible representations of the rotation group R_3 are given in terms of U as follows: Consider the space of normalized homogeneous monomials

$$X_m^j = \frac{1}{N} \xi_{\frac{1}{2}}^{j+m} \xi_{-\frac{1}{2}}^{j-m}, \tag{A3.20}$$

$$m = -j, -j+1, \ldots, +j; \quad j = 0, \tfrac{1}{2}, 1, \tfrac{3}{2}, \ldots,$$

where $\xi = \begin{pmatrix} \xi_{\frac{1}{2}} \\ \xi_{-\frac{1}{2}} \end{pmatrix}$ is the spinor transforming according to U and $N^2 = (j-m)!(j+m)!$. For each j the vector X^j has $(2j+1)$ components.

Under R_3, the quantities X_m^j transform as

$$X_{m'}^{\prime j} = D_{m'}^{jm}(U)X_m^j \equiv \frac{1}{N} \xi_{\frac{1}{2}}^{\prime j+m'} \xi_{-\frac{1}{2}}^{\prime j-m'}. \tag{A3.21}$$

This equation defines the $(2j+1)$-dimensional *irreducible unitary* representations $D^j(U)$ of R_3.

The irreducible finite-dimensional representations of the restricted Lorentz groups are defined in terms of the homogeneous monomials

$$X_{\beta}^{(j_1 \cdot j_2)\alpha} = \frac{1}{N} (\eta^{\frac{1}{2}})^{j_1 + \alpha} (\eta^{-\frac{1}{2}})^{j_1 - \alpha} \xi_{\frac{1}{2}}^{j_1 + \beta} \xi_{\frac{1}{2}}^{j_2 - \beta}, \tag{A3.22}$$

$$\dot{\alpha} = j_1, j_1 - 1, \ldots, -j_1; \quad \beta = j_2, j_2 - 1, \ldots, -j_2,$$

where ξ_α and η^β are spinors transforming according to A and $A^{\dagger -1}$, respectively. Under $\Lambda_+^{\uparrow}$ we have the transformation property

$$X_{\beta'}^{\prime \dot{\alpha}'} = D^{j_1 j_2}(A)_{\beta' \dot{\alpha}}^{\dot{\alpha}' \beta} X_{\beta}^{\dot{\alpha}}, \tag{A3.23}$$

which defines the $(2j_1 + 1)(2j_2 + 1)$ representations $D^{j_1 j_2}(A)$ of $\Lambda_+^{\uparrow}$ which are, however, now not unitary.

We obtain immediately the following relations:

$$D^{0\frac{1}{2}}(A) = A,$$

$$D^{0j}(U) = D^j(U),$$

$$D^{j_1 j_2}(A) = D^{j_1 0}(A) \otimes D^{0 j_2}(A), \qquad\qquad (A3.24)$$

$$D^{0j}(A^*, A^{T-1}, A^{\dagger-1}) = D^{0j}(A)^{*, \text{ or } T-1, \dagger-1},$$

$$D^{j0}(A) = D^{0j}(A)^{\dagger-1},$$

$$D^{0j}(C^{-1}) D^{0j}(A) D^{0j}(C) = D^{0j}(A)^{T-1}.$$

Thus we can take as raising and lowering spinors

$$D^{0j}(C^{-1})^{\alpha\beta} \qquad \text{and} \qquad D^{0j}(C)_{\alpha\beta}, \qquad\qquad (A3.25)$$

respectively, which can also be written as

$$D^{0j}(C^{-1})^{\alpha\beta} = (-1)^{j-\alpha} \delta^{\alpha, -\beta}$$

$$D^{0j}(C)_{\alpha\beta} = (-1)^{-j+\beta} \delta_{-\alpha,\beta}. \qquad\qquad (A3.26)$$

APPENDIX 4

Clebsch–Gordan Coefficients

The direct products of the irreducible representations of the rotation group are completely reducible into a sum of again irreducible parts. This is done by a unitary transformation, which brings the product into a diagonal box form. Or in terms of basis vectors in the representation space, the unitary transformations take the basis $X_{m_1}^{I_1} X_{m_2}^{I_2}$ into the bases X_m^I. We have the result

$$D_{\alpha_1}^{I_1\beta_1} D_{\alpha_2}^{I_2\beta_2} = \sum_I [I_1 I_2 I]_{\beta_1\beta_2}^{\beta_1\beta_2} \{I_1 I_2 I\}_{\alpha_1\alpha_2}^\alpha D_\alpha^{I\beta}, \tag{A4.1}$$

where the coefficients are the matrix elements of the reducing unitary operator, the Clebsch–Gordan coefficients, which also indicate the number of times an irreducible representation D^I occurs in the expansion (1). The unitarity condition on these coefficients are

$$\sum_{\alpha_1\alpha_2} [I_1 I_2 I]_{\alpha_1\alpha_2}^{\alpha} \{I_1 I_2 I'\}_{\alpha_1\alpha_2}^{\alpha'} = \delta_\alpha^{\alpha'} \delta^{II'}, \tag{A4.2}$$

and

$$\sum_I [I_1 I_2 I]_{\alpha_1\alpha_2}^{\alpha} \{I_1 I_2 I\}_{\beta_1\beta_2}^{\alpha} = \delta_{\beta_1}^{\alpha_1} \delta_{\beta_2}^{\alpha_2}, \tag{A4.3}$$

for each fixed α.

We have chosen a particular notation for the Clebsch–Gordan coefficients to indicate the nature of the spinor indices. The usual notations in the literature $C(I_1 I_2, I, \alpha_1\alpha_2, \alpha)$ or $C_{I_1 I_2}(I, \alpha; \alpha_1\alpha_2)$ or $(I_1 I_2 I\alpha | I_1 I_2 \alpha_1\alpha_2)$ do not show this property. To prove the spinor character of the coefficients, we multiply both sides of Eq. (A4.1) with $[I_1 I_2 I']_\gamma^{\alpha_1\alpha_2}$, sum over $\alpha_1\alpha_2$, and use (A4.3) to obtain

$$\sum_{\alpha_1\alpha_2} [I_1 I_2 I]_\alpha^{\alpha_1\alpha_2} D_{\alpha_1}^{I_1\beta_1} D_{\alpha_2}^{I_2\beta_2} = [I_1 I_2 I]_{\beta_1\beta_2}^{\beta_1\beta_2} D_\alpha^{I\beta}. \tag{A4.4}$$

Now because D^I's are unitary, i.e.,

$$D_\alpha^{I\beta} D_\beta^{I\gamma^*} = \delta_\alpha^\gamma, \tag{A4.5}$$

we can write Eq. (A4.4) in the form

$$[I_1 I_2 I]_\alpha^{\alpha_1\alpha_2} = D_\alpha^{I\beta} D_{\beta_1}^{I_1\alpha_1^*} D_{\beta_2}^{I_2\alpha_2^*} [I_1 I_2 I]_{\beta_1\beta_2}^{\beta_1\beta_2}, \tag{A4.6}$$

301

which shows indeed that the index α transforms according to D^I and the two indices, $\alpha_1 \alpha_2$ according to $D^{I'}$ and that the Clebsch–Gordon coefficients are *isotropic* tensors. Similarly, one proves the transformation property of $\{I_1 I_2 I\}^{\alpha}_{\alpha_1 \alpha_2}$. The numerical values of $[I_1 I_2 I]^{\alpha_1 \alpha_2}_{\alpha}$ and $\{I_1 I_2 I\}^{\alpha}_{\alpha_1 \alpha_2}$ are the same. But using raising and lowering operators we find

$$[I_1 I_2 I]^{\alpha}_{\alpha_1 \alpha_2} = (-1)^{2I}[I_1 I_2 I]^{\alpha_1 \alpha_2}_{\alpha}, \tag{A4.7}$$

where we have made use of the following symmetry property of the Clebsch–Gordan coefficients:

$$[I_1 I_2 I]^{\alpha_1 \alpha_2}_{\alpha} = (-1)^{I_1 + I_2 - I}[I_1 I_2 I]^{-\alpha_1, -\alpha_2}_{-\alpha}. \tag{A4.8}$$

Another useful symmetry property of the C-G coefficients is

$$[I_1 I_2 I]^{\alpha_1 \alpha_2}_{\alpha} = (-1)^{I_1 + I_2 - I}[I_2 I_1 I]^{\alpha_2 \alpha_1}_{\alpha}. \tag{A4.9}$$

Finally, we give *the tables of numerical values* of the Clebsch–Gordan coefficients. Note that quite generally

$$[I_1 I_2 I]^{\alpha_1 \alpha_2}_{\alpha} = 0, \tag{A4.10}$$

unless

$$\alpha = \alpha_1 + \alpha_2; \quad I = I_1 + I_2, I_1 + I_2 - 1, \ldots, |I_1 - I_2|,$$

and

$$-I_1 < \alpha_1 < I_1, \quad -I_2 < \alpha_2 < I_2, \quad -I < \alpha < I.$$

In the following tables of $[I_1 I_2 I]^{\alpha_1 \alpha_2}_{m}$, α_1 is the row index from $+I_1$ to $-I_1$, α_2 is the column index from $+I_2$ to $-I_2$; m can be found from $m = \alpha_1 + \alpha_2$.

(a) $[\tfrac{1}{2}\tfrac{1}{2}0] = \begin{bmatrix} 0 & \dfrac{1}{\sqrt{2}} \\ -\dfrac{1}{\sqrt{2}} & 0 \end{bmatrix}$, $[\tfrac{1}{2}\tfrac{1}{2}1] = \begin{bmatrix} 1 & \dfrac{1}{\sqrt{2}} \\ \dfrac{1}{\sqrt{2}} & 1 \end{bmatrix}$.

(b) $[1\tfrac{1}{2}\tfrac{1}{2}] = \begin{bmatrix} 0 & \sqrt{\tfrac{2}{3}} \\ -\sqrt{\tfrac{1}{3}} & \sqrt{\tfrac{1}{3}} \\ -\sqrt{\tfrac{2}{3}} & 0 \end{bmatrix}$, $[1\tfrac{1}{2}\tfrac{3}{2}] = \begin{bmatrix} 1 & \sqrt{\tfrac{1}{3}} \\ \sqrt{\tfrac{2}{3}} & \sqrt{\tfrac{2}{3}} \\ \sqrt{\tfrac{1}{3}} & 1 \end{bmatrix}$.

(c) $[110] = \begin{bmatrix} 0 & 0 & \sqrt{\tfrac{1}{3}} \\ 0 & -\sqrt{\tfrac{1}{3}} & 0 \\ \sqrt{\tfrac{1}{3}} & 0 & 0 \end{bmatrix}$, $[111] = \begin{bmatrix} 0 & \sqrt{\tfrac{1}{2}} & \sqrt{\tfrac{1}{2}} \\ -\sqrt{\tfrac{1}{2}} & 0 & \sqrt{\tfrac{1}{2}} \\ -\sqrt{\tfrac{1}{2}} & -\sqrt{\tfrac{1}{2}} & 0 \end{bmatrix}$,

$[112] = \begin{bmatrix} 1 & \sqrt{\tfrac{1}{2}} & \sqrt{\tfrac{1}{6}} \\ \sqrt{\tfrac{1}{2}} & \sqrt{\tfrac{2}{3}} & \sqrt{\tfrac{1}{2}} \\ \sqrt{\tfrac{1}{6}} & \sqrt{\tfrac{1}{2}} & 1 \end{bmatrix}$.

(d)
$$[\tfrac{1}{2}\,\tfrac{3}{2}\,1] = \begin{bmatrix} 0 & \dfrac{1}{2} & \dfrac{\sqrt{2}}{2} & \dfrac{\sqrt{3}}{2} \\ -\dfrac{\sqrt{3}}{2} & \dfrac{-\sqrt{2}}{2} & -\dfrac{1}{2} & 0 \end{bmatrix},$$

$$[\tfrac{1}{2}\,\tfrac{3}{2}\,2] = \begin{bmatrix} 1 & \dfrac{\sqrt{3}}{2} & \dfrac{\sqrt{2}}{2} & \dfrac{1}{2} \\ \dfrac{1}{2} & \dfrac{\sqrt{2}}{2} & \dfrac{\sqrt{3}}{2} & 1 \end{bmatrix}.$$

(e)
$$[1\,\tfrac{3}{2}\,\tfrac{1}{2}] = \begin{bmatrix} 0 & 0 & 1/\sqrt{6} & 1/\sqrt{2} \\ 0 & -\tfrac{1}{3} & -1/\sqrt{3} & 0 \\ 1/\sqrt{2} & 1/\sqrt{6} & 0 & 0 \end{bmatrix},$$

$$[1\,\tfrac{3}{2}\,\tfrac{3}{2}] = \begin{bmatrix} 0 & 2/\sqrt{10} & 4/\sqrt{30} & \sqrt{\tfrac{2}{3}} \\ -\sqrt{\tfrac{3}{5}} & -\sqrt{\tfrac{1}{15}} & \sqrt{\tfrac{1}{15}} & \sqrt{\tfrac{3}{5}} \\ -\sqrt{\tfrac{2}{5}} & -4/\sqrt{30} & -2/\sqrt{10} & 0 \end{bmatrix},$$

$$[1\,\tfrac{3}{2}\,\tfrac{5}{2}] = \begin{bmatrix} 1 & \sqrt{\tfrac{3}{5}} & \sqrt{\tfrac{3}{10}} & \sqrt{\tfrac{1}{10}} \\ \sqrt{\tfrac{2}{5}} & \sqrt{\tfrac{3}{5}} & \sqrt{\tfrac{3}{5}} & \sqrt{\tfrac{2}{5}} \\ \sqrt{\tfrac{1}{6}} & \sqrt{\tfrac{2}{10}} & \sqrt{\tfrac{3}{5}} & 1 \end{bmatrix}.$$

(f)
$$[\tfrac{3}{2}\,\tfrac{3}{2}\,0] = \begin{bmatrix} 0 & 0 & 0 & \tfrac{1}{2} \\ 0 & 0 & -\tfrac{1}{2} & 0 \\ 0 & \tfrac{1}{2} & 0 & 0 \\ -\tfrac{1}{2} & 0 & 0 & 0 \end{bmatrix},$$

$$[\tfrac{3}{2}\,\tfrac{3}{2}\,1] = \begin{bmatrix} 0 & 0 & \sqrt{\tfrac{3}{10}} & \sqrt{\tfrac{3}{20}} \\ 0 & -2/\sqrt{10} & -1/\sqrt{20} & \sqrt{\tfrac{3}{10}} \\ \sqrt{\tfrac{3}{10}} & -1/\sqrt{20} & -2/\sqrt{10} & 0 \\ 3/\sqrt{20} & \sqrt{\tfrac{3}{10}} & 0 & 0 \end{bmatrix},$$

$$\left[\tfrac{3}{2}\,\tfrac{3}{2}\,2\right] = \begin{bmatrix} 0 & 1/\sqrt{2} & 1/\sqrt{2} & \tfrac{1}{2} \\ -1/\sqrt{2} & 0 & \tfrac{1}{2} & 1/\sqrt{2} \\ -1/\sqrt{2} & -\tfrac{1}{2} & 0 & 1/\sqrt{2} \\ -\tfrac{1}{2} & -1/\sqrt{2} & -1/\sqrt{2} & 0 \end{bmatrix},$$

$$\left[\tfrac{3}{2}\,\tfrac{3}{2}\,3\right] = \begin{bmatrix} 1 & 1/\sqrt{2} & 1/\sqrt{5} & 1/\sqrt{20} \\ 1/\sqrt{2} & \sqrt{\tfrac{3}{5}} & \sqrt{\tfrac{3}{20}} & 1/\sqrt{5} \\ 1/\sqrt{5} & 3/\sqrt{20} & \sqrt{\tfrac{3}{5}} & 1/\sqrt{5} \\ 1/\sqrt{20} & 1/\sqrt{5} & 1/\sqrt{2} & 1 \end{bmatrix}.$$

APPENDIX 5

Connection between Two- and Four-Component Form of the Amplitudes

a. Introduction of Four-Component Spinors

Given a two-component (dotted) spinor $\Phi_{\dot\alpha}$, e.g., which in a particular frame has the components

$$\Phi_{\frac{1}{2}} = \frac{1}{\sqrt{2}}\begin{pmatrix}1\\0\end{pmatrix}, \quad \Phi_{-\frac{1}{2}} = \frac{1}{\sqrt{2}}\begin{pmatrix}0\\1\end{pmatrix}, \tag{A5.1}$$

we define a four-component spinor by

$$u(k)_\alpha = \begin{pmatrix} B\Phi_{\dot\alpha} \\ B^{-1\dagger}\Phi_{\dot\alpha} \end{pmatrix}, \tag{A5.2}$$

where B is the 2×2 matrix corresponding to a Lorentz transformation from rest frame to an arbitrary momentum k (see Sec. 2.3):

$$B \equiv B_{k \leftarrow p} = \sqrt{\frac{k \cdot \sigma}{m}}\, U,$$

$$B^{-1} = U^{-1}\sqrt{\frac{k \cdot \tilde\sigma}{m}}, \quad B^{-1\dagger} = \sqrt{\frac{k \cdot \tilde\sigma}{m}}\, U; \tag{A5.3}$$

then the four-component spinor $u(k)$ satisfies the Dirac equation:

$$(\gamma \cdot k - m)u(k) = 0, \tag{A5.4}$$

$$\gamma \cdot k = \gamma^\mu k_\mu.$$

Proof: We can choose

$$\gamma_\mu = \begin{pmatrix} 0 & \sigma_\mu \\ \tilde\sigma_\mu & 0 \end{pmatrix}. \tag{A5.5}$$

Then Eq. (A5.4) becomes

$$\gamma \cdot ku = \begin{pmatrix} 0 & \sigma \cdot k \\ \tilde\sigma \cdot k & 0 \end{pmatrix}\begin{pmatrix} B\Phi \\ B^{-1\dagger}\Phi \end{pmatrix} = \begin{pmatrix} k \cdot \sigma\, B^{-1\dagger}\Phi \\ k \cdot \tilde\sigma\, B\Phi \end{pmatrix}$$

$$= m\begin{pmatrix} \sqrt{k \cdot \sigma/m}\; U\Phi \\ \sqrt{k \cdot \tilde\sigma/m}\; U\Phi \end{pmatrix} = mu(k),$$

305

which proves the statement. We also *define* the conjugate spinor by

$$\bar{u}(k) = u(k)^\dagger \gamma_0 \tag{A5.6}$$

or

$$\bar{u}(k) = \overbrace{B^\dagger \Phi^* \quad B^{-1}\Phi^*}^{} \begin{pmatrix} 0 & 1 \\ 1 & 0 \end{pmatrix} = \begin{pmatrix} B^{-1}\Phi^* \\ B^\dagger \Phi^* \end{pmatrix},$$

and the spinor

$$v(k) \equiv C\bar{u}(k)^T = \begin{pmatrix} CB^{-1^T}\Phi^* \\ CB^{\dagger T}\Phi^* \end{pmatrix} \tag{A5.7}$$

then $v(k)$ satisfies the Dirac equation

$$(\gamma \cdot k + m)v(k) = 0. \tag{A5.8}$$

Proof:

$$\gamma \cdot kv = \begin{pmatrix} 0 & k\cdot\sigma \\ k\cdot\tilde{\sigma} & 0 \end{pmatrix}\begin{pmatrix} CB^{-1^T}\Phi^* \\ CB^{\dagger T}\Phi^* \end{pmatrix} = \begin{pmatrix} k\cdot\sigma CB^{\dagger T}\Phi^* \\ k\cdot\tilde{\sigma} CB^{-1^T}\Phi^* \end{pmatrix}$$

$$= \begin{pmatrix} k\cdot\sigma C\sqrt{k\cdot\sigma^T/m}\ U^*\Phi^* \\ k\cdot\tilde{\sigma} C\sqrt{k\cdot\tilde{\sigma}^T/m}\ U^*\Phi^* \end{pmatrix} = -\begin{pmatrix} k\cdot\sigma C^{-1}\sqrt{k\cdot\sigma^T/m}\ CC^{-1}U^*CC^{-1}\Phi^* \\ k\cdot\tilde{\sigma} C^{-1}\sqrt{k\cdot\tilde{\sigma}^T/m}\ CC^{-1}U^*CC^{-1}\Phi^* \end{pmatrix}$$

$$= -\begin{pmatrix} k\cdot\sigma\sqrt{k\cdot\tilde{\sigma}/m}\ UC^{-1}\Phi^* \\ k\cdot\tilde{\sigma}\sqrt{k\cdot\sigma/m}\ UC^{-1}\Phi^* \end{pmatrix} = -m\begin{pmatrix} BC^{-1}\Phi^* \\ B^{-1\dagger}C^{-1}\Phi^* \end{pmatrix} = -m\begin{pmatrix} CB^{-1^T}\Phi^* \\ CB^{\dagger T}\Phi^* \end{pmatrix}$$

$$= -mv(k),$$

where we have used the relations

$$CM^{-1}C^{-1} = M^T$$

for any 2×2, det $M = 1$;

$$CU^*C^{-1} = U,$$

$$\tilde{\sigma}_\mu = C^{-1}\sigma_\mu^T C; \quad \sigma_\mu = C^{-1}\tilde{\sigma}_\mu^T C; \quad C = \begin{pmatrix} 0 & -1 \\ 1 & 0 \end{pmatrix}.$$

b. Amplitudes

We now consider the amplitudes in the four-component form:

$$R = \bar{u}(k')_\alpha T^{\alpha\dot\alpha} u(k)_{\dot\alpha},$$

i.e.,

$$R = \overbrace{\Phi_\alpha^* B^{-1} \quad \Phi_\alpha^\dagger B^\dagger}^{} \begin{pmatrix} T_{11} & T_{12} \\ T_{21} & T_{22} \end{pmatrix}\begin{pmatrix} B\Phi_{\dot\alpha} \\ B^{-1\dagger}\Phi_{\dot\alpha} \end{pmatrix} \tag{A5.9}$$

or

$$R = \Phi_\alpha^* B^{-1}(k')T_{11}B(k)\Phi_{\dot\alpha}(k) + \Phi_\alpha^* B^\dagger(k')T_{21}B(k)\Phi_{\dot\alpha}$$
$$+ \Phi_\alpha^* B^{-1}(k')T_{12}B^{-1\dagger}(k)\Phi_{\dot\alpha} + \Phi_\alpha^* B^\dagger(k')T_{22}B^{-1\dagger}(k)\Phi_{\dot\alpha}.$$

In the frame where (A5.1) holds, the quantities $\Phi_\alpha^* B^{-1}$, $B\Phi_{\dot\alpha}, \ldots$ act as follows:

$$\Phi_{\alpha,i}^* B^{-1ij} = \frac{1}{\sqrt{2}}\begin{pmatrix} 1 \\ 0 \end{pmatrix}\begin{pmatrix} \cdot & \cdot \\ \cdot & \cdot \end{pmatrix} = B^{-1}(k')_{\dot\alpha}^j,$$

i.e., Φ, Φ^* just pick up definite elements of B. Thus we have the two-component form

$$R = \tfrac{1}{2}[B^{-1}(k')T_{11}B(k) + B^\dagger(k')T_{21}B(k)$$
$$+ B^{-1}(k')T_{12}B^{-1\dagger}(k) + B^\dagger(k')T_{22}B^{-1\dagger}(k)]. \quad (A5.10)$$

Here a 2×2 matrix multiplication is understood.

Finally using the connection between the R and the spinorial amplitudes,

$$R = B^{-1}(k')MB^{\dagger-1}(k),$$

we obtain the connection between M and the T-matrix in (A5.9):

$$M = \tfrac{1}{2}[T_{11}B(k)B^\dagger(k) + B(k')B^\dagger(k')T_{21}B(k)B^\dagger(k)$$
$$+ T_{12} + B(k')B^\dagger(k')T_{22}]. \quad (A5.11)$$

The matrix T is made up of Dirac matrices. The following table shows the values of T_{ij} in the representation (A5.5):

T	T_{11}	T_{12}	T_{21}	T_{22}	
I	I	0	0	I	
$\gamma_\mu\gamma_\nu - \gamma_\nu\gamma_\mu$	$\sigma_\mu\tilde{\sigma}_\nu - \sigma_\nu\tilde{\sigma}_\mu$	0	0	$\tilde{\sigma}_\mu\sigma_\nu - \tilde{\sigma}_\nu\sigma_\mu$	
$\gamma_5\gamma_\mu$	0	$-\sigma_\mu$	$\tilde{\sigma}_\mu$	0	(A5.12)
γ_μ	0	σ_μ	$\tilde{\sigma}_\mu$	0	
γ_5	$-I$	0	0	I	

Given now a four-component T-matrix, we can easily evaluate M in two component form using Eqs. (A5.12) and (A5.11), and vice versa.

APPENDIX 6

Functions of One Complex Variable

We discuss here some theorems useful in analytic S-matrix theory.

Limit. $\lim\limits_{z \to z_0} f(z) = w_0$ means that whenever $|z - z_0| < \delta$ there exists an ε such that $|f(z) - w_0| < \varepsilon$.

Continuity. $f(z)$ is continuous at z_0 if $\lim\limits_{z \to z_0} f(z) = f(z_0)$.

Differentiation. $f(z)$ is differentiable at z_0 if

$$\left| \frac{f(z) - f(z_0)}{z - z_0} - f(z_0) \right| < \varepsilon \quad \text{if} \quad |z - z_0| < \delta.$$

Definition. $f(z)$ *is holomorph in a domain G if its derivative exists at every point of G, it is single valued and* $f'(z)$ *is continuous in G.*

Theorem. *If* $f = u + iv$ *is holomorph in G, then u and v have continuous partial derivatives satisfying the Cauchy-Riemann differential equations*

$$\frac{\partial u}{\partial x} = \frac{\partial v}{\partial y}, \quad \frac{\partial u}{\partial y} = -\frac{\partial v}{\partial x}.$$

Proof. The differentiation is independent of the direction in which one goes to the limit.

$$\frac{df}{dz} = \frac{\left(\dfrac{\partial u}{\partial x} + i \dfrac{\partial v}{\partial x} \right) dx + \left(\dfrac{\partial u}{\partial y} + i \dfrac{\partial v}{\partial y} \right) dy}{dx + i\,dy}$$

is independent of dy/dx if

$$i \left(\frac{\partial u}{\partial x} + i \frac{\partial v}{\partial x} \right) = \frac{\partial u}{\partial y} + i \frac{\partial v}{\partial y},$$

which gives the desired equations.

Converse. Given two real and continuous functions u and v in G satisfying the Cauchy-Riemann equations, then $f = u + iv$ *is holomorph in G and continuously differentiable with*

$$f'(z) = \frac{\partial u}{\partial x} + i \frac{\partial v}{\partial x}.$$

Corollary. *u and v are harmonic functions, $\Delta u = 0$, $\Delta v = 0$. Conversely, given a harmonic function u, it can be considered as the real or imaginary part of an holomorphic function.*

Point $z = \infty$. $f(z)$ is differentiable at $z = \infty$ if the limit

$$df(z)/dz|_{z=\infty} = -df(1/w)/dw\ w^2|_{w=0}$$

exists. Thus, $f(z)$ is holomorph at $z = \infty$ if $f(1/w)$ is holomorph at $w = 0$.

Integration. *Given a curve in G in parametric form $z = z(t)$ we define*

$$\oint_C f(z)\,dz = \int_{t=0}^{1} f(z(t))\frac{dz}{dt}\,dt$$

or

$$= \lim_{\substack{|\Delta z_n| \to 0 \\ N \to \infty}} \sum_{n=1}^{N} f(a_n)\,\Delta z_n.$$

We can estimate: If $|f(z)| \leqslant M > 0$ along C then

$$\left|\oint_C f(z)\,dz\right| \leq Ms,$$

where s is the length of the curve C.

Theorem of Cauchy-Goursat. *Let $f(z)$ be a holomorphic function in G, C a contour (consisting of continuous or discontinuous cycles, double cycles, etc.); then*

$$\oint_C f(z)\,dz = 0.$$

Converse (Theorem of Morera). *$f(z)$ continuous and $\oint f(z)\,dz = 0$, then $f(z)$ is holomorph in G.*

Proof. According to Stokes' formula,

$$\iint_S \nabla \times \vec{A} \cdot d\vec{f} = \oint_C \vec{A} \cdot d\vec{s}$$

or

$$\oint_C (A_x\,dx + A_y\,dy) = \int_S \left(\frac{\partial A_y}{\partial x} - \frac{\partial A_x}{\partial y}\right)dx\,dy.$$

Let once $A_x = v$, $A_y = u$ and then $A_y = v$ and $A_x = -u$ and apply the Cauchy-Riemann equations to obtain

$$\oint f(z)\,dz = \oint_C (u\,dx - v\,dy) + i\oint_C (u\,dy + v\,dx) = 0.$$

The Cauchy Integral Formula. If $f(z)$ holomorph in G, $z_0 \in G$, $C = $ cycle which goes around z_0 once in positive direction (counterclockwise), then

$$f(z_0) = \frac{1}{2\pi i}\oint_C \frac{f(z)\,dz}{z - z_0}.$$

Note. The Cauchy formula solves a boundary-value problem. The values of the function on C determine its value in the interior. There is no analogy in the theory of real functions.

Proof. Let C' be a small circle around z_0 of radius ρ. By Cauchy-Goursat theorem,

$$\oint_C = \oint_{C'}$$

or

$$\oint_{C'} \frac{f(z)\,dz}{z - z_0} = f(z_0) \underbrace{\oint_{C'} \frac{dz}{z - z_0}}_{2\pi i} + \underbrace{\oint \frac{|f(z) - f(z_0)|}{z - z_0}\,dz}_{2\pi\varepsilon},$$

where $|f(z) - f(z_0)| < \varepsilon$.

Formulas for the Derivatives. Given $f(z)$ on a curve C, then $f(z_0)$ defined by the Cauchy formula for a point inside the contour is holomorph. Hence one can differentiate:

$$f'(z_0) = \frac{1}{2\pi i} \oint_C \frac{f(z)\,dz}{(z - z_0)^2}, \ldots \quad f^{(n)}(z_0) = \frac{n!}{2\pi i} \oint_C \frac{f(z)\,dz}{(z - z_0)^{n+1}}.$$

Series Expansion of Holomorphic Functions

The sum of a power series $\sum a_n z^n$ is a holomorphic function in the interior of the circle of convergence. The radius of convergence is given by *Hadamard's formula*:

$$1/R = \varlimsup_{n \to \infty} |a_n|^{1/n}.$$

A uniform convergent series can be integrated and differentiated term by term; sum and integral can be exchanged. A power series around a point a converges in every point of the circle of convergence. There is at least one singular point on the periphery of the circle of convergence.

Given two finite points a and b, we have

$$\frac{1}{z - b} = \frac{1}{(z - a) - (b - a)} = \frac{1/(z - a)}{1 - (b - a)/(z - a)}$$

$$= \sum_{n=0}^{\infty} (b - a)^n/(z - a)^{n+1},$$

and the series converges uniformly for all z with $|z - a| > |a - b|$.

Taylor Series. $f(z)$ holomorph in G, c a cycle in G and $a \in G$. Then

$$f(z) = \frac{1}{2\pi i} \oint_C \frac{f(\xi)\,d\xi}{\xi - z} = \frac{1}{2\pi i} \oint \frac{f(\xi)}{\xi - a} \frac{1}{1 - \dfrac{z - a}{\xi - a}}\,d\xi.$$

For $|z - a|/|\xi - a| < 1$, we have

$$f(z) = \frac{1}{2\pi i} \oint \frac{f(\xi)}{\xi - a} \left[1 + \frac{z - a}{\xi - a} + \frac{(z - a)^2}{(\xi - a)^2} + \cdots \right] d\xi$$

or, integrating by parts, we obtain the Taylor Series:

$$f(z) = f(a) + f'(a)(z - a) + (1/2!)f''(a)(z - a)^2 + \cdots,$$

which converges in the largest open disk in G with center at a.

Laurent Series. Let $f(z)$ be holomorph inside an annular ring between two circles C_1 and C_2 and z a point inside the ring, $a = $ a point inside the small circle C_1. Then

$$f(z) = \frac{1}{2\pi i} \left(\oint_{C_2} \frac{f(\xi)\, d\xi}{\xi - z} - \oint_{C_1} \frac{f(\xi)\, d\xi}{\xi - z} \right).$$

Because the expansions

$$\frac{1}{\xi - z} = \frac{1}{\xi - a} \left[1 + \frac{z - a}{\xi - a} + \left(\frac{z - a}{\xi - a} \right)^2 + \cdots \right]$$

$$= -\frac{1}{z - a} \left[1 + \frac{\xi - a}{z - a} + \left(\frac{\xi - a}{z - a} \right)^2 + \cdots \right]$$

are convergent on C_2 and C_1, respectively, we have

$$f(z) = \frac{1}{2\pi i} \left\{ \oint_{C_2} \frac{f(\xi)\, d\xi}{\xi - a} \left(1 + \frac{z - a}{\xi - a} + \cdots \right) \right.$$

$$\left. + \oint_{C_1} \frac{f(\xi)\, d\xi}{z - a} \left(1 + \frac{\xi - a}{z - a} + \cdots \right) \right\}$$

$$= \sum_{\nu = -\infty}^{+\infty} A_\nu (z - a)^\nu,$$

where for $\nu \geqslant 0$:

$$A_\nu = \frac{1}{2\pi i} \oint_{C_2} \frac{f(\xi)\, d\xi}{(\xi - a)^{\nu + 1}}$$

and for $\nu < 0$:

$$A_\nu = \frac{1}{2\pi i} \oint_{C_1} \frac{f(\xi)\, d\xi}{(\xi - a)^{\nu + 1}}$$

or, taking a contour K inside the ring, we have in both cases

$$A_\nu = \frac{1}{2\pi i} \oint_K f(\xi)(\xi - a)^{\nu - 1}\, d\xi.$$

If a is an isolated singularity the Laurent series will begin with some negative power m:

$$f(z) = \frac{A_{-m}}{(z - a)^m} + \cdots + \frac{A_{-1}}{z - a} + A_0 + A_1(z - a) + \cdots.$$

In particular, if $m = 1$ the point a is a simple pole with *residue*

$$A_{-1} = \frac{1}{2\pi i} \oint_C f(\xi)\, d\xi,$$

$m > 1$: a pole of order m. If $m = \infty$ the point a is an *essential singularity*.

Theorem (Weierstrass). *In every neighborhood of an essential singularity* $f(z)$ *fluctuates in such a way that it comes arbitrarily close to every complex number.*

The Connection with the Fourier Series. Consider $f(w)$ holomorph in the band (see Fig. A6.1) in w-plane and the conformal mapping $z = e^{iw}$.

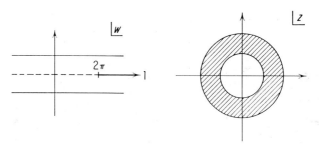

Figure A6.1

By previous result,

$$f(z) = \sum_{-\infty}^{+\infty} A_\nu z^\nu, \qquad A_\nu = \frac{1}{2\pi i} \oint f(\xi)\xi^{-\nu-1}\, d\xi.$$

Hence in the variable w we get

$$f(w) = \sum_{-\infty}^{+\infty} A_\nu e^{i\nu w}, \qquad A_\nu = \frac{1}{2\pi} \int_0^{2\pi} f(w)e^{-i\nu w}\, dw.$$

Lemma of Jordan. $f(z)$ *holomorph in the upper half-plane except for a finite number of poles,* $C = $ *a half-circle of radius r in the upper half-plane. Let* $f(z) \to 0$ *uniformly when* $|z| \to \infty$, *then*

$$\lim_{r \to 0} \int_C e^{itz}f(z)\, dz \to 0, \quad \text{if } t > 0.$$

Proof. Let $z = re^{i\varphi}$

$$\left| e^{i\,\mathrm{tr}\cos\varphi - \mathrm{tr}\sin\varphi} \right| = e^{-\mathrm{tr}\sin\varphi}.$$

Hence for $|f(z)| < \varepsilon$ there exists an $N(\varepsilon)$ such that for $r > N(\varepsilon)$

$$\left| \oint e^{itz}f(z)\, dz \right| < \varepsilon r \int_0^{\pi} e^{-\mathrm{tr}\sin\varphi}\, d\varphi$$

$$\leqslant 2\varepsilon r \int_0^{\pi/2} e^{-\mathrm{tr}\frac{2}{\pi}\varphi}\, d\varphi \quad \text{because } \sin\varphi/\varphi \geqslant 2/\pi$$

$$= \frac{2\pi\varepsilon}{t}(1 - e^{-rt}) < \frac{2\varepsilon\pi}{t}.$$

Similarly, for $t < 0$ the same statement holds in the lower half-plane, and

$$\lim_{R \to \infty} \int e^{tz} f(z) \, dz = 0 \qquad \begin{array}{l} \text{for} \quad t > 0 \text{ in the left-hand plane,} \\ \text{for} \quad t < 0 \text{ in the right-hand plane.} \end{array}$$

Application. The step function $\theta(t)$ has the following Cauchy representation:

$$\theta(t) = \frac{1}{2\pi i} \oint \frac{e^{i\omega t}}{\omega} \, d\omega$$

or

$$\theta(t) = \tfrac{1}{2} + (1/\pi) \int_0^\infty \frac{\sin \omega t}{\omega} \, d\omega.$$

Cauchy or Dispersion Relations

If $f(z)$ is holomorphic, then $f(z)/(z - z')$ is no longer holomorphic. Assume $f(z') \neq 0$; the Cauchy formula reads

$$\frac{1}{2\pi i} \oint_C \frac{f(z) \, dz}{z - z'} = \begin{cases} f(z') & \text{if } z' \text{ is inside } C, \\ 0 & \text{if } z' \text{ is outside } C. \end{cases}$$

Thus the integral does not define a holomorphic function. If we define *the index* of a point z_0 with respect to a curve C by

$$n(C, z_0) = \frac{1}{2\pi i} \oint_C \frac{dz}{z - z_0},$$

we can then write Cauchy's theorem as

$$2\pi i n(C, z_0) f(z_0) = \oint_C \frac{f(z) \, dz}{z - z_0}.$$

Simple Dispersion Relations. Let $f(z)$ be holomorphic in the whole upper half-plane (including the real axis from above). Let $z_{(\pm)} = x' \pm i\varepsilon$, $\varepsilon > 0$, small, then

$$\frac{1}{2\pi i} \oint \frac{f(z) \, dz}{z - z_\pm} = \begin{cases} f(x' + i) & \text{for } (+) \text{ sign,} \\ 0 & \text{for } (-) \text{ sign.} \end{cases}$$

Assume now that the modulus $|f(z)| \to 0$ as $R \to \infty$; then

$$\frac{1}{2\pi i} \int_{-\infty}^{+\infty} \frac{f(x) \, dx}{x - z_\pm} = \begin{cases} f(x' + i\varepsilon) & (+) \\ 0 & (-). \end{cases}$$

We could put the right-hand side always equal to zero provided we take contours of the form

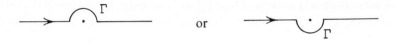

Figure A6.2

Relation to Principal Value Integral

$$\lim_{\varepsilon \to 0} \int_{-\infty}^{+\infty} \frac{f(x)\,dx}{x - (x' \pm i\varepsilon)} = \lim_{\rho \to 0} \left[\left(\int_{-\infty}^{x'-\rho} + \int_{x'+\rho}^{+\infty} \right) \frac{f(x)\,dx}{x - x'} + \int_{\Gamma} \frac{f(x)\,dx}{x - x'} \right]$$

$$= P \int_{-\infty}^{+\infty} \frac{f(x)\,dx}{x - x'} + 2\pi i \begin{cases} f(x')/2 & (+ \text{ sign}) \\ -f(x')/2 & (- \text{ sign}). \end{cases}$$

This would be equal to $2\pi i f(x')$ for $(+)$ sign and 0 for $(-)$ sign. Hence in both cases we get

$$f(x') = (1/i\pi)P \int_{-\infty}^{+\infty} \frac{f(x)\,dx}{x - x'}.$$

Note. We can write symbolically

$$\lim_{\varepsilon \to 0} \frac{1}{z \pm i\varepsilon} = P\frac{1}{z} \mp i\pi\delta(z)$$

or

$$\lim_{\varepsilon \to 0} \frac{1}{x - z_\pm} = P\frac{1}{x - x'} \pm i\pi\delta(x - x'),$$

for we then obtain the same relation as above:

$$\lim_{\varepsilon \to 0} \frac{1}{2\pi i} \int_{-\infty}^{+\infty} \frac{f(x)\,dx}{x - z_\pm} = \frac{1}{2\pi i} P \int_{-\infty}^{+\infty} \frac{f(x)\,dx}{x - x'} \pm \frac{i\pi}{2\pi i} \int \delta(x - x')f(x)\,dx$$

$$= \begin{cases} f(x') & (+ \text{ sign}) \\ 0 & (- \text{ sign}). \end{cases}$$

Dispersion Relations for the Real and Imaginary Parts

On the real axis let $f(x) = D(x) + iA(x)$. Then

$$D(x') + iA(x') = -\frac{i}{\pi} P \int_{-\infty}^{+\infty} \frac{D(x) + iA(x)}{x - x'}\,dx.$$

Hence

$$D(x') = \frac{1}{\pi} P \int_{-\infty}^{+\infty} \frac{A(x)}{x - x'}\,dx \qquad A(x') = \frac{1}{\pi} P \int_{-\infty}^{+\infty} \frac{D(x)}{x' - x}\,dx,$$

A and D are said to be the *Hilbert transform* of each other. If, in particular,

$$f(-x) = \overline{f(x)} \qquad \text{i.e.,} \quad D(-x) = D(x), \quad A(-x) = -A(x),$$

we have

$$\pi D(x') = P \int_0^\infty \frac{A(x)\,dx}{x - x'} + \int_0^\infty \frac{A(x)\,dx}{x + x'} = 2P \int_0^\infty \frac{xA(x)\,dx}{x^2 - x'^2}.$$

Dispersion Relations with More Than One Pole

Let $f(z)$ be holomorph; then

$$\oint \frac{f(z)\,dz}{z(z - z')} = 2\pi i(\text{Res}\,(0) + \text{Res}\,(z')) = 2\pi i\left(\frac{f(z')}{z'} - \frac{f(0)}{z'} \right).$$

Hence

$$f(z') - f(0) = \frac{z'}{i\pi} P \int_{-\infty}^{+\infty} \frac{f(x)\, dx}{x(x - x')},$$

if $|f(z)| \to z$ as $R \to 0$. In terms of real and imaginary parts,

$$D(x') - D(0) = \frac{z'}{\pi} P \int \frac{A(x)\, dx}{x(x - x')}.$$

These are the dispersion relations with one *subtraction* at $z = 0$. Again, if $f(-x) = \overline{f(x)}$,

$$D(x') - D(0) = P \frac{x'}{\pi} \int_0^\infty \frac{A(x)\, dx}{x(x^2 - x'^2)}.$$

Generalization. The assumption that $|f(z)| \to 0$ as $R \to \infty$ is too stringent. Let $f(z)$ be holomorphic in the upper half-plane and assume that there exists an integer $n > 0$ such that for any δ we may find constants $A_j(\delta)$ such that

$$|f(z)| \leqslant A_0(\delta)|z|^n + A_1(\delta)|z|^{n-1} + \cdots + A_n(\delta)$$

for $Im(z) > \delta$ (i.e., a pole of order n at infinity). Let

$$g(z) = f(z)/(z - z_0 + i\varepsilon)^{n+1}.$$

For $g(z)$ we have

$$g(x) = \frac{1}{i\pi} P \int_{-\infty}^{+\infty} \frac{g(x')\, dx'}{x' - x}.$$

Hence

$$f(x) = \frac{(x - x_0 + i\varepsilon)^{n+1}}{i\pi} P \int_{-\infty}^{+\infty} \frac{f(x')\, dx'}{(x' - x)(x' - x_0 + i\varepsilon)^{n+1}}.$$

Using the symbolic identity

$$\lim_{\substack{\varepsilon \to 0 \\ \varepsilon > 0}} \frac{1}{(x' - x_0 + i\varepsilon)^{n+1}} = P \frac{1}{(x' - x_0)^{n+1}} - \frac{i\pi(-1)^n}{n!} \delta^{(n)}(x' - x_0),$$

we obtain the dispersion relation with $(n + 1)$ subtractions:

$$f(x) = \frac{(x - x_0)^{n+1}}{i\pi} P \int_{-\infty}^{+\infty} \frac{f(x')\, dx'}{(x' - x)(x' - x_0)^{n+1}}$$

$$- f(x_0) - \frac{f'(x_0)}{1}(x - x_0) - \cdots - \frac{f^{(n)}(x_0)}{n!}(x - x_0).$$

Dispersion Relations without the Holomorphy in the Upper Half-Plane Theorem of Cauchy-Bremmermann

Given any function $f(x)$ of class (C^n) (n times differentiable) such that $f(x) \xrightarrow[|z| \to \infty]{} 0(|x|^{-\alpha})$ and $f^{(n)}(x) \to 0(|x|^{-\alpha})$, $0 < m \leqslant n$, $\alpha > 0$, then there exists a function $\check{f}$, holomorphic in the entire plane except the real axis, such that

$$\lim_{\substack{\varepsilon > 0 \\ \varepsilon \to 0}} \{\check{f}(x + i\varepsilon) - \check{f}(x - i\varepsilon)\} = f(x)$$

and

$$\lim_{\substack{\varepsilon \to 0 \\ \varepsilon > 0}} \{\check{f}^{(n)}(x + i\varepsilon) - \check{f}^{(n)}(x - i\varepsilon)\} = f^{(n)}(x);$$

$\check{f}$ is explicitly given by

$$\check{f}(z) = \frac{1}{2\pi i} \int_{-\infty}^{+\infty} \frac{f(x)}{x - z} \, dx, \qquad Imz \neq 0.$$

The proof is almost evident from the explicit form of $\check{f}$. To obtain the dispersion relation, let $\alpha = 1$; we then have

$$f(x_0) = \lim_{\varepsilon \to 0} \frac{1}{2\pi i} \int_{-\infty}^{+\infty} f(x) \left[\frac{1}{x - x_0 - i\varepsilon} - \frac{1}{x - x_0 + i\varepsilon} \right] dx$$

$$= \frac{1}{\pi i} \int_{-\infty}^{+\infty} P\left(\frac{1}{x - x_0}\right) f(x) \, dx.$$

This representation theorem also holds for functions given in an interval along the real axis:

$$\check{f}(z) = \frac{1}{2\pi i} \int_{a}^{b} \frac{f(x)}{x - z} \, dx, \qquad Imz \neq 0.$$

A further generalization is obtained as follows. Suppose we have a meromorphic function (holomorphic with a finite number of poles) in the lower half-plane. Let $f(x)$ be the restriction of this function to the real axis. If we form

$$\check{f}(z) = \frac{1}{2\pi i} \int_{-\infty}^{+\infty} \frac{f(x)}{x - z} \, dx,$$

then $\check{f}(z)$ is holomorphic in the upper half-plane and zero in the whole lower half-plane. As an example, consider $f(z) = 1/(z + i\varepsilon)$. We find

$$\check{f} = 0 \qquad\qquad \text{for } Imz < 0,$$

$$\check{f} = 1/(z + i\varepsilon) \qquad \text{for } Imz > 0.$$

The theorem also holds for distributions. Let T be a tempered distribution, and $T = 0(|x|^{-\beta})$, $\beta > 0$ for large x, and let

$$\check{T}(z) = (1/2\pi i)T \cdot [1/(x - z)].$$

Then

$$\lim_{\substack{\varepsilon \to 0 \\ \varepsilon > 0}} \int_{-\infty}^{+\infty} (\check{T}(x + i\varepsilon) - \check{T}(x - i\varepsilon))\varphi(x) \, dx = T \cdot \varphi$$

for any test function φ.

Examples.

(1) $\quad \check{\delta}(z) = \frac{1}{2\pi i} \int_{-\infty}^{+\infty} \frac{\delta(x)}{x - z} \, dx = -\frac{1}{2\pi i z}.$

(2) $\quad \delta^{(n)}(z) = (-1)^{n+1} \dfrac{n!}{2\pi i z^{n+1}}.$

(3) $\quad \delta_+ \cdot \varphi = \lim_{\substack{\text{Def.}\ \varepsilon > 0 \\ \varepsilon \to 0}} - \dfrac{1}{i\pi} \int_{-\infty}^{+\infty} \dfrac{1}{x + i\varepsilon}\, \varphi(x)\, dx \quad (= -\varphi(0)).$

$$\delta_+(z) = \begin{cases} -\dfrac{1}{\pi i z} & Imz > 0, \\[2mm] 0 & Imz < 0. \end{cases}$$

(4) $\quad \displaystyle\int_{-\infty}^{+\infty} P\left(\dfrac{1}{x^n}\right)\varphi(x)\, dx \equiv \lim_{\substack{\varepsilon \to 0 \\ \varepsilon > 0}} \dfrac{1}{2} \int_{-\infty}^{+\infty} \left[\dfrac{1}{(x + i\varepsilon)^n} + \dfrac{1}{(x - i\varepsilon)^n}\right]\varphi(x).$

$$\check{P}\left(\dfrac{1}{z^n}\right) = \begin{cases} \dfrac{1}{2z^n} & Imz > 0, \\[2mm] -\dfrac{1}{2z^n} & Imz < 0. \end{cases}$$

The Maximum Principle. *If $f(z)$ is holomorphic and nonconstant in a region G then its absolute value $|f(z)|$ has no maximum in G.*

Proof. Let $z_0 \in G$ be the point where $|f(z_0)|$ is a maximum and let $w_0 = f(z_0)$. But w_0 has a neighborhood in the w-plane which contains points of modulus greater than $|w_0|$. This is a contradiction.

Corollary. If $f(z)$ is holomorphic on a closed bounded set B, then the maximum of $|f(z)|$ is taken on the boundary of B.

Proof. If $f(z_0)$ is a maximum, then $|f(z)|$ would have a maximum in the neighborhood $|z - z_0| < \delta$ in B, but this is impossible unless $f(z)$ is constant in this neighborhood; but then $f(z)$ is constant throughout the region.

The theorem can also be proved analytically from Cauchy theorem. The value of $f(z)$ in the middle of the circle is the mean value of $f(z)$ along the periphery of the circle.

Under special circumstances stronger statements can be made:

Lemma of Schwarz. *If $f(z)$ is holomorphic for $|z| < 1$ and satisfies $|f(z)| \leqslant 1$, $f(0) = 0$, then $|f(z)| \leqslant z$ and $|f'(0)| \leqslant 1$. Equality holds only if $f(z) = cz$ where c is a constant of absolute value one.*

Entire Functions, Meromorphic Functions

Definition. *A function holomorphic in the entire finite plane is said to be an entire (integral) function. A function $f(z)$ is meromorph, if it has only isolated singularities which are poles and outside of these points it is holomorph.*

Convergence of Infinite Products. *A necessary and sufficient condition for the absolute convergence of the product $\displaystyle\prod_{1}^{\infty} (1 + a_n)$ is the convergence of the series $\displaystyle\sum_{1}^{n} |a_n|$. (Note that the convergence of $\displaystyle\sum_{1}^{n} a_n$ is neither sufficient nor necessary.)*

Proof. Consider the series $\sum_1^\infty \log(1 + a_n)$, with the principal branch of logarithm in each term. If this series converges with the partial sum S_n approaching S, then the product $P = \prod(1 + a_n)$ converges to e^S, which is different from zero. The convergence of the series is also necessary for the convergence of the product. Because

$$\lim_{z \to 0} \frac{\log(1 + z)}{z} = 1$$

we have

$$(1 - \varepsilon)|a_n| < |\log(1 + a_n)| < (1 + \varepsilon)|a_n|,$$

and the two series $\sum|a_n|$ and $\sum\log(1 + a_n)$ are simultaneously absolutely convergent.

Theorem of Weierstrass. *There exists an entire function with arbitrarily prescribed zeros a_n provided that, in the case of infinitely many zeros, $a_n \to \infty$. Every entire function with these and no other zeros can be written in the form*

$$f(z) = z^m e^{g(z)} \prod_{\substack{n=1 \\ (a_n \neq 0)}}^\infty (1 - z/a_n)e^{(z/a_n) + \frac{1}{2}(z/a_n)^2 + \cdots + (1/m_n)(z/a_n)^{m_n}},$$

where m_n are certain integers, and $g(z)$ is an entire function.

Proof. If $g(z)$ is entire then $f(z) = \exp[g(z)]$ is also entire and different from zero. Conversely, every entire function that is different from zero is of the form $\exp(g)$. If there were a finite number of zeros we have

$$f(z) = z^m e^{g(z)} \prod_1^N (1 - z/a_n).$$

In the case of infinite zeros we have to see that the product converges, i.e., if the series $\sum_1^\infty 1/|a_n|$ converges. To achieve this one can always add convergence-producing factors shown in the statement of the theorem.

Examples.

(1) $\sin \pi z = \pi z \prod_1^\infty (1 - z^2/n^2) = \pi z \prod_{n \neq 0}(1 - z/n)e^{z/n}.$

(2) $\Gamma(z)^{-1} = e C_z z \prod_{n=1}^\infty [(1 + z/n)e^{-z/n}], \quad C = 0.5772156649\ldots.$

$z\Gamma(z)\Gamma(-z) = \sin \pi z/z.$

$\Gamma(z + 1) = z\Gamma(z).$

$\Gamma(z)$ is meromorphic with poles at $z = 0, -1, -2, \ldots$, but has no zeros. Another definition:

$$\Gamma(z) = \int_0^\infty t^{z-1}e^{-t}\, dt, \qquad Re\, z > 0.$$

An entire function in the *extended plane* (plane with the point at infinity included) must be a constant by the maximum principle.

Mittag-Leffler Theorem. *Given a sequence of distinct complex numbers* $\{z_n\}$ *with* $\lim\limits_{n \to \infty} z_n = \infty$ *(no limiting point in the finite plane) and polynomials* $P_n(z)$ *without a constant term, i.e.,* $P_n(0) = 0$, *then the most general meromorphic function having poles at* z_n *and the corresponding singular parts* $P_n[1/(z - z_n)]$ *is, assuming* $z_0 = 0$, *of the form*

$$f(z) = P_0\left(\frac{1}{z}\right) + \sum_{n=1}^\infty \left[P_n\left(\frac{1}{z - z_n}\right) - p_n(z)\right] + g(z),$$

where $p_n(z)$ *are suitable chosen polynomials, given below, and* $g(z)$ *is an entire function.*

Proof. $P_n[1/(z - z_n)]$ is holomorphic for $|z| < |z_n|$; we expand it around $z = 0$ in a Taylor series $\sum_\nu A_{n\nu}z^\nu$. We now choose $p_n(z)$ to be the partial sum of this series ending, say, with the term ν_n:

$$p_n(z) = \sum_{\nu=0}^{\nu_n} A_{n\nu}z^\nu.$$

If $|P_n| \leqslant M_n$, we have the following estimate for $|z| \leqslant |z_n|/2$:

$$\left|P_n\left(\frac{1}{z - z_n}\right) - p_n(z)\right| \leqslant M_n(4|z|/|z_n|)^{\nu_n+1}; \quad z \leqslant |z_n|/4.$$

Thus the Mittag-Leffler series can be made convergent by choosing ν_n large enough. The series $\sum\limits_n M_n(4z/z_n)^{\nu_n+1}$ converges in the whole plane if $\lim\limits_{n \to \infty} M_n^{1/\nu_n}/|z_n| = 0$; this is assured by choosing $n_\nu > \log M_n$. For $|z| < R$, R arbitrary, the series $\sum\limits_n (P_n - p_n)$ has only a finite number of terms that become infinite. From a certain term n onwards the above estimate for $|P_n - p_n|$ holds in the disk $|z| \leqslant R$. If the terms with $|z_n| \leqslant R$ are omitted, the remaining series converges absolutely and uniformly in $|z| \leqslant R$. Because R is arbitrary the series converges in the whole plane, $z \neq z_n$.

Special Case. *If* $P_n(z) = z$ *for every* n *and if there exists an integer* k *such that*

$$\sum_{n=1}^\infty 1/|z_n|^k = \infty, \quad \text{but} \quad \sum_{n=1}^\infty 1/|z_n|^{k+1} < \infty, \qquad k \geqslant 0,$$

then

$$f(z) = 1/z + \sum_{n=1}^{\infty} \left[\frac{1}{z - z_n} + \frac{1}{z_n} + \frac{z}{z_n^2} + \cdots + \frac{z^{k-1}}{z_n^k} \right] + g(z),$$

if $k > 0$, *and*

$$f(z) = \sum_{n=0}^{\infty} \frac{1}{z - z_n} + g(z), \qquad \text{if } k = 0.$$

Theorem. *A function that is meromorphic in the extended plane is necessarily a rational function—i.e., the ratio of two polynomials.*

Theorem. *Every function that is meromorphic in the whole plane is the ratio of two entire functions. If $F(z)$ is meromorphic in the whole plane, we can find entire functions $g(z)$ with the poles of F as its zeros. Then the product $F(z)g(z) = f(z)$ is an entire function.*

Examples of Mittag-Leffler Theorem.

(1) $\pi^2/\sin^2 \pi z = \sum_{-\infty}^{+\infty} 1/(z - n)^2.$

(2) $\pi \cot \pi z = 1/z + \sum_{n=1}^{\infty} 2z/(z^2 - n^2) = \lim_{m \to \infty} \sum_{-m}^{m} 1/(z - n).$

(3) $\pi/\sin \pi z = \lim_{m \to \infty} \sum_{-m}^{m} (-1)^m [1/(z - n)].$

Branch-Point Singularities

So far we have considered only poles and essential singularities. Consider now the function $w = z^n$. The ray $\arg z = \theta$ is mapped into $\arg w = n\theta$; the circle $|z| = r$ goes into $|w| = r^n$ covered n times. The segment $k2\pi/n \leqslant \arg z < (k + 1)2\pi/n$ is mapped into the whole circle $|w| = r^n$ in the w-plane. The inverse function is many valued. To have a single-valued mapping we introduce *Riemann surfaces*: n copies of the w-plane each having the points $w = 0$ and $w = \infty$ in common; these are the so-called *branch points*. We join the successive sheets along any curve connecting the points 0 and infinity, but the same in all sheets (*branch line* of the Riemann surface), e.g., along the positive real line. The nth surface will be joined with the first. The topology of the Riemann surface so obtained is as follows: If we go counterclockwise around the origin from the point $(x + iy)$ in the sheet S_k we arrive at the point $(x - iy)$ still in the same sheet; but if we go down vertically from $(x + iy)$ to the real axis we go to sheet S_{k-1}. Similarly, a vertical line up from $(x - iy)$ goes into the sheet S_{k+1}. A neighborhood of a point on the branch line consists of a half-circle in S_{k+1} and a half-circle in S_k (or S_k and S_{k-1}). Starting from S_k we go counterclockwise $S_k, S_{k+1}, \ldots, S_n, S_1, \ldots, S_k$ and clockwise $S_k, S_{k-1}, \ldots, S_1, S_n, \ldots, S_k$.

Roots. We have n determinations of $z = w^{1/n}$:

$$z_1(w), \ldots, z_n(w).$$

The first one is the *principal determination* of the root.

Logarithmic Branch Point

The equation $e^w = z$, $z \neq 0, \infty$, has infinitely many solutions:

$$w = \log z = \log |z| + i \arg z.$$

The various determinations of w differ by $2\pi i$. The principal determination is characterized by

$$-\pi < \arg z \leqslant \pi.$$

Again we may introduce Riemann sheets connected along the branch line joining the two branch points $z = 0$ and $z = \infty$. The branch line is customarily taken along the negative real axis. The two branch points here are of infinite order; no neighborhood is defined for them in contrast to the previous algebraic branch points of $z^{1/n}$.

The function $\log z$ is holomorphic everywhere in the cut plane. For the principal determination we have the relations

$$\log z = \int_1^z dt/t, \quad |\arg z| < \pi$$

and

$$\log z = \sum_{n=1}^{\infty} (-1)^{n-1}/n(z-1)^n, \quad |z-1| < 1.$$

For $-\pi < \arg z < \pi$ we get the mapping

$$\text{cut } z\text{-plane} \to (2k-1)\pi < Imw < (2k+1)\pi.$$

Counterclockwise through the cut we go from the sheet S_k to S_{k+1}, clockwise from S_k to S_{k-1}:

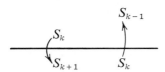

Figure A6.3

Analytic Continuation

Theorem. *If $f(z)$ is holomorphic in G and $f(z) = 0$ on an arc A in G, then $f(z) = 0$ everywhere in G.*

Proof. $f(z) = 0$ on A implies $f'(z) = 0$ on A, because we can take the limit $\Delta z \Rightarrow 0$ along the arc. Thus all derivatives vanish along A. Then by Taylor expansion around some point z_0 of A, $f(z) = 0$ inside some circle C with center at z_0. Now we can take another arc A' along which $f(z) = 0$, etc. Continuing this process everywhere in G we prove the theorem.

Theorem. *If $f(z)$ is holomorph in G, then $f(z)$ is determined uniquely by its values on an arc in G. (More generally on a set with an accumulation point in G.)*

Corollary. *Two single-valued holomorphic functions defined in the same domain are identical. (Analytic functions are strongly tied up with domains.)*

Definition. *Let $f_1(z)$ be holomorphic in G_1, $f_2(z)$ holomorphic in G_2, G_1, and G_2 intersecting along an arc A (or a domain D) and $f_1 = f_2$ on A (or D), then f_1 and f_2 are analytic continuations of each other and*

$$f(z) = \begin{cases} f_1(z), & z \in G_1 \\ f_2(z), & z \in G_2 \end{cases}$$

is holomorphic in the union of G_1 and G_2.

Example.

$1 + z + z^2 + \cdots$ $\qquad$ is holomorphic in $|z| < 1$,

$e^{-(1-z)t} \, dt$ $\qquad$ is holomorphic in $Rez > 1$,

$-(1 + 1/z + 1/z^2 + \cdots)$ $\quad$ is holomorphic in $|z| > 1$.

All these functions represent $f(z) = 1/(1 - z)$ in different domains, which is holomorphic everywhere except at $z = 1$. The above forms are then analytic continuations of each other.

There are various ways of performing the analytic continuation.

Analytic Continuation by Rearrangement of Power Series

Let

$$f(z) = \sum_{n=0}^{\infty} c_n (z - a)^n$$

with a circle of convergence of radius $R(a)$ where

$$1/R(a) = \limsup_{n \to \infty} |c_n|^{1/n}.$$

Set $z = (z - b) + b$ and use the binomial expansion

$$z^n = (z - a + a)^n = \sum_{k=0}^{\infty} \binom{n}{k} (z - a)^k a^{n-k}$$

to obtain the following direct rearrangement of $f(z)$ at the point b:

$$f(z;b) = \sum_{0}^{\infty} c_n(b)(z - b)^n.$$

One finds

$$c_n(b) = \sum_{k=0}^{\infty} k(k-1)\ldots(k-n+1)c_k(b-a)^{k-n} = \frac{f_{(b)}^{(n)}}{n!}.$$

Because of the result

$$R(a) - |a - b| \leqslant R(b) \leqslant R(a) + |a - b|$$

we have the possibility of analytic continuation if the circle of convergence of $f(z;b)$ has points outside that of $f(z;a)$. If the two circles touch each other the tangent point is a singular point; we know that we must have at least one singular point on the circle of convergence.

There are of course functions that cannot be continued further; in this case the circle of convergence is a *natural boundary* of the function.

Examples.

(1) The series $\sum_{n=0}^{\infty} (1/n!)z^{2^n}$ has the circle $|z| = 1$ as its natural boundary.

(2) The lacunary series $\sum_{k=1}^{\infty} a_k z^{n_k} a_k \neq 0$ where $\lim_{k \to \infty} (k/n_k) = 0$ has its circle of convergence as a natural boundary.

Definition. *A finite or infinite sequence of power series*

$$f_n(z) = \sum_{k=0}^{\infty} C_{k,n}(z - a_n)^k, \quad |z - a_n| < R_n, \quad n = 1, 2, 3, \ldots$$

forms a chain if for each $n > 1$, $|a_n - a_{n+1}| < R_{n+1}$, and if $f_n(z)$ is a direct arrangement of f_{n+1}.

Definition. *Two power series $f(z;a)$ and $g(z;b)$ are equivalent, $f \sim g$ if there exists a finite chain joining $f(z)$ with $g(z)$.*

$f \sim g$ is an equivalence relation; $f \sim f$; $f \sim g \to g \sim f$, and $f \sim g$, $g \sim h \to f \sim h$. Hence all power series separate into equivalent classes.

Definition. *An equivalent class of power series is an analytic function. We may include poles, branch points, and the point at infinity in the domain of definition of analytic functions. (The definition includes many-valued functions.)*

Theorem. *Let G be simple connected, $a \in G$. If $f(z;a)$ can be continued analytically along every path in G, then the continuation defines a holomorphic function.*

Domain of Holomorphism. An equivalence class of power series containing at most one element for each center c defines a single-valued function $f(z)$. The set $\{c\}$ is the domain of holomorphism D of f (plus possible the point at infinity). The domain of existence is the union of D with the set of poles, if any.

The following theorem tells us that the number of Riemann sheets of a function is at most countable infinite.

Theorem of Poincaré and Volterra. *The number of different power series in* $(z - a)$, *a fixed, which belong to an equivalence class, is finite or countable infinite.*

Theorem (Mittag-Leffler, Acta Math., 1884). *Given any domain D in the complex plane, there exists a function* $f(z)$ *having D as a domain of holomorphism.*

That is, given any domain there exists a function which cannot be continued analytically outside this domain; any domain is a domain of holomorphism. This theorem is not true for functions of more than one complex variable (see App. 9).

Analytic continuation by means of functional equations.

Consider the functional equation

$$F(z,f_1(z),f_2(z)) = 0, \quad z \in G$$

where f_i can also be the derivatives, so that we have an ordinary differential equation. We have the following theorem:

Theorem. *Analytic continuation of the solutions of the above functional equation are the solutions of the analytic continuation of the functional equation itself.* (Law of permanence of functional equations.)

In the case of differential equations, the following theorem is useful (E. Ince, *Ordinary Differential Equations*, New York, Dover, 1944, p. 72).

Theorem of Poincaré. *If a differential equation depends holomorphically on a parameter and the boundary conditions are independent of that parameter, then the solutions of the equation are holomorphic functions of the parameter.* (H. Poincaré, *Les méthodes nouvelles de la méchanique céleste*, Vol. 1, Chap. 1, Paris, 1892, Gauthier-Villars.)

In particular, if the coefficients of the equation are entire functions of the parameter then the solution is also an entire function of the parameter.

For the analytic properties of integral equations, see App. 7.

Schwarz' Reflection Principle. *Let* $f(z)$ *be holomorphic in G, which contains a segment A of the real axis, and let* G^* *be the reflected domain; then* $F(z) = [f(z^*)]^*$ *is holomorphic in* G^*; f *and F are analytic continuations of each other, if f real on A.*

Proof. We first note that if $f(z)$ is holomorphic, $f(z^*)$ and $f^*(z)$ are not; it suffices to consider the Cauchy-Riemann differential equations. But $f^*(z^*)$ again satisfies these equations if $f(z)$ does. One can also look directly at the power series expansion at a point a. If

$$f(z) = \sum a_n(z - a)^n$$

we get

$$f^*(z^*) = \left[\sum a_n(z^* - a)\right]^* = \sum a_n^*(z - a_n^*).$$

Generalization. *Let G be a domain inside a circle C of radius r having an arc A common with C, and $\bar{G}$ domain obtained by reflecting G through the circle C. Let $f(z)$ be holomorphic in G and continuous on A, and $w = f(z)$ be in some circle $C': |w - b| \leqslant R$ for z on A. Define*

$$\bar{z} = a + r^2/(z^* - a^*).$$

Then the function

$$f(\bar{z}) = b + R^2/(f^*(z) - b^*)$$

is holomorphic in $\bar{G}$. (* means complex conjugation, ⁻ reflection with respect to the circle.)

Definition. *A function $f(z)$ is said to be real analytic (or holomorphic) if it takes real values along some segment A of the real axis. The Schwarz reflection principle makes it therefore possible to continue real analytic functions from upper half-plane to lower half-plane, and vice versa.*

Titchmarch Theorem. Special case (Titchmarch, *Fourier Integral*, p. 119, Oxford U.P., 1959). *If the Fourier transform $\tilde{f}(k)$ of a function $f(x)$*

$$f(x) = \int_{-\infty}^{+\infty} \tilde{f}(k)e^{ixk}\, dk$$

is (i) bounded and square integrable, (ii) $f(k) = 0$ for $k < 0$, then

$$f(z) = \int_{-\infty}^{+\infty} \tilde{f}(k)e^{izk}\, dk = \int_{0}^{\infty} \tilde{f}(k)e^{izk}\, dk$$

is the analytic continuation of $f(x)$ to the upper half-plane; $f(x)$ is the boundary value of the holomorphic function $f(z)$.

Proof. The factor

$$e^{ikz} = e^{ikx}e^{-ky}$$

with $k > 0$ decreases exponentially for $y \to +\infty$ (upper half-plane). Furthermore, because $\tilde{f}(k)$ is bounded in the upper half-plane, $|f(z)|$ is bounded:

$$|f(z)| = \left|\int_{0}^{\infty} \tilde{f}(k)e^{ikz}\, dk\right| \leqslant \int_{0}^{\infty} |\tilde{f}(k)|e^{-ky}\, dk \leqslant K\int_{0}^{\infty} e^{-ky}\, dk = K/y,$$

$f(z)$ is not only bounded but decreases at least as rapidly as $1/R$. The holomorphy of $f(z)$ follows then from this boundedness and its being a super-position of holomorphic functions e^{ikz}.

Application. Analyticity of Wightman functions—Let $W(x_1, \ldots, x_n)$ be a function of n fourvectors. Let

$$W(x_1, \ldots, x_n) = \int e^{-i\sum p\cdot x} W(p_1, \ldots, p_n)\, dp_1 \ldots dp_n$$

such that each p_k is in the future light cone: $p_k^2 \geqslant 0$, $p_k^0 > 0$. Then the Fourier transform W is zero outside the light cone. If we introduce the complex variable $z = x + iy$ the exponential e^{-ipz} converges for $p \cdot y > 0$, i.e., y in the future light cone. Hence $W(z)$ is holomorphic in the $8n$-dimensional region with y's in the future light cone, the so-called future *tube*.

Examples and Exercises

1. Prove the triangular inequality $\left| \sum\limits_{i=1}^{n} z_i \right| \leqslant \sum\limits_{1}^{n} |z_i|$.

2. Prove the Cauchy inequality $\left| \sum\limits_{1}^{n} z_i w_i \right| \leqslant \sum\limits_{1}^{n} |z_i|^2 \sum\limits_{1}^{n} |w_i|^2$.

3. A real function of a complex variable either has the derivative zero or the derivative does not exist; if the derivative exists everywhere the function is a constant.

4. Theorem. *The only possible finite singular points of the solutions of a linear differential equation $w^{(n)} + p_1(z)w^{(n-1)} + \cdots = 0$ are the singular points of the coefficients themselves.* (F. Tricomi, *Differential Equations*, London, Blackie, 1961.)

5. Theorem of Herglotz. *If $f(z)$ is holomorphic for $\operatorname{Im} z > 0$ and if $\operatorname{Im} f(z) \geqslant 0$ for $\operatorname{Im} z > 0$, then there exists a bounded nondecreasing function $\eta(t)$ such that*

    $$f(z) = Az + \int_{-\infty}^{+\infty} \frac{1 + tz}{t - z} \, d\eta(t) + C,$$

    where A and C are real constants and $A \geqslant 0$. Furthermore, $f(z)/z \to A$ as $z \to \infty$ in any sector $0 < \varepsilon \leqslant \arg z \leqslant \pi - \varepsilon$; $0 < \varepsilon < \pi/2$.

6. Study the three branch points of the functions arc sin z, log log z, and $[1 - (1 - z)^{1/2}]^{1/2}$.

7. The function sin (cot $1/z$) has infinitely many essential singularities with a limit point at $z = 0$.

8. Given a solution of the integral equation of Volterra type $f(z) = g(z) + \int K(z - w)f(w)\,dw$, where $g(z)$ and $K(z)$ are given entire functions, which is holomorphic in some neighborhood of the origin, then this solution can be extended to the finite plane as entire function.

9. Carlson's Theorem. *$f(z)$ holomorphic in $\operatorname{Re} z > 0$, $f(z) = 0(e^{a|z|})$ as $z \to \infty$ in $\operatorname{Re} z > 0$ with $a < \pi$. Then if $f(z) = 0$ for positive integer z, $f(z)$ vanishes identically.*

10. Show that the poles of the function $y = \dfrac{1}{z} \tan \dfrac{1}{z_n}$ accumulate at $z = 0$, but this point behaves like a pole (*quasipole*) if one approaches it within a sector between the series of poles. Obtain the "residues" $[\lim_{z \to 0} zy]$ within each sector. (For quasi poles of the scattering amplitude see A. O. Barut and T. Sawada, *Nuovo Cimento*, **37**, 1531 (1965)).

APPENDIX 7

Necessary Conditions for the Singularities of Complex Integral Transforms

The following lemma, originally due to Hadamard, is very useful in studying the singularities of integral expressions and also in making the analytic continuation of integral transforms.

Lemma. *Consider the integral*

$$g(w) = \int_C f(z,w) \, dz$$

over an arc C in the z-plane. Let D be a neighborhood of the arc C, and let G be a domain in the w-plane. Let further f(z,w) be regular in both variables, except for a finite number of isolated singularities or branch points, for any value of the other variable, when $z \in D$ and $w \in G$; D and G may extend over many Riemann sheets of the function f. Under these conditions g(w) can be singular at a point $w_0 \in G$ only if

   (1) *$f(z,w_0)$ in z-plane has a singularity coinciding with the end points of the arc C (end point singularity),*

   (2) *two singularities of f, $z_1(w)$ and $z_2(w)$, approach the arc C from opposite sides and pinch the arc precisely at $w = w_0$ (coincident or pinching singularities),*

   (3) *a singularity z(w) tends to infinity as $w \to w_0$ deforming the contour with itself to infinity; one has to make a change of variables to bring the point ∞ to the finite plane to see what happens.*

For a fixed contour C and $w \in G$, the integral defines $g(w)$ to be holomorphic in some domain. If one singularity approaches C we can modify the contour, thereby obtaining an analytic continuation of the function $g(w)$ in w-plane. Clearly this procedure of analytic continuation breaks down if one of the three situations in the lemma occurs. These are, however, necessary conditions, not sufficient. It may be that the integral is still regular in spite of these conditions.

To illustrate the lemma we consider the following situation. Suppose we get a branch point at P due to an end point singularity at A; i.e., when

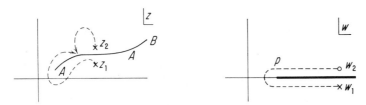

Figure A7.1

$w_0 = P$, $f(z,w_0)$ has a singularity at A. Suppose further that f has two pinching singularities z_1 and z_2, when $w \to w_1$, then w_1 may be a singular point. We change now w_1 along the dotted line to w_2. If z_1 and z_2 approach C from the same side, then w_2 is not a singular point.

The condition for an end point singularity may be expressed as follows:

$$f^{-1}(z,w_0) = 0, \quad \text{if } z \text{ is one end point of } C,$$

and the coincident singularities, if they are two poles, occur if

$$f^{-1}(z,w_0) = 0 \quad \text{and} \quad [f^{-1}(z,w_0)]' = 0 \quad \text{for some } z \text{ on } C.$$

In the latter case one has actually to look explicitly whether the two singularities are approaching C from the opposite sides.

The lemma can be generalized to multiple integrals involving several complex variables. It has been extensively used in determining the singularities of Feynman diagrams in perturbation theory. We use it in many places to obtain the singularities of the amplitudes from the unitarity condition.[1]

Analytic Properties of Linear Integral Equations

Consider first the homogeneous integral equation of the form

$$f(k) = \int G(k;x,y) \, dx \, dy.$$

If the kernel G is holomorphic in k in a certain region of the complex k-plane, and if G is continuous in D and on its boundary B, then $f(k)$ is also holomorphic in D provided G is bounded; i.e.,

$$G(k;x,y) \leqslant g(x,y) \quad \text{for all } k \text{ on } B,$$

with

$$\int g(x,y) \, dx \, dy < \infty.$$

[1] See also J. C. Polkinghorne and G. R. Screaton, *Nuovo Cimento*, **15**, 289, 925 (1960); J. Tarski, *J. Math. Phys.*, **1**, 149 (1960).

It is sufficient to require this bound on the boundary B because a holomorphic function takes its maximum value on B.

The inhomogeneous equation (Fredholm)

$$f(k,x) = f_0(k,x) + \lambda \int dy\, G(k;x,y)f(k,y),$$

with a square integrable, holomorphic (in k) kernel G and bounded kernel, (as above) has the unique and *meromorphic* (in k) solution:

$$f(k,x) = f_0(k,x) + \frac{\lambda}{\Delta(\lambda,k)} \int dy\, \Delta(\lambda,k;x,y)f_0(k,y)$$

where

$$\Delta(\lambda,k) = 1 + \sum_{n=1}^{\infty} \frac{(-\lambda)^n}{n!} \int dx_1 \ldots dx_n \det G(k;x_r,x_s),$$

$$\Delta(\lambda,k;x,y) = G(k;x,y) + \sum_{n=1}^{\infty} \frac{(-x)^n}{n!} \int dx_1 \ldots dx_n \det G(k;x_r,x_s),$$

$$\det G(k;x_r,x_s) = \begin{vmatrix} G(k;x_1x_1) & \cdots & G(k;x_1x_n) \\ G(k;x_nx_1) & \cdots & G(k;x_nx_n) \end{vmatrix}.$$

APPENDIX 8

Legendre Functions $P_\nu(z)$ and $Q_\nu(z)$; Hypergeometric Function $F(a,b;c,z)$

The properties of the Legendre functions $P_\nu(z)$ and $Q_\nu(z)$ for complex ν and z are essential in the analytic continuation of the amplitude in $\cos\theta$ and in angular momentum.

The spherical harmonics $P_\nu^\mu(z)$ and $Q_\nu^\mu(z)$ can be defined as the solutions of the differential equation

$$(1 - z^2)\frac{d^2u}{dz^2} - 2z\frac{du}{dz} + \left[\nu(\nu + 1) - \frac{\mu^2}{1 - z^2}\right]u = 0, \qquad (A8.1)$$

where ν and μ are arbitrary complex numbers. (This is a special case of the hypergeometric differential equation.) In general, the solutions have branch points at $z = +1, -1, \infty$. We denote the solutions which are regular and single-valued for $Rez > 1$ by $P_\nu^\mu(z)$ and $Q_\nu^\mu(z)$; and those which are regular and single-valued for $|z| < 1$ by $\bar{P}_\nu^\mu(z)$ and $\bar{Q}_\nu^\mu(z)$.

For $\mu = 0$ and $\nu =$ integer (and only for these values), Eq. (A8.1) has polynomial solutions: $P_\ell(z)$, Legendre polynomials.

For $\mu = 0$ and $\nu =$ complex, the solutions are the Legendre functions of the first and second kind, $P_\nu(z)$ and $Q_\nu(z)$, respectively, regular and single-valued in the cut z-plane as follows:

Figure A8.1

When ν is an integer, $P_\nu(z)$ has no cut; in fact it is then equal to the Legendre polynomials with the property $P_\ell(z) = P_{-\ell-1}(z)$. The cut of $Q_\nu(z)$ for $\nu =$ positive integer runs between -1 and $+1$ and $Q_\ell(z)$ is regular at $z = \infty$.

331

(For v = negative integers see below). Because of the positions of the cuts we have in general

$$P_v(z) = P_{-v-1}(z) = \bar{P}_v(z) = \bar{P}_{-v-1}(z), \tag{A8.2}$$

but we have to distinguish between Q_v and $\bar{Q}_v$. We have

$$\bar{Q}_v(x) = (1/2)[Q_v(x + i0) + Q_v(x - i0)], \quad |x| < 1, \tag{A8.3}$$

and $P_v(z)$ and $Q_v(z)$ are linearly independent; they form a fundamental system for Legendre equation in the region $Re z > 1$. The same is true for $\bar{P}_v(z)$ and $\bar{Q}_v(z)$ in the region $-1 < z < +1$, z real.

We have furthermore the following important relations:

$$P_v(-z) = e^{\pm i\pi v}P_v(z) - (2/\pi) \sin \pi v Q_v(z), \tag{A8.4}$$

$$Q_v(-z) = -e^{\mp i\pi v}Q_v(z) \tag{A8.5}$$

$(+, -$ according to $Im z > 0$ or $<0)$.

$$Q_v(z) \sin \pi v - Q_{-v-1}(z) \sin \pi v = \pi \cos \pi v P_v(z); \quad \sin \pi v \neq 0, \tag{A8.6}$$

$$Q_v(x \pm i0) = \bar{Q}_v(x) \mp (i\pi/2)P_v(x). \tag{A8.7}$$

Thus the discontinuity of Q_v between -1 and $+1$ is $\pi P_v(x)$. And because the cut of Q_v for v = positive integer is between $+1$ and -1 we obtain from the Cauchy formula

$$Q_n(z) = (1/2) \int_{-1}^{+1} \frac{P_n(y)\,dy}{z - y}, \tag{A8.8}$$

for n positive integer and for all z except z real and between $+1$ and -1. Note that the integral $\oint_C dz\, Q_n(z)/(z - z_0)$ over a large circle in the whole z-plane vanishes.

The discontinuity of $P_v(z)$ from $z = -1$ to $z = -\infty$ is proportional to $P_v(-z)$. We have

$$P_v(z) = -(\sin \pi v/\pi) \int_{-\infty}^{-1} \frac{P_v(-z')\,dz'}{z - z'} \tag{A8.9}$$

or

$$P_v(-z) = -(\sin \pi v/\pi) \int_1^\infty \frac{P_v(z')\,dz'}{z' - z}. \tag{A8.9'}$$

The discontinuity of $Q_v(z)$ between $z = -1$ and $-\infty$ is, similarly, proportional to $Q_v(-z)$ so that with Eq. (A8.8) we have for arbitrary v,

$$Q_v(z) = (1/2) \int_{-1}^{+1} \frac{P_v(y)\,dy}{z - y} - (\sin \pi v/\pi) \int_{-\infty}^{-1} \frac{Q_v(-y)\,dy}{y - z}. \tag{A8.10}$$

Another useful relation connected with Eq. (A8.8) is the formula of Heine:

$$(z - y)^{-1} = \sum_{n=0}^{\infty} (2n + 1)P_n(y)Q_n(z), \tag{A8.11}$$

which is valid for $|y + \sqrt{y^2 - 1}| < |z + \sqrt{z^2 - 1}|$, i.e., y must be in the interior of the ellipse passing through z with foci $+1$, -1. This follows from the *Faber's theorem*[1] about the convergence of the Legendre series:

$$\sum_{n=0}^{\infty} (2n + 1)A_n P_n(y)$$

The Legendre series converges absolutely and uniformly in an ellipse with semimajor axis $(h \pm h^{-1})/2$ where

$$h = \lim_{n \to \infty} |1/A_n|^{1/n}.$$

The asymptotic value of Q_n for large n is discussed below.

We next give the integral representations of the Legendre functions the so-called *Laplace's first integrals*:

$$P_\nu(z) = (1/\pi) \int_0^\pi [z + \sqrt{z^2 - 1} \cos \phi]^\nu \, d\phi \qquad (A8.12)$$

valid for $|\arg z| < (\pi/2)$; when $\phi = (\pi/2)$: $\arg (z + \sqrt{z^2 - 1} \cos \varphi) = \arg z$:

$$Q_\nu(z) = \int_0^\infty (z + \sqrt{z^2 - 1} \cosh \theta)^{-\nu-1} \, d\theta \qquad (A8.13)$$

valid for $Re(\nu + 1) > 0$, for $\nu \neq n$, $\arg (z + \sqrt{z^2 - 1} \cosh \theta)$ has its principal value when $\theta = 0$.

From these representations we obtain

$$\cdot P_\nu(z) \xrightarrow[|z| \to \infty]{} z^\nu \int_0^\pi (1 + \cos \varphi)^\nu \, d\varphi, \quad |\arg z| < (\pi/2) \qquad (A8.14)$$

and

$$Q_\nu(z) \xrightarrow[|z| \to \infty]{} z^{-\nu-1} \int_0^\infty (1 + \cosh \theta)^{-\nu-1} \, d\theta, \quad Re(\nu + 1) > 0. \quad (A8.15)$$

In the ν-plane the functions $P_\nu(z)$ and $Q_\nu(z)$ are entire functions with an essential singularity at infinity. In addition $Q_\nu(z)$ has poles at negative integers, $\nu = -1, -2, -3, \ldots$.

To find the asymptotic behavior in the ν-plane we consider the connection of the Legendre functions with the hypergeometric functions of various arguments.[2] The following formulas are most useful:

$$P_\nu(z) = F(-\nu, \nu + 1; 1; (1 - z)/2), \qquad (A8.16)$$

$$Q_\nu(z) = (1/2) \frac{\Gamma^2(\nu + 1)}{\Gamma(2\nu + 1)} \left(\frac{z^2 - 1}{2}\right)^{-\nu-1} F\left(\nu + 1, \nu + 1; 2\nu + 2; \frac{2}{1 - z}\right).$$

$$(A8.17)$$

[1] See Ref. 2 of this Appendix, p. 95. Prove Eq. (A8.7) using Eq. (A8.17) and this theorem.
[2] For further formulas of this kind see tables in Ref. 3 of this Appendix, p. 129.

The *hypergeometric function* $F(a,b;c;z)$ is an analytic function in the z-plane

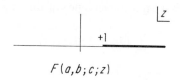

$$F(a,b;c;z)$$

Figure A8.2

cut from $z = 1$ to $z = \infty$. For fixed a and b, and fixed z, $|z| < 1$, and $|c| \to \infty$ we have

$$F(a,b;c;z) = 1 + (ab/c)z + \cdots . \tag{A8.18}$$

This formula is still valid for all $|z| > 1$, if $|\arg(1 - z)| < \pi$ (i.e., z not on the cut) and $Re\, c \to \infty$. As a function of the parameters $F(a,b;c;z)/\Gamma(c)$ is an entire function of a, b, and c if z is fixed such that $Re\, z < \frac{1}{2}$, or if $|z| < 1$. If $(c - a)$ or $(c - b)$ is a negative integer, then F is an elementary function.
    Using Eqs. (A8.16), (A8.17), and (A8.18) we obtain

$$P_\nu(z) \xrightarrow[|\nu| \to \infty]{} \frac{e^{-\xi/2}}{(\pi\nu)^{\frac{1}{2}}(1 - e^{-2\xi})^{\frac{1}{2}}} \left[e^{(\nu + \frac{1}{2})\xi} + e^{\pm i(\pi/2)} e^{-(\nu + \frac{1}{2})\xi} \right] \tag{A8.19}$$

for $-\pi/2 - \varepsilon_2 \leqq \arg\nu \leqq \pi/2 + \varepsilon_1$, ε_1, $\varepsilon_2 > 0$, and

$$Q_\nu(z) \xrightarrow[|\nu| \to \infty]{} (\pi/\nu)^{\frac{1}{2}} \frac{e^{-(\nu + \frac{1}{2})\xi}}{(1 - e^{-2\xi})^{\frac{1}{2}}} \tag{A8.20}$$

for $|\arg(z \pm 1)| \leqq \pi$, $|\arg\nu| \leqq \pi - \delta$. In these formulas $z = \cosh\xi$ and the $\pm$ sign in the formula for $P_\nu(z)$ is according to $Im\, z \gtrless 0$.
    Finally we give some special values. For $-1 < x < 1$:

$$P_0(x) = 1,$$

$$P_1(x) = x,$$

$$P_2(x) = (3x^2 - 1)/2, \ldots$$

$$Q_0(x) = (1/2) \ln\frac{1 + x}{1 - x},$$

$$Q_1(x) = (x/2) \ln\frac{1 + x}{1 - x} - 1, \ldots$$

$$P_\nu(1) = 1,$$

$$P_\nu(0) = -(\sin\pi\nu/2\pi^{3/2})\Gamma\left(\frac{\nu + 1}{2}\right)\Gamma(-\nu/2),$$

$$Q_\nu(0) = (\tfrac{1}{4}\pi^{1/2})(1 - \cos\pi\nu)\Gamma\left(\frac{\nu + 1}{2}\right)\Gamma(-\nu/2).$$

References

1. Erdelyi, A. (ed.), *Higher Transcendental Functions*, Vol. I (New York: McGraw-Hill, 1953).

2. Jahnke-Emde-Lösch, *Tables of Higher Functions* (New York: McGraw-Hill, 1960).

3. Oberhettinger, F., and Magnus, F., *Special Functions of Mathematical Physics* (New York: Chelsea, 1949).

4. Whittaker, E. T., and Watson, G. N., *Modern Analysis* (New York: Cambridge U. P., 1952).

APPENDIX 9

Some Important Properties of Analytic Functions of Several Complex Variables

Many results valid for functions of a single variable (App. 6) have either no counterpart, or are no longer valid for functions of several complex variables. Thus, great care is necessary in the use of these functions. We shall point out in this appendix the similarities and the differences between these two cases.

1 Domains

The underlying space is the vector space $C^{(n)}$ of n complex variables $z = (z_1, z_2, \ldots, z_n)$. It is also isomorphic to the real space of $2n$ dimensions, $R^{(2n)}$, but with a complex structure. The open connected sets in $C^{(n)}$ are called *domains*. Some special domains are of interest:

(a) *A product domain* is defined by $\{z \mid z \in D_1, z_2 \in D_2, \ldots, z_n \in D_n\}$, where $D_1, D_2, \ldots, D_n$ are usual domains in one complex variable.

(b) *A circular domain* (Reinhardt domain) is given by the set

$$\{z \mid (|z_1|, \ldots, |z_n|) \in E\},$$

where E is a set in the space of absolute values (n-dimensional real space). The *polycircle*,

$$\{z \mid (|z_1| < r_1, \ldots, |z_n| < r_n\}$$

and the *hypersphere*,

$$\{z \mid (|z_1|^2 + \cdots + |z_n|^2 \leq r\}$$

are special cases of circular domains. (Figure A9.1.) The polycircle is also a special case of a product domain. The point DB in Fig. A9.1b, which belongs to both of the boundaries of D_1 and D_2, is *the distinguished boundary* (DB); it is the product of the boundaries. The domain of convergence of multiple power series and of Laurent series are circular domains.

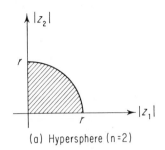

(a) Hypersphere (n = 2)

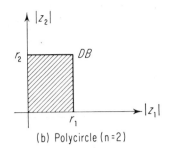

(b) Polycircle (n = 2)

Figure A9.1

(c) *A tube domain with base d is the product of a domain in* $R^{(2n)}$ *of the real parts* x_k *of* z_k, *with arbitrary complex components* y_k, *i.e.,* $\{z \mid x \in d, y$ *arbitrary*$\}$. *A semitube domain is defined by*

$$\{(z, W) \mid z \in D, g(z) < Rew < f(z)\},$$

where $f(z)$ and $g(z)$ are real-valued functions in D.

An *analytic* 1-*plane* in $C^{(n)}$ consists of points of the form $\{z \mid z = z_0 + z_1, A_1\}$, where z_0 and A_1 are fixed in $C^{(n)}$. For $z_0 = 0$, $A_1 = 1$, it is the plane z_1 itself with 2 real dimensions. But not every plane of dimension 2 is an analytic plane. In general, an *analytic k-plane* is the set $\{z \mid z = z_0 + z_1 A_1 + \cdots + z_k A_k\}$, $z_0, z_1, \ldots, z_k$ and $A_1 \ldots A_k \in C^{(n)}$ fixed, and $z = (z_1, \ldots, z_n) \in C^{(k)}$.

2 Holomorphic Functions

Consider the complex-valued function $F(z_1, \ldots, z_n)$. All variables are on equal footing. The point at infinity is not singled out from any finite point.

The analyticity (more precisely, the holomorphy) in several complex variables can be defined either by the existence of partial derivatives in each variable, keeping the other fixed (Riemann), or by the convergence of an n-fold power series [Taylor series around $(a_1, a_2, \ldots, a_n)$]

$$\sum_{m_1, \ldots, m_n} C_{m_1 m_2 \cdots m_n} (z_1 - a_1)^{m_1} (z_2 - a_2)^{m_2} \cdots (z_n - a_n)^{m_n} \qquad (A9.1)$$

in the polycircle $|z_1 - a_i| < r_i$ $(i = 1, 2, \ldots, n)$ (Weierstrass).

These two definitions are equivalent. That is, if $F(z_1, \ldots, z_n)$ satisfies Cauchy formula in each variable separately and is continuous, then it satisfied the expansion (A9.1), as can be shown by a successive application of the Cauchy theorem. For the convergence of Eq. (A9.1), it is sufficient that at least one of the simple series inside Eq. (A9.1) is convergent.

Note that for real variables the continuity does not follow from the existence of partial derivatives.

Cauchy's formula for the polycircle,

$$f(z_1, \ldots, z_n) = \frac{1}{(2\pi)^n} \int\limits_{|\xi_i - a_i| = \Gamma_i} \frac{d\xi_1, \ldots, d\xi_n}{\prod\limits_{j} (\xi_j - z_j)} f(\xi_1, \ldots, \xi_n), \qquad \text{(A9.2)}$$

shows that a holomorphic function is completely determined by its values on the distinguished boundary of the polycircle.

In contrast to the case for a single complex variable, a holomorphic function $W = f(z)$ is not a conformal map at all points where $f'(z) \neq 0$; only analytic planes are mapped conformally; i.e., two curves lying on the same analytic ℓ-planes will make the same angle after the mapping.

Substitution Rule. If $f(z_1, \ldots, z_n)$ is holomorphic in $D \in C^{(n)}$ and we let $z_i = g_i(w_1, \ldots, w_K)$, where g_i are holomorphic in $G \in C^{(k)}$, then $f[g_1(w), \ldots, g_n(w)]$ is holomorphic in G. This follows from the partial derivatives

$$\frac{\partial f}{\partial w_j} = \sum_{k=1}^{n} \frac{\partial f}{\partial z_k} \frac{\partial z_k}{\partial w_j}.$$

As a consequence, the restrictions of a holomorphic function on analytic k-planes are also holomorphic in the intersection.

3 Holomorphic Continuation

If a function f_1 is analytic in a polycylinder C_1, f_2 on the polycylinder C_2, and if $f_1 = f_2$ in the common interior points of C_1 and C_2, then there is a unique function f of several complex variables, which is analytic in the union of C_1 and C_2 and coincides with f_1 in C_1 and f_2 in C_2. This is the uniqueness of analytic continuation as in the case of analytic functions of a single complex variable.

To obtain the analog of Riemann surfaces in the case of several variables, one introduces a *function element* consisting of the triplet: a point X in $C^{(n)}$ (more generally in a topological space), a neighborhood U of z, and function f in some class (X, U, f). Two function elements are equivalent if and only if in $U_1 \cap U_2$ we have $z_1 = z_2$ and $f_1 = f_2$. The equivalent class of function elements is called the *germ* of the holomorphic function. New germs can be generated by a germ, by using power series expansion, for example. At each point a new germ is generated. The new germs

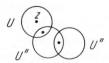

Figure A9.2

generate other germs and so forth. In particular, one can continue the germs holomorphically along arcs. The continuations along two arcs which can be continuously transformed into each other (homotopic arcs) are identical. The collection of all germs generated by a given function element is called the *germ space*, or *the domain of holomorphy of the function f*. The domain of holomorphy is independent of the domain D in which the function is given initially.

4 Holomorphy Domains

In the case of one complex variable ($n = 1$) any domain is a *holomorphy domain*, i.e., the holomorphy domain of some function. One can always construct a function which is holomorphic inside the given domain, but has singularities on the boundary. (L. Bieberbach, *Lehrbuch der Funktionen-theorie*, vol. I, Teubner, Leipzig, 1923, p. 295.)

For $n \geqslant 2$, there are domains which are not holomorphy domains. That is, *any* function which is holomorphic in such a domain is also automatically holomorphic in a larger domain. The holomorphy domains in the case of several complex variables therefore need further specification. Clearly, it is very useful to recognize such domains, because if the function is known to be holomorphic in some domain G, it is also holomorphic in a holomorphy domain D, containing G. If all functions holomorphic in the domain D are algebraically continuable to the domain D', then D' is called a *holomorphic extension* of the domain D. A domain D not allowing holomorphic extensions is a *domain of holomorphy*. For a family of functions, the largest domain in which these functions are holomorphic is called the *envelope of holomorphy*. Thus, the holomorphy envelope of a domain D is the intersection of the holomorphy domains of all functions holomorphic in D. The additional requirement for a domain to be a holomorphy domain is that it be *convex*. The convex hull of a domain $K \in D$ with respect to a function f (holomorphic in D) consists of all points P in D for which $|f(p)| \leqslant \sup |f(K)|$. We note that if f is holomorphic in an open subset of D and continuous on the boundary, then $|f(z)|$ takes its maximum on the boundary (Theorem of the Maximum, as in Appendix 6, for $n = 1$). We then find the convex hull for all functions holomorphic in D. Such a domain is called *holoconvex*. And, *not only is every holomorphy domain holoconvex, but, conversely, every holoconvex domain is a holomorphy domain*.

5 Singularity Surfaces

In the case of one complex variable ($n = 1$) the term analytic is used even in the presence of isolated singularities (more precisely meromorphic functions). For $n \geqslant 2$, an analytic function cannot have isolated singu-

is not a domain of holomorphy, for $n \geqslant 2$. Any function that is holomorphic on such a sphere is also automatically holomorphic in the ball $\{z \mid |z_1|^2 + \cdots + |z_n|^2 \leqslant r^2\}$ (Hartog's second theorem). Because an isolated point is inside a sphere, it is always inside the domain of holomorphy. Similarly, the exterior of any bounded set in $C^{(n)}$, for $n \geqslant 2$, cannot be a domain of holomorphy. The singularities of the functions of several complex variables are then necessarily surfaces. For example, if $f = g/h$, the zeros of the holomorphic functions $h(z_1, z_2, \ldots, z_n) = 0$ form a $(2n - 2)$ dimensional analytic hyposurface.

References

Behnke, H., and Thullen, P., "Theorie der Funktionen mehrerer komplexen Veränderlichen," *Ergeb. Math. Grenz.*, no. 3 (Berlin: Springer, 1934).

Bremmermann, H. J., "Complex Analysis in Several Variables," lecture notes (Berkeley: U. of California Press, 1962).

Fuks, B. A., "Analytic Functions of Several Complex Variables," *Amer. Math. Soc. Translations of Mathematical Monographs*, Vols. 8, 14 (Providence, R.I., 1965).

Gleason, A. M., "The Cauchy-Weil Formula," *Journ. Math. Mech.*, **12**, 429 (1963).

Lelong, P., *Leçons sur la théorie des fonctions de plusieurs variables complexes*, Commissariat de L'energie Atomique, Saclay 1960 (mimeographed).

Wightman, A. S., "Analytic Functions of Several Complex Variables," in C. De Witt (ed.), *Dispersion Relations and Elementary Particles* (New York: Wiley, 1960).

MONOGRAPHS AND REVIEW ARTICLES ON *S*-MATRIX THEORY AND DISPERSION RELATIONS TECHNIQUES (GENERAL DISCUSSION)

Amati, D., and Fubini, S., "Dispersion Relations Methods in Strong Interactions," *Ann. Rev. Nucl. Sci.*, **12**, 354 (1962).

Barut, A. O., "The Framework of *S*-Matrix Theory," in *Strong Interactions and High Energy Physics* (Edinburgh: Oliver and Boyd, 1964).

Berestetskii, V. B., "Dynamical Properties of Elementary Particles and the Theory of the Scattering Matrix," *Sov. Phys. Uspekhi*, **5**, 7 (1962).

Chew, G. F., *S-Matrix Theory of Strong Interactions* (New York: Benjamin, 1961).

Chew, G. F., "The Analytic *S*-Matrix," in C. De Witt and M. Jacob (eds.), *High Energy Physics* (New York: Gordon and Breach, Science Publishers, 1966).

Eden, R. J., Landshoff, P., Olive, D. I., and Polkinghorne, J., *Analytic S-Matrix Theory* (Cambridge University Press, 1966).

Frautschi, S. C., *Regge Poles and S-Matrix Theory* (New York: Benjamin, 1963).

Froissart, M., and Omnès, R., "Introduction to the Theory of Strong Interactions (New York: Gordon and Breach, Science Publishers, 1966).

Goldberger, M. L., "Dispersion Relations," in C. De Witt (ed.), *Dispersion Relations and Elementary Particles* (New York: Wiley, 1960).

Mandelstam, S., "Dispersion Relations in Strong Coupling Physics," *Reports Progr. Phys.*, **25**, 99 (1962).

Omnès, R., and Froissart, M., *Mandelstam Theory and Regge Poles* (New York: Benjamin, 1963).

Squires, E. J., "An Introduction to Relativistic *S*-Matrix Theory," in *Strong Interactions and High Energy Physics* (Edinburgh: Oliver and Boyd, 1964).

Squires, E. J., *Complex Angular Momenta and Particle Physics* (New York: Benjamin, 1963).

Stapp, H. P., "Analytic *S*-Matrix Theory," in *International Seminar in Elementary Particles* (Vienna: International Atomic Energy Agency, 1965).

Werle, J., *Relativistic Theory of Reactions* (Amsterdam: North-Holland Publ. Co., 1966).

Zachariasen, F., "Lectures in Bootstraps," Pacific International Summer School in Physics, Univ. of Hawai, 1966.

AUTHOR INDEX

Acharya, R., 166
Adair, R., 183
Ahmadzadeh, A., 147, 148
Alston, M., *et al.,* 198, 199, 200
Alvarez, L., 183
Amati, D., 341
Ambrose, W., 19
Andersen, C. D., 177

Backenstoss G., *et al.,* 179, 189
Balasz, L., 217, 222, 259
Ball, J., 222
Bardakci, K., 162
Bardon, M., *et al.,* 181
Bargmann, V., 18
Barut A. O., 15, 29, 51, 55, 81, 102,
    147, 164, 166, 170, 203, 270, 281,
    341
Bass, L., 175
Behnke, H., 340
Behrends, E., *et al.,* 200
Bell, J. S., 182, 204
Berestetskii, V. B., 341
Bertanza, L., *et al.,* 200
Bhattacharjie, A., 175
Bieberbach, L., 339
Blade, R., 270
Blanckenbecler, R., 123
Block, M., *et al.,* 200
Bottino, A., 123, 147
Branscomb, E., 202
Bransden, B. H. *et al.,* 222
Branson, D., 11
Breit, G., 182, 204
Bremmermann, H. J., 315, 340
Brisson, J. C., 196
Brown, H. L., *et al.,* 183
Brown, J., *et al.,* 179

Burcham, W., 187
Burke, P., 147, 148

Calogero, F., 147
Carruthers, P., 81
Cartwright, W. F., *et al.,* 177
Case, K. M., 202
Cerulus, F., 159
Chamberlain, O., *et al.,* 89, 178, 179
Cheng, H., 147, 166
Chew, G. F., 128, 135, 211, 212, 259,
    341
Chinowski, W. *et al.,* 199
Christenson, J. H., 182
Combes, C. *et al.,* 179
Cook, V. *et al.,* 200
Cowan, C. L., 176
Cronin, J. W., 182
Cziffra, P., 176

Dahl, O. *et al.,* 200
Dalitz, R. H., 89, 178, 179
Darby, G., 176
Day, T. *et al.,* 183
De Alfaro, V., vi
Diddens, A. N. *et al.,* 154
Dilley, J., 147, 170
Dirac, P. A. M., 6
Downs, B. W., 187

Eden, R. J., vi, 95, 113, 153, 341
Eisler, P., 183
Erdelyi, A., 335
Erwin, A. *et al.,* 197

Feldman, D., 188
Finn, A. C., 161
Fitch, V. L., 182

343

SUBJECT INDEX